LEADING CERTIFICATE ORD

GW00992119

Active Maths 3
Book 1

Michael Keating, Derek Mulvany and James O'Loughlin

Special Advisors:
Oliver Murphy, Colin Townsend and Jim McElroy

FOLENS

Editor: Priscilla O'Connor, Sarah Reece

Designer: Liz White

Layout: Compuscript

Illustrations: Compuscript, Denis M. Baker, Rory O'Neill

ISBN: 978-1-78090-076-6

© Michael Keating, Derek Mulvany, James O'Loughlin, Oliver Murphy and Colin Townsend, 2012

Folens Publishers, Hibernian Industrial Estate, Greenhills Road, Tallaght, Dublin 24, Ireland

Acknowledgements

The authors would like especially to thank Jim McElroy for his work on the written solutions and his invaluable advice.

The authors and publisher wish to thank the following for permission to reproduce photographs:
Alamy, Corbis, Getty, iStockphoto, Moviestore Collection, Science Photo Library, Sportsfile, Thinkstock.

The authors and publisher wish to thank Bank of Ireland and Bord Gáis Energy for permission to reproduce copyright material.

Contents

Introduction

Active Maths 3 is a comprehensive **two-book series** covering the **complete Leaving Certificate Ordinary Level course**. *Active Maths 3* covers all five strands of the new Project Maths syllabus.

- **Book 1** corresponds to **Paper 1** and therefore contains **Strands 3 (Number), 4 (Algebra) and 5 (Functions)**.

- **Book 2** corresponds to **Paper 2** and therefore contains **Strands 1 (Statistics and Probability) and 2 (Geometry and Trigonometry) plus the Strand 3 topic Length, Area and Volume.**

Teachers and students will find that they have the new syllabus fully covered.

- A separate **free Activity Book** provides a wealth of activities designed to develop students' understanding of each topic in a hands-on way. The textbooks are linked throughout with the Activity Book to introduce topics and emphasise key Learning Outcomes.

Active Maths 3 is packed with student-friendly features:

- Prepares students for the new style of exam question with comprehensive **graded exercises** on each topic and **end-of-chapter revision exercises** include Project Maths-type exam questions based on all material that has been released by the NCCA and SEC.

- **Learning Outcomes** from the new syllabus are stated at the beginning of each chapter.

- Each chapter includes a **You Should Remember** section so that students can check they are fully prepared before starting the chapter.

- A list of **Key Words** at the start of each chapter helps students to consolidate learning. On first occurrence in each chapter, key words are set apart in **Definition boxes** to reinforce the importance of understanding their meaning.

- Clear and concise **Worked Examples** show students how to set out their answers, including step-by-step instructions with excellent diagrams to explain constructions.

- Essential formulae are set apart in **Formula boxes**.

- **Answers** to exercises are given at the end of each book.

  Additional **teacher resources, including digital activities** and **fully worked-out solutions** for the textbooks, will be available online at www.folensonline.ie.

Active Maths 3 allows teachers to meet the challenge of the new syllabus for Leaving Certificate Ordinary Level, and encourages students to discover for themselves that mathematics can be enjoyable and relevant to everyday life.

Note: Constructions in Book 2 are numbered according to the NCCA syllabus for Project Maths Ordinary Level.

chapter 1

Algebra I

Learning Outcomes

In this chapter you will learn to:

- ➲ Evaluate algebraic expressions
- ➲ Add and subtract algebraic terms
- ➲ Multiply algebraic terms
- ➲ Simplify algebraic fractions
- ➲ Factorise a quadratic expression
- ➲ Divide algebraic terms
- ➲ Divide expressions of the form $(ax^2 + bx + c) \div (dx + e)$

1.1 ALGEBRA: AN INTRODUCTION

Algebra is a method of problem-solving. In algebra, we use letters to represent an unknown quantity.

The word 'algebra' comes from a phrase used by Muhammad ibn Musa al–Khwarizmi in his ninth-century book *al-Jabr wa'l Muqabala* or *The Compendious Book on Calculation by Completion and Balancing*.

al-Jabr is usually translated as 'balancing both sides of an equation'.

Algebra has many uses, from computer software to economics. To be able to use algebra to solve problems, we must first understand the notation and rules that are used.

al-Khwarizmi

Notation in Algebra

> A **variable** is a letter (usually x or y) that represents a number. The number may change or be unknown.

- In $5x$, the variable is x.
- In $20y$, the variable is y.

> A **coefficient** is a number or symbol multiplied with a variable in an algebraic term.

- In $5x$, the coefficient is 5.
- In $20y$, the coefficient is 20.

> A **constant** is something that does not change value, i.e. a number by itself.

In $10x + 2$, the **constant** is 2.

> A constant, a variable or a constant multiplied by a variable are all considered **terms**.

$12(x)$ would be an example of a **term**. This is written as $12x$.

$5x + 2$ is an **expression**. Other examples of expressions include $10x$, $8y^2$ and $4pr^3$.

> An **algebraic expression** is an expression that contains one or more numbers, one or more variables, and one or more arithmetic operations.

1.2 SUBSTITUTION

One of the many cases where we encounter algebra is when we are given a formula and asked to substitute in certain values. This requires us to replace letters with numbers.

We must always remember to follow BIMDAS.

x^2 Worked Example 1.1

If $a = 2$ and $b = -3$, find the value of the following expressions:

(i) $4a - 2b$ (ii) $-a + 4b$ (iii) $2a^2 - 3b^2$ (iv) $2ab^2$

Solution

Rewrite the expression, using brackets to replace the variables, and insert (substitute) the given value of a and b.

(i) $4a - 2b$

$= 4(2) - 2(-3)$

$= 8 + 6$

$= 14$

(ii) $-a + 4b$

$= -(2) + 4(-3)$

$= -2 - 12$

$= -14$

(iii) $2a^2 - 3b^2$

$= 2(2)^2 - 3(-3)^2$

$= 2(4) - 3(9)$ (BIMDAS)

$= 8 - 27$

$= -19$

(iv) $2ab^2$

$= 2(2)(-3)^2$

$= 2(2)(9)$

$= 36$

x^2 Worked Example 1.2

If $x = 4$ and $y = -1$, evaluate the following expressions:

(i) $x^2 - y^2$ (ii) $\sqrt{y^2 + 3x^2}$ (iii) $\dfrac{5x^3 - y^7}{3y}$

Solution

Again we rewrite the expression, using brackets to replace the variable, and insert the given value of x and y.

(i) $x^2 - y^2$

$= (4)^2 - (-1)^2$

$= 16 - 1$

$= 15$

(ii) $\sqrt{y^2 + 3x^2}$

$= \sqrt{(-1)^2 + 3(4)^2}$

$= \sqrt{1 + 3(16)}$

$= \sqrt{1 + 48}$

$= \sqrt{49}$

$= 7$

(iii) $\dfrac{5x^3 - y^7}{3y}$

$= \dfrac{5(4)^3 - (-1)^7}{3(-1)}$

$= \dfrac{5(64) - (-1)}{-3}$

$= \dfrac{320 + 1}{-3}$

$= -107$

 ACTIVITY 1.1

Exercise 1.1

1. If $x = 1$ and $y = -3$, find the value of:

(i) $2x$ (iii) $3(x + y)$ (v) x^3 (vii) $3y^2$ (ix) x^2y (xi) xy^3

(ii) $2y$ (iv) $2(x - 2y) + 3x$ (vi) $4x^2$ (viii) xy (x) x^2y^2 (xii) x^2y^3

2. If $x = 2$, $y = 1$ and $z = -5$, find the value of:

(i) $x + y + z$ (iii) $4x - 3z - 3y$ (v) $100x - 2y - 6z$ (vii) $3y - 2x$ (ix) $-x - y - z$

(ii) $2x + 6y + 4z$ (iv) $2x + y - 5$ (vi) $12x + 2z - 8y$ (viii) $3x + 4y$ (x) $-6x + 2y - 4z$

3. If $a = 4$, $b = -2$ and $c = 6$, evaluate:

(i) abc (iii) $a^2 + 2b^4 - 3c$ (v) $ab + bc$ (vii) $(a^3)^2 - (bc)^2$ (ix) $a^2b^2c^2$

(ii) $a^2 + b$ (iv) $a^2 + 3b^3 - c^2$ (vi) $a^2b - c^3$ (viii) $a^c - a^2c$ (x) $(2a^2)^{b^2} - c^2$

4. If $p = -1$, $q = 2$ and $r = 5$, find the value of:

(i) $2(p + q)$ (iii) $5(q + p) - 2r$ (v) $\dfrac{3p + 1}{4q - r^2}$ (vii) $\dfrac{1}{5}r + \dfrac{1}{2}q + 2q$ (ix) $\sqrt{\dfrac{q^2 + (r + p)}{4q}}$

(ii) $4(q + r - p)$ (iv) $3(p - r)^2 - pq$ (vi) $\dfrac{p}{5} - \dfrac{r}{2} - q$ (viii) $\sqrt{p + q}$ (x) $\sqrt{\dfrac{-2(rpq)^5}{q^r - 6q}}$

5. The volume of a cone can be found using the formula:

FORMULA

Volume $= \dfrac{1}{3}\pi r^2 h$

Work out the volume of each of the following cones:

Cone	π	r	h
1	3.14	5 cm	10 cm
2	3.14	4 m	5 m
3	3.14	30 mm	75 mm
4	$\dfrac{22}{7}$	14 cm	19 cm
5	$\dfrac{22}{7}$	56 mm	200 mm

6. The surface area of a cuboid can be found using the formula:

FORMULA

Surface area $= 2lb + 2lh + 2bh$

Work out the surface area of each of the following cuboids:

Cuboid	l	b	h
1	2 m	2 m	3 m
2	3.5 cm	12 cm	9 cm
3	2 m	1.8 m	0.9 m
4	1 cm	12 cm	14 cm
5	8 m	9 m	12 m

7. The height in metres of a projectile after it has been fired up in the air is given by the formula:

FORMULA

Height $= 30t - 5t^2$

with t being the time in seconds.

(a) Complete the following table:

t	Height
0	
1	
2	
3	
4	
5	
6	

(b) (i) Draw a graph of $h = 30t - 5t^2$, with time (in seconds) on the x-axis and height (in metres) on the y-axis.

Estimate from the graph:

(ii) The maximum height reached by the projectile

(iii) How many seconds it takes the projectile to reach its maximum height

(iv) The number of seconds for which the projectile is above a height of 25 metres

1.3 ADDING AND SUBTRACTING TERMS

When adding or subtracting algebraic terms we must always remember the following rules:

Algebra Rule: Only terms that have the exact same letter(s) raised to the same power (like terms) can be added or subtracted.

Example: $5x + 6y + 4x - 3y = 9x + 3y$

Algebra Rule: When adding or subtracting like terms, the powers of the variables do not change; only the number (coefficient) in front of the variable changes.

Example: $20y^2 + 8y^2 = 28y^2$

 ACTIVITY 1.2

x^2 Worked Example 1.3

Simplify each of the following:

'Simplify' means to make the question simpler by adding, subtracting, multiplying or dividing.

(i) $5a - 4b - 3c - a + 5b - 6c$

(ii) $x^2 - 2x - 10 + 4 - 3x + 4x^2$

(iii) $10x^4 - 3x^3y - 2xy + 3yx + 3xy^3 - 4x^4$

Solution

(i) $5a - 4b - 3c - a + 5b - 6c$

We put the like terms together. This is called grouping the terms.

$= 5a - a - 4b + 5b - 3c - 6c$

$= 4a + b - 9c$

(ii) $x^2 - 2x - 10 + 4 - 3x + 4x^2$

$= x^2 + 4x^2 - 2x - 3x - 10 + 4$

$= 5x^2 - 5x - 6$

We usually put the term with the highest power first, the term with the next highest power second, etc.

(iii) $10x^4 - 3x^3y - 2xy + 3yx + 3xy^3 - 4x^4$

$= 10x^4 - 4x^4 - 3x^3y - 2xy + 3yx + 3xy^3$

Notice that xy and yx are like terms but yx^3 and xy^3 are **not**.

$= 6x^4 - 3x^3y + 3xy^3 + xy$

Exercise 1.2

Simplify each of the following:

1. (i) $a + a + a$

    (ii) $2b + 5b + 4b$

    (iii) $c + 3c - 4c$

    (iv) $8d + 5d - 12d$

    (v) $a + 5a - 10a$

2. (i) $b - b - 2b$

    (ii) $-c + 7c - 9c$

    (iii) $-d - 3d - 2d$

    (iv) $p - 4p - 4p + 3$

    (v) $2x - 4x - 6 - 8x$

3. (i) $4e - 3e - 6f + f$

    (ii) $2g + 3g + 4h - 7$

    (iii) $12j + 5j + 5k - 7k$

    (iv) $7m - 7n + m$

    (v) $2p - 4q - 3p + 2q$

4. (i) $2x - 3y + 4x - 2y + 3y + 4x$

    (ii) $14x + 2y - 3z - 10x + 3y - 11z$

    (iii) $2a + 5b - 2c + 5a - 2b - c$

    (iv) $4l + 2n + 5l - 3m - 2n - 5m$

    (v) $-p + 2 - q - 5r - 2p + r$

5. (i) $2ab + ab + ab$

    (ii) $ab - 2ab - 4ab$

    (iii) $xy + xy + 2xy$

    (iv) $2xy + 5xy - 7xy$

    (v) $2pq - 3pq + 4qp$

6. (i) $-pq - 7qp - 3pq$

    (ii) $mn + 10nm - 2nm - 10mn$

    (iii) $3pq + 4rq + 8pq - 7rq - 8qp$

    (iv) $4y + 9x + 2xy - 5x + 2y$

    (v) $ab + 2dc - 4ba + c$

7. (i) $a^2 + a^2$

    (ii) $a^3 + a^3$

    (iii) $b^2 + 2b^2a + 4ab^2 + 4b^2a$

    (iv) $b^3 - 2b^3 + 3b^3$

    (v) $xy^2 - 2yx^2 + y^2x$

8. (i) $p^2 + p^2 + p^3$

    (ii) $6p^4 - 2p^4 + p^4$

    (iii) $4x^2 + 3x^2 + x$

    (iv) $xa^2 - 2ax^2 - x^2a + 2x^2a$

    (v) $x^3 + 2yx^3 + y^2x^3 - 4x^3y - 3x^3$

9. (i) $9p^2 + 2q^2 + 7p^2 + 3q^2$

    (ii) $3x^3 - 2y^2 + 3x^3 - 3y^2$

    (iii) $5m^2 - 8n^2 + 2m^2 - 3n^2$

    (iv) $mn^2 - 3mn^2 + 5nm^2 - 2m^2n$

    (v) $2yz^2 - 2zy^2 + z^2y - y^2z$

10. (i) $3x^3y + yx^3 + xy^3 - 3y^3x$

    (ii) $pr^2 + 2p^2r + 2rp^2 - rp^2 + pr^2$

    (iii) $-3ab^2 + 3a^2b + 5b^2a - 3ba^2$

    (iv) $2x^2y - 2xy^2 - 4x^2y - 5xy^2$

    (v) $2xy + 2x^2y^2 + 2xy^2 - 5xy^2$

1.4 MULTIPLYING TERMS

Unlike when adding or subtracting, in algebra any term may be multiplied by another term. When we multiply terms, we encounter another set of rules that are important to understand.

Example: $(4x)(5y)$

$= (4)(x)(5)(y)$

$= (4)(5)(x)(y)$... Commutative

$= 20xy$.

> **Algebra Rule:** To multiply terms:
> number × number, variable × variable.

Algebra Rule: When multiplying terms that are alike, we **add** the powers or indices.

This rule is also written as $a^p a^q = a^{p+q}$.

Example: $4x^3 \times 3x^5$

$\quad = (4)(x)(x)(x)(3)(x)(x)(x)(x)(x)$

$\quad = (4)(3)(x)(x)(x)(x)(x)(x)(x)(x)$... Commutative

$\quad = 12x^8$.

x^2 Worked Example 1.4

Simplify each of the following:

    (i) $(3x)^3$ (iii) $(2pq^2r^3)(-5pq^2r^4)$ (v) $(3a^2b)^2$

    (ii) $(2ab)(3a^2b^4)$ (iv) $(7xy^3)(2xy^{-2})$

Solution

    (i) $(3x)^3$

        $= (3x)(3x)(3x)$

        $= 27x^3$

    (ii) $(2ab)(3a^2b^4)$

        $= (2)(3)(a)(b)(a^2)(b^4)$

        $= (2)(3)(a)(a^2)(b)(b^4)$

        $= 6a^3b^5$

    (iii) $(2pq^2r^3)(-5pq^2r^4)$

        $= (2)(-5)(pq^2r^3)(pq^2r^4)$

        $= -10p^2q^4r^7$

    (iv) $(7xy^3)(2xy^{-2})$

        $= (7)(2)(xy^3)(xy^{-2})$

        $= 14x^2y$ $y^3 \times y^{-2} = y^{3-2} = y^1$ or y

    (v) $(3a^2b)^2$

        $= (3a^2b)(3a^2b)$

        $= (3)(3)(a^2b)(a^2b)$

        $= 9a^4b^2$

Exercise 1.3

Simplify each of the following:

1. (i) $(2a)(5a)$

    (ii) $(3b)(4)$

    (iii) $(4c)(2c)$

    (iv) $(-d)(d)$

    (v) $(-5e)(-2e)$

2. (i) $(3a)(b)$

    (ii) $(2b)(-c)$

    (iii) $(-2c)(-2d)$

    (iv) $(2d)(e)(d)$

    (v) $(-e)(-e)(f)$

3. (i) $(x^2)(x^2)$

    (ii) $(x^3)(y^2)$

    (iii) $(3x^5)(2x^2)$

    (iv) $(-y^2)(2y^3)$

    (v) $(-4y^2)(-5y^3)$

4. (i) $(x^5)(x^3)$

    (ii) $(2a^4)(3a^6)$

    (iii) $(10y^3)(-y^2)$

    (iv) $(-b^{12})(-4b^3)$

    (v) $(5x^5)(2x)$

5. (i) $(a)(ab)$

    (ii) $(ab)(ab)$

    (iii) $(2dc)(3d)$

    (iv) $(a)(a^2b)$

    (v) $(4xy)(xy^2)$

6. (i) $(3x^5)(-2xy^5)$

    (ii) $(a)(-a)(-a)$

    (iii) $(x)(2x)(-x)$

    (iv) $(-3y)(y^2)(y^2)$

    (v) $(-5y)(-y)(2)$

7. (i) $(2x)(4x)(-y)$

    (ii) $(-3y)(3x^2)(y^2)$

    (iii) $(-5n)(-5n)(2m^2)$

    (iv) $(3a^5)(4a^2)(-2a)$

    (v) $(3a)(-a)(-4b)$

8. (i) $(2xy)(4xy)(xy)$

    (ii) $(xy)(x^2y)(2)$

    (iii) $(pq)(5p^2q)(2pq^2)$

    (iv) $(-p^2q)(4p^2q)(2qp^4)$

    (v) $(2t^2p)(t^2p^2)(5t^3p)$

9. (i) $(b)^2$

    (ii) $(2b)^2$

    (iii) $(-3b)^2$

    (iv) $(-3b)^3$

    (v) $(4ab)^3$

10. (i) $(-2ab)^2$

     (ii) $(4x^2y)^2$

     (iii) $(-2x^2y)^3$

     (iv) $(-xy^2)^4$

     (v) $(4y^2x^3)^3$

1.5 MULTIPLYING TERMS WITH BRACKETS

We may have to deal with multiplying an expression by a number or a term.

The distributive property of the real numbers is used to simplify expressions involving brackets.

$x(y + z) = xy + xz$, for $x, y, z \in R$ (Distributive property)

x^2 Worked Example 1.5

Simplify the following:

> The same question may be phrased as expand the brackets and simplify.

(i) $6(x - 2y + 1) - 2(x + y)$

(ii) $5(3a^2 + 4a + 5) - (a^2 + 3a - 2)$

(iii) $2y(y + 2) - 5y(y - 1)$

(iv) $3x(x^2 + y - 1) - 2xy(x^2 + x - 1)$

Solution

(i) $6(x - 2y + 1) - 2(x + y)$

> Every term inside the bracket will be multiplied by the term outside the bracket.

$= 6(x) + 6(-2y) + 6(1) - 2(x) - 2(y)$

$= 6x - 12y + 6 - 2x - 2y$

Group the terms and then simplify.

$= 6x - 2x - 12y - 2y + 6$

$= 4x - 14y + 6$

(ii) $5(3a^2 + 4a + 5) - (a^2 + 3a - 2)$

To aid in the multiplying we insert a 1 outside the second bracket.

$= 5(3a^2 + 4a + 5) - 1(a^2 + 3a - 2)$

We must also pay special attention to the signs.

$= 15a^2 + 20a + 25 - a^2 - 3a + 2$

Group the terms and then simplify.

$= 15a^2 - a^2 + 20a - 3a + 25 + 2$

$= 14a^2 + 17a + 27$

(iii) $2y(y + 2) - 5y(y - 1)$

$= 2y^2 + 4y - 5y^2 + 5y$

$= 2y^2 - 5y^2 + 4y + 5y$

$= -3y^2 + 9y$

(iv) $3x(x^2 + y - 1) - 2xy(x^2 + x - 1)$

$= 3x^3 + 3xy - 3x - 2x^3y - 2x^2y + 2xy$

$= 3x^3 - 2x^3y - 2x^2y + 3xy + 2xy - 3x$

$= 3x^3 - 2x^3y - 2x^2y + 5xy - 3x$

ACTIVITY 1.3

Exercise 1.4

In each part, remove the brackets and simplify:

1. (i) $3(a + 3)$

(ii) $2(a + 2)$

(iii) $5(b + 2)$

(iv) $3(b - 3)$

(v) $-4(c - 4)$

(vi) $2(2x + y - 3)$

(vii) $5(x - 3y - 1)$

(viii) $2(-2x + 2y - 2)$

(ix) $-(2x - y - 1)$

(x) $-4(-x - 5y + 7)$

2. (i) $3(x + 2) + 4(x + 1)$

(ii) $2(x + 4) + 5(x + 2)$

(iii) $4(y - 2) + 2(y - 4)$

(iv) $2(y + 2) - 3(y - 8)$

(v) $2(a - 4) - 5(a - 1)$

3. (i) $1(2a + 2) + 2(3a + 1)$

(ii) $4(3b + 4) - 5(2b + 1)$

(iii) $3(4b - 2) - 3(b - 4)$

(iv) $-2(7x - 1) + 2(4x - 8)$

(v) $3(-2x + 2) - 2(4 - 3x)$

4. (i) $5(5y - 1) - 2(5y - 8)$

(ii) $-(y - 2) - 2(8 - 5y)$

(iii) $2(a^2 - a + 1) + 2(a^2 + 5a + 4)$

(iv) $-4(3a^2 + a - 1) - (4a^2 - 2a - 4)$

(v) $5(b^2 - 2b - 1) - 2(-2b - b^2 - 1)$

5. (i) $x(x + 3)$

(ii) $2x(x + 4)$

(iii) $5y(y - 2)$

(iv) $y(y - 6)$

(v) $a(2a - 1)$

6. (i) $2a(2a + 1)$

(ii) $4b(2b - 2)$

(iii) $-b(4b - 3)$

(iv) $x^2(x + 1)$

(v) $2x(x^2 - 1)$

7. (i) $3y(y^2 + 3y - 2)$

(ii) $a(2a^2 - 3a + 1)$

(iii) $2a(5a^2 - 4a - 4)$

(iv) $-2b(2b^2 + 2b - 9)$

(v) $-b(-1 - 3b - b^2)$

8. (i) $a(a + 1) + a(a + 1)$

(ii) $a(4a + 3) + 2a(2a + 3)$

(iii) $b(b - 3) + b(2b + 2)$

(iv) $b(3b - 1) - 2b(3b + 4)$

(v) $2x(3x - 7) - 2x(x - 5)$

9. (i) $3a(7a - 2) - 4a(3a + 1)$

(ii) $-3a(a - 3) - 2a(2a - 3)$

(iii) $5b(2b - 9) + 2b(4b - 8)$

(iv) $8b(3b - 1) - 11b(b - 2)$

(v) $-2q(3q - 3) - 4q(q + 5)$

10. (i) $q(2 - 5q) + 2q(2 - 2q)$

(ii) $3(x^2 - 3x + 1) + 5x(x + 3)$

(iii) $3y(2y - 3) - (y + 3)(2y)$

(iv) $a(2a^2 + 3a + 1) - 4a(a^2 + 1)$

(v) $2x(4x^2 + 2x - 1) - 2x(x^2 - x - 3)$

1.6 ALGEBRAIC FRACTIONS I

When we are asked to add or subtract two algebraic fractions, we first must find the **lowest common denominator** (LCD).

x^2 Worked Example 1.6

Write as a single fraction:

$$\frac{4x + 1}{4} - \frac{2x + 3}{5} + 2$$

Solution

Rewrite the expression, putting the whole number over 1.

$$\frac{4x + 1}{4} - \frac{2x + 3}{5} + \frac{2}{1}$$

The LCD of 4, 5 and 1 is 20.

4 into 20 goes 5 times.

5 into 20 goes 4 times.

1 into 20 goes 20 times.

$$= \frac{5(4x + 1) - 4(2x + 3) + 20(2)}{20}$$

$$= \frac{20x + 5 - 8x - 12 + 40}{20}$$

$$= \frac{12x + 33}{20}$$

Do not omit the denominator.

x^2 Worked Example 1.7

Write as a single fraction:

$$\frac{3x + 2}{3} + \frac{5x}{2} - \frac{2x - 4}{6}$$

Solution

The LCD of 3, 2 and 6 is 6.

$$\frac{3x + 2}{3} + \frac{5x}{2} - \frac{2x - 4}{6}$$

$$= \frac{2(3x + 2) + 3(5x) - 1(2x - 4)}{6}$$

$$= \frac{6x + 4 + 15x - 2x + 4}{6}$$

$$= \frac{19x + 8}{6}$$

ACTIVITY 1.4

Exercise 1.5

Simplify each of the following:

1. $\frac{x}{2} + \frac{x}{5}$

2. $\frac{y}{8} + \frac{y}{4}$

3. $\frac{a}{5} - \frac{a}{3}$

4. $\frac{b}{5} + \frac{b}{10} - 2$

5. $\frac{3c}{2} - \frac{c}{4}$

6. $\frac{2x}{3} + \frac{4x}{7}$

7. $\frac{5x}{2} - \frac{3x}{4} + 3$

8. $\frac{6x}{5} + \frac{3x}{20} + \frac{7x}{4}$

9. $\frac{9y}{14} + \frac{5y}{2} - \frac{4y}{7}$

10. $\frac{8x}{3} + \frac{4x}{9} - \frac{5}{6}$

11. $\frac{2a + 1}{4} + \frac{a + 5}{3}$

12. $\frac{4a + 1}{5} + \frac{3a - 1}{3}$

13. $\frac{2x - 3}{4} + \frac{x - 2}{8}$

14. $\frac{5x + 3}{9} - \frac{x + 2}{3}$

15. $\frac{2y - 4}{4} - \frac{3y - 5}{2} + y$

16. $\frac{3y - 1}{8} - \frac{4y - 5}{3}$

17. $\frac{2x + 5}{2} + \frac{x - 1}{9} + 2$

18. $\frac{x - 7}{10} - \frac{2x - 2}{20} + \frac{4}{5}$

19. $\frac{4x - 2}{12} - \frac{x - 2}{24} - \frac{2}{3}$

20. $\frac{x - 1}{5} - \frac{3x - 4}{15} + \frac{7}{3}$

21. $\frac{7a - 2}{4} + \frac{2a - 5}{3} - \frac{5a}{3}$

22. $\frac{2x + 2}{5} - \frac{x - 2}{6} - \frac{9x}{30}$

23. $\frac{x}{5} - \frac{3x + 2}{2} - \frac{3x - 4}{10}$

24. $\frac{x + 1}{2} + \frac{3x + 1}{6} - \frac{2x + 1}{3}$

25. $2x - 3 - \frac{4x - 3}{5} - \frac{5x - 4}{3}$

26. $\frac{2x - 7}{2} - \frac{x - 5}{4} - \frac{x - 4}{6}$

27. $\frac{3y + 1}{9} - \frac{3y + 1}{18} - \frac{y - 1}{6}$

28. $\frac{1}{3}(x + 1) - \frac{3}{2}(3x - 2) - \frac{5}{6}(x - 4)$

29. $\frac{2}{3}(a + 6) + \frac{3}{4}(2a - 1)$

30. $\frac{3}{5}(5x + 1) - \frac{2}{3}(2x + 3) + 3\frac{1}{15}$

1.7 EXPRESSIONS

Another type of algebra question involves the multiplication of two or more expressions.
For example: $(x + 3)(x - 4)$.

x^2 Worked Example 1.8

Remove the brackets and simplify:

    (i) $(x + 2)(x - 3)$ (iii) $(2a - 4)(a^2 - 4a - 1)$

    (ii) $(2y - 1)(y - 2)$ (iv) $(5b - 2)^2$

Solution

    (i) $(x + 2)(x - 3)$

> First term by second bracket + Second term by second bracket

$$= x(x - 3) + 2(x - 3)$$

> Both brackets are the same.

$$= x^2 - 3x + 2x - 6$$
$$= x^2 - x - 6$$

    (ii) $(2y - 1)(y - 2)$

$$= 2y(y - 2) - 1(y - 2)$$
$$= 2y^2 - 4y - y + 2$$
$$= 2y^2 - 5y + 2$$

    (iii) $(2a - 4)(a^2 - 4a - 1)$

$$= 2a(a^2 - 4a - 1) - 4(a^2 - 4a - 1)$$
$$= 2a^3 - 8a^2 - 2a - 4a^2 + 16a + 4$$
$$= 2a^3 - 8a^2 - 4a^2 + 16a - 2a + 4$$
$$= 2a^3 - 12a^2 + 14a + 4$$

    (iv) $(5b - 2)^2$

$$= (5b - 2)(5b - 2)$$
$$= 5b(5b - 2) - 2(5b - 2)$$
$$= 25b^2 - 10b - 10b + 4$$
$$= 25b^2 - 20b + 4$$

ACTIVITY 1.5

We can also use the area model to multiply two expressions.

x^2 Worked Example 1.9

Simplify the following expressions:

    (i) $(x + 3)(x + 5)$ (ii) $(x - 3)(x^2 + 4x - 5)$

Solution

    (i) $(x + 3)(x + 5)$

We draw a rectangle with sides $x + 3$ and $x + 5$ and then work out the area of each of the smaller rectangles.

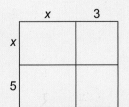

Area $= x^2 + 3x + 5x + 15$

$\therefore (x + 3)(x + 5) = x^2 + 8x + 15$

    (ii) $(x - 3)(x^2 + 4x - 5)$

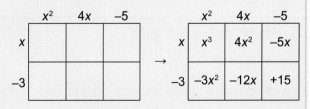

Area $= x^3 + 4x^2 - 5x - 3x^2 - 12x + 15$

$\therefore (x - 3)(x^2 + 4x - 5) = x^3 + x^2 - 17x + 15$

Exercise 1.6

Multiply each of the following expressions and simplify your answers:

1.   (i) $(x + 3)(x + 2)$

    (ii) $(x + 4)(x + 1)$

    (iii) $(x + 2)(x + 7)$

    (iv) $(x - 7)(x + 3)$

    (v) $(x - 1)(x + 5)$

2.   (i) $(y - 4)(y - 8)$

    (ii) $(y - 7)(y + 7)$

    (iii) $(y - 4)(y - 2)$

    (iv) $(y - 3)(y + 3)$

    (v) $(y - 12)(y - 5)$

3.   (i) $(a - 2)(a - 9)$

    (ii) $(a - 11)(a + 3)$

    (iii) $(a + 14)(a - 7)$

    (iv) $(a - 1)(a - 1)$

    (v) $(5 + a)(5 - a)$

4.   (i) $(x + 2)(3x + 2)$

    (ii) $(4x + 1)(2x + 1)$

    (iii) $(x - 2)(4x + 3)$

    (iv) $(3x - 3)(5x - 2)$

    (v) $(2x - 8)(3x - 9)$

5.   (i) $(2y - 4)(3y + 1)$

    (ii) $(6y - 3)(2y - 4)$

    (iii) $(7y - 1)(3y - 5)$

    (iv) $(8 - y)(2 - 3y)$

    (v) $(1 - 2y)(3y - 1)$

6.   (i) $(5b - 4)(b - 1)$

    (ii) $(12b + 1)(2b - 5)$

    (iii) $(4b - 3)(2b - 4)$

    (iv) $(9b - 2)(7 - 5b)$

    (v) $(2 - 2b)(2b - 1)$

7.   (i) $(x + 1)(x^2 + x + 1)$

    (ii) $(x - 3)(2x^2 + x - 1)$

    (iii) $(4x + 1)(4x^2 - 2x - 3)$

    (iv) $(3x^2 - 2x - 2)(x - 3)$

    (v) $(1 - x)(7x^2 - 4x - 1)$

8.   (i) $(x + 1)^2$

    (ii) $(x + 3)^2$

    (iii) $(x - 2)^2$

    (iv) $(x - 5)^2$

    (v) $(2y + 1)^2$

9.   (i) $(3y - 2)^2$

    (ii) $(y - 2)^3$

    (iii) $2(2y - 4)^2$

    (iv) $(y + 5)(y + 3)$ $+ (y + 5)(y - 4)$

    (v) $(y + 1)(2y - 3)$ $- (2y + 1)(y - 1)$

1.8 FACTORISING I

> Factorising is the reverse of expanding. We turn the given expression into a product.

$x(x + 5) = x^2 + 5x \rightarrow$ Expanding

$x^2 + 5x = x(x + 5) \rightarrow$ Factorising

In our course we will encounter three types of **expressions** that will have to be factorised.

Highest Common Factor

To factorise $x^2 - 3x$, we pick the **highest common factor** (HCF) of the two terms and use that as the outside term of our bracket.

$\therefore x^2 - 3x = x(x - 3)$

Difference of Two Squares

Multiply two expressions that differ only by their sign.

$$(x - 4)(x + 4)$$

$$= x(x + 4) - 4(x + 4)$$

$$= x^2 + 4x - 4x - 16$$

$$= x^2 - 16$$

Working backwards, we can factorise:

$$x^2 - 16$$

$$= (x)^2 - (4)^2 \quad \text{(writing each term as a square)}$$

$$= (x - 4)(x + 4)$$

> Note: There must always be a minus sign between the two given terms in order to use this method.

Quadratic Trinomials

When we multiply the two expressions $(x + 3)(x + 4)$, we end up with a type of expression called a **quadratic trinomial**.

> A quadratic trinomial in x has an x^2 term, an x term and a constant.

$(x + 3)(x + 4) = x^2 + 7x + 12$

If we are asked to factorise $x^2 + 7x + 12$, we know we are looking for:

(i) The factors of 12 (factors of the constant)

(ii) That add up to 7 (the coefficient of x)

x^2 Worked Example 1.10

Factorise fully the following expressions:

  (i) $y^2 + 4y$ (ii) $x^2 - 11x$

Solution

(i) $y^2 + 4y$

   y is the highest common factor for both terms.

   $\therefore y^2 + 4y = y(y + 4)$

(ii) $x^2 - 11x$

   $x(x - 11)$

   > We can always check our answer by multiplying out the factors.

x^2 Worked Example 1.11

Factorise:

  (i) $x^2 - 49$ (ii) $a^2 - 225$

Solution

(i) $x^2 - 49$

   Write each term as a square.

   $x^2 = (x)^2$

   $49 = (7)^2$

   $\therefore (x)^2 - (7)^2 = (x - 7)(x + 7)$

(ii) $a^2 - 225$

   $(a)^2 - (15)^2$

   $(a - 15)(a + 15)$

x^2 **Worked Example 1.12**

Factorise:

 (i) $x^2 + 5x + 4$ (ii) $x^2 + 12x + 32$

Solution

 (i) $x^2 + 5x + 4$

 We need to find the factors of $+4$ (positive 4) that add up to $+5$ (positive 5).

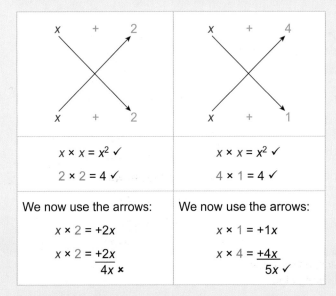

$x \times x = x^2$ ✔ $2 \times 2 = 4$ ✔	$x \times x = x^2$ ✔ $4 \times 1 = 4$ ✔
We now use the arrows: $x \times 2 = +2x$ $\underline{x \times 2 = +2x}$ $4x$ ✘	We now use the arrows: $x \times 1 = +1x$ $\underline{x \times 4 = +4x}$ $5x$ ✔

 So $(x + 4)(x + 1)$ is correct.

> Note: $(x + 4)(x + 1)$ could also be written as $(x + 1)(x + 4)$.

 (ii) $x^2 + 12x + 32$

 We are looking for the factors of $+32$ that add up to $+12$.

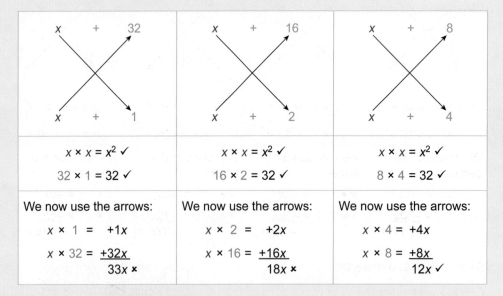

$x \times x = x^2$ ✔ $32 \times 1 = 32$ ✔	$x \times x = x^2$ ✔ $16 \times 2 = 32$ ✔	$x \times x = x^2$ ✔ $8 \times 4 = 32$ ✔
We now use the arrows: $x \times 1 = +1x$ $\underline{x \times 32 = +32x}$ $33x$ ✘	We now use the arrows: $x \times 2 = +2x$ $\underline{x \times 16 = +16x}$ $18x$ ✘	We now use the arrows: $x \times 4 = +4x$ $\underline{x \times 8 = +8x}$ $12x$ ✔

 So $(x + 8)(x + 4)$ is correct.

x^2 **Worked Example 1.13**

Factorise:

(i) $x^2 + 5x - 14$ (ii) $x^2 - 11x + 30$

Solution

> We must be very careful when dealing with expressions that have negative terms.

(i) $x^2 + 5x - 14$

We are looking for factors of -14 (negative 14) that add to give us $+5$ (positive 5).

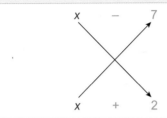

$x \times x = x^2$ ✓	$x \times x = x^2$ ✓
$-7 \times 2 = -14$ ✓	$7 \times -2 = -14$ ✓
We now use the arrows: $x \times 2 = +2x$ $x \times -7 = \underline{-7x}$ $\quad\quad\quad -5x$ ✗	We now use the arrows: $x \times -2 = -2x$ $x \times 7 = \underline{+7x}$ $\quad\quad\quad 5x$ ✓
We must be on the right track, as we have the correct number but the wrong sign.	

So $(x + 7)(x - 2)$ is correct.

(ii) $x^2 - 11x + 30$

> Both factors must be negative.

We are looking for factors of $+30$ that add to give us -11.

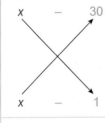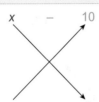

$x \times x = x^2$ ✓	$x \times x = x^2$ ✓	$x \times x = x^2$ ✓	$x \times x = x^2$ ✓
$-30 \times -1 = 30$ ✓	$-10 \times -3 = 30$ ✓	$-15 \times -2 = 30$ ✓	$-6 \times -5 = 30$ ✓
We now use the arrows: $x \times -1 = -1x$ $x \times -30 = \underline{-30x}$ $\quad\quad\quad\quad -31x$ ✗	We now use the arrows: $x \times -3 = -3x$ $x \times -10 = \underline{-10x}$ $\quad\quad\quad\quad -13x$ ✗	We now use the arrows: $x \times -2 = -2x$ $x \times -15 = \underline{-15x}$ $\quad\quad\quad\quad -17x$ ✗	We now use the arrows: $x \times -5 = -5x$ $x \times -6 = \underline{-6x}$ $\quad\quad\quad\quad -11x$ ✓

So $(x - 6)(x - 5)$ is correct.

Don't forget to check your answer.

ACTIVITY 1.6

- If the constant term is positive, then the signs in brackets are either both positive or both negative.
- If the constant term is negative, then one sign is positive and the other sign is negative.

We can also use the area model to factorise quadratic trinomials.

x^2 Worked Example 1.14

Factorise:

(i) $x^2 + 5x + 4$ (ii) $x^2 - 4x - 12$

Solution

(i) $x^2 + 5x + 4$

From using the area model to multiply expressions, we can fill in the areas of two of the smaller rectangles.

	x	
x	x^2	
		4

We fill in the empty spaces in the rectangle.

We know that the area of these two rectangles adds up to $5x$, but the expression must also have coefficients that multiply to give us 4.

	x	
x	x^2	$4x$
	$1x$	4

From this we can fill in the sides of the large rectangle and, hence, the factors of the trinomial.

	x	4
x	x^2	$4x$
1	$1x$	4

Factors: $(x + 1)(x + 4)$

(ii) $x^2 - 4x - 12$

From using the area model to multiply expressions, we can fill in the areas of two of the smaller rectangles.

	x	
x	x^2	
		-12

We now fill in two factors of -12 that add to give us -4 and check to see if they are correct.

	x	
x	x^2	$-6x$
	$2x$	-12

→

	x	-6
x	x^2	$-6x$
2	$2x$	-12

Factors: $(x - 6)(x + 2)$

Factorise the following:

1. $x^2 + 6x + 9$	15. $x^2 - 16x + 64$	29. $x^2 - 10x + 9$	43. $x^2 - 4x + 3$
2. $x^2 + 8x + 7$	16. $x^2 - 5x - 14$	30. $x^2 + 2x - 48$	44. $x^2 - 2x - 24$
3. $x^2 + 13x + 36$	17. $x^2 - 3x - 18$	31. $x^2 - 10x + 24$	45. $y^2 - 121$
4. $x^2 + 8x + 12$	18. $x^2 + 9x + 18$	32. $b^2 - 25$	46. $x^2 - x - 90$
5. $x^2 + 5x$	19. $x^2 - 6x - 27$	33. $x^2 + 12x$	47. $x^2 + 2x - 63$
6. $x^2 - 7x$	20. $x^2 + 6x - 16$	34. $x^2 + x - 72$	48. $x^2 - 15x + 56$
7. $x^2 + 14x + 40$	21. $x^2 - 10x + 21$	35. $y^2 - 169$	49. $x^2 + x - 42$
8. $x^2 - 16$	22. $x^2 + 18x + 81$	36. $x^2 + 15x + 56$	50. $x^2 + 3x - 70$
9. $x^2 + 11x + 24$	23. $x^2 - 2x$	37. $x^2 - 225$	51. $x^2 - 10x - 39$
10. $x^2 - 12x + 27$	24. $x^2 - 100$	38. $x^2 - 2x - 63$	52. $9 - x^2$
11. $x^2 + 4x + 4$	25. $x^2 - 12x + 32$	39. $x^2 - 15x$	53. $x^2 - 11x + 30$
12. $x^2 + 5x - 14$	26. $x^2 - 3x - 4$	40. $x^2 + 7x - 18$	54. $x^2 - 45 + 4x$
13. $x^2 - 9x$	27. $x^2 - 4$	41. $x^2 + 5x - 36$	55. $x^2 - 80 - 10x + 5$
14. $x^2 - 9$	28. $x^2 - 2x - 15$	42. $x^2 - 14x$	56. $x^2 - 7x + 6 + 2x$

1.9 FACTORISING II

The previous section dealt with factorising expressions where the x^2 term only had a coefficient of 1.

We must also be able to factorise expressions where the coefficient of x^2 is greater than 1.

x^2 Worked Example 1.15

Factorise fully the following expressions:

(i) $5a^2 + 20a$ (ii) $2x^2 - 3x$

Solution

(i) $5a^2 + 20a$

The highest common factor of both terms is $5a$.

$\therefore 5a^2 + 20a = 5a(a + 4)$

(ii) $2x^2 - 3x$

In this case, the highest common factor of both terms is x.

$\therefore 2x^2 - 3x = x(2x - 3)$

x^2 Worked Example 1.16

Factorise:

(i) $4x^2 - 81$ (ii) $25a^2 - 144y^2$

Solution

(i) $4x^2 - 81$

Write each term as a square.

$= (2x)^2 - (9)^2$

$= (2x - 9)(2x + 9)$

(ii) $25a^2 - 144y^2$

$= (5a)^2 - (12y)^2$

$= (5a - 12y)(5a + 12y)$

x^2 **Worked Example 1.17**

Factorise:

(i) $2x^2 + 13x + 15$ (ii) $5x^2 - 16x + 3$ (iii) $3x^2 + 11x - 20$

Solution

(i) $2x^2 + 13x + 15$

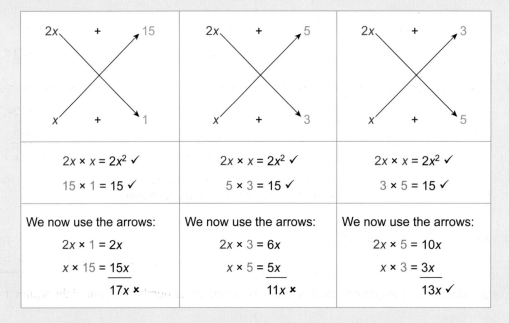

$2x \times x = 2x^2$ ✓	$2x \times x = 2x^2$ ✓	$2x \times x = 2x^2$ ✓
$15 \times 1 = 15$ ✓	$5 \times 3 = 15$ ✓	$3 \times 5 = 15$ ✓
We now use the arrows:	We now use the arrows:	We now use the arrows:
$2x \times 1 = 2x$	$2x \times 3 = 6x$	$2x \times 5 = 10x$
$x \times 15 = \underline{15x}$	$x \times 5 = \underline{5x}$	$x \times 3 = \underline{3x}$
$17x$ ✗	$11x$ ✗	$13x$ ✓

So $(2x + 3)(x + 5)$ is correct.

(ii) $5x^2 - 16x + 3$

If the constant term is positive, then the factors are either both positive or both negative. As we have a negative term ($-16x$) already, both factors must be negative.

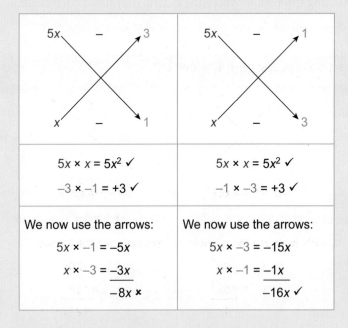

$5x \times x = 5x^2$ ✓	$5x \times x = 5x^2$ ✓
$-3 \times -1 = +3$ ✓	$-1 \times -3 = +3$ ✓
We now use the arrows:	We now use the arrows:
$5x \times -1 = -5x$	$5x \times -3 = -15x$
$x \times -3 = \underline{-3x}$	$x \times -1 = \underline{-1x}$
$-8x$ ✗	$-16x$ ✓

So $(5x - 1)(x - 3)$ is correct.

(iii) $3x^2 + 11x - 20$

If the constant term is negative, then one factor is positive and the other is negative.

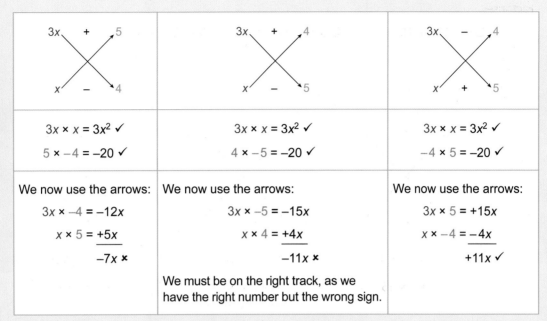

$3x \times x = 3x^2$ ✓	$3x \times x = 3x^2$ ✓	$3x \times x = 3x^2$ ✓
$5 \times -4 = -20$ ✓	$4 \times -5 = -20$ ✓	$-4 \times 5 = -20$ ✓
We now use the arrows: $3x \times -4 = -12x$ $x \times 5 = \underline{+5x}$ $\quad\quad -7x$ ✗	We now use the arrows: $3x \times -5 = -15x$ $x \times 4 = \underline{+4x}$ $\quad\quad -11x$ ✗ We must be on the right track, as we have the right number but the wrong sign.	We now use the arrows: $3x \times 5 = +15x$ $x \times -4 = \underline{-4x}$ $\quad\quad +11x$ ✓

So $(3x - 4)(x + 5)$ is correct.

We may also encounter quadratic trinomials that have a non-prime number in front of the squared term.

x^2 **Worked Example 1.18**

Factorise fully the following expressions:

(i) $4x^2 + 21x + 5$ (ii) $24x^2 - 100x + 16$

Solution

(i) $4x^2 + 21x + 5$

4 has two pairs of factors that we must consider: 1, 4 **and** 2, 2.

$2x \times 2x = 4x^2$ ✓	$4x \times x = 4x^2$ ✓	$4x \times x = 4x^2$ ✓
$5 \times 1 = 5$ ✓	$5 \times 1 = 5$ ✓	$1 \times 5 = 5$ ✓
We now use the arrows: $2x \times 1 = +2x$ $2x \times 5 = \underline{+10x}$ $\quad\quad 12x$ ✗	We now use the arrows: $4x \times 1 = +4x$ $x \times 5 = \underline{+5x}$ $\quad\quad 9x$ ✗	We now use the arrows: $4x \times 5 = +20x$ $x \times 1 = \underline{+1x}$ $\quad\quad +21x$ ✓

$(4x + 1)(x + 5)$ is correct.

(ii) $24x^2 - 100x + 16$

Step 1 Take out the HCF:
$4(6x^2 - 25x + 4)$

Step 2 Factorise $6x^2 - 25x + 4$.

6 has two pairs of factors that we need to consider: 1, 6 **and** 3, 2.

Also, the factors of 4 are 4×1 and 2×2.

This question may require multiple attempts before we get a correct answer.

$\therefore 6x^2 - 25x + 4 = (6x - 1)(x - 4)$

Step 3 Write the fully factorised expression:

$24x^2 - 100x + 16 = 4(6x - 1)(x - 4)$

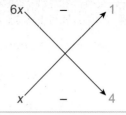

$6x \times x = 6x^2$ ✓

$-1 \times -4 = +4$ ✓

We now use the arrows:

$6x \times -4 = -24x$

$x \times -1 = \underline{-1x}$

$\qquad -25x$ ✓

ACTIVITY 1.7

Another method of factorising quadratic trinomials is the **Guide Number Method**.

x^2 Worked Example 1.19

Factorise $6x^2 - 11x + 3$.

Solution

Step 1 Multiply the coefficient of x^2 by the constant.

6 by 3 = 18

Step 2 Find two factors of 18 that add to give the coefficient of the middle term, $-11x$.

-2 and -9

Step 3 Use the answers from Step 2 to rewrite $6x^2 - 11x + 3$ as follows:

$6x^2 - 2x - 9x + 3$

$2x(3x - 1) - 3(3x - 1)$ (Factorise by grouping)

$(2x - 3)(3x - 1)$ (Distributive property)

The factors of $6x^2 - 11x + 3$ are $(2x - 3)(3x - 1)$.

Exercise 1.8

Factorise fully the following expressions:

1. $2x^2 + 6x$	14. $5x^2 + 13x + 6$	27. $900x^2 - 196$	40. $5x^2 + 12x + 4$
2. $3x^2 + 21x$	15. $2b^2 + 3b$	28. $4x^2 - 13x + 3$	41. $3x^2 - 18x + 24$
3. $7x^2 + 2x - 5$	16. $25x^2 - 100$	29. $81y^2 - 196$	42. $2x^2 + 10x + 12$
4. $2x^2 + 5x + 3$	17. $3x^2 + 17x + 10$	30. $5x^2 + 2x$	43. $2x^2 - 2x - 12$
5. $7x^2 + 15x + 2$	18. $2x^2 - x - 10$	31. $7x^2 - x - 8$	44. $5x^2 - 18x + 9$
6. $64x^2 - 49$	19. $7x^2 + 14x - 21$	32. $3x^2 + 7x + 4$	45. $6x^2 + 3x - 3$
7. $5x^2 + 6x + 1$	20. $5x^2 + 8x - 21$	33. $4x^2 - 16x$	46. $2x^2 - 14x + 20$
8. $4x^2 - 16$	21. $121x^2 - 25$	34. $3x^2 + 8x + 4$	47. $4x^2 - x - 5$
9. $3x^2 + 6x + 3$	22. $2x^2 - 2x - 24$	35. $3x^2 - 4x - 7$	48. $6x^2 + 4x - 2$
10. $7x^2 + 9x + 2$	23. $3x^2 - 24x + 36$	36. $2x^2 - x - 15$	49. $10x^2 + 33x + 9$
11. $2x^2 - 4x + 2$	24. $5y^2 - 7y$	37. $5x^2 + 28x - 49$	50. $6x^2 + 10x + 4$
12. $5x^2 - 25x$	25. $2x^2 - 15x + 18$	38. $2x^2 - 13x + 15$	51. $4x^2 + 5x - 21$
13. $3x^2 - 8x + 5$	26. $5x^2 + 17x - 12$	39. $8x^2 + 17x + 2$	

1.10 SIMPLIFYING ALGEBRAIC FRACTIONS

When we simplify an algebraic fraction, we need to divide above and below by a common factor.

Simplifying algebraic fractions is similar to simplifying normal fractions.

x^2 Worked Example 1.20

Simplify the following:

(i) $\dfrac{40x^2y^4}{8x^2y^3}$

(ii) $\dfrac{20a^3b^5}{25a^2b^6}$

Solution

(i) $\dfrac{40x^2y^4}{8x^2y^3}$

$$= \frac{\cancel{(40)}\cancel{(x)}\cancel{(x)}\cancel{(y)}\cancel{(y)}\cancel{(y)}(y)}{\cancel{(8)}\cancel{(x)}\cancel{(x)}\cancel{(y)}\cancel{(y)}\cancel{(y)}}$$

$= 5y$

Divide above and below by the HCF $8x^2y^3$.

(ii) $\dfrac{20a^3b^5}{25a^2b^6}$

Divide above and below by $5a^2b^5$.

$\therefore \dfrac{20a^3b^5}{25a^2b^6} = \dfrac{4a}{5b}$

x^2 **Worked Example 1.21**

Simplify the following:

(i) $\dfrac{x^2 - 16}{x^2 - 4x}$

(ii) $\dfrac{y^2 + 11y + 28}{y^2 + 4y - 21}$

Solution

(i) $\dfrac{x^2 - 16}{x^2 - 4x}$

We factorise both numerator and denominator.

$= \dfrac{(x - 4)(x + 4)}{x(x - 4)}$

$= \dfrac{\overset{1}{\cancel{(x-4)}}(x + 4)}{x\underset{1}{\cancel{(x-4)}}}$

$= \dfrac{x + 4}{x}$

(ii) $\dfrac{y^2 + 11y + 28}{y^2 + 4y - 21}$

$= \dfrac{(y + 4)(y + 7)}{(y + 7)(y - 3)} = \dfrac{(y + 4)\overset{1}{\cancel{(y + 7)}}}{\underset{1}{\cancel{(y + 7)}}(y - 3)}$

$= \dfrac{y + 4}{y - 3}$

When factorising, you will find that there is usually at least one factor that is common to both the top and the bottom of the fraction.

Long Division in Algebra

Another approach to simplifying an algebraic expression is to use long division. We can use this method of long division when dividing an expression by an expression of lower degree:

Expression	Degree	Reason
$x - 3$	1	Highest power is 1
$x^2 + x + 9$	2	Highest power is 2

Example: Divide 456 by 19.

Solution:

```
           24
    19 | 45⑥
       -(38)↓
        ─────
         7 6
       - (7 6)
        ─────
           0
```

Steps: ■ $45 \div 19 = 2$ Remainder 7

■ Bring down the 6

■ $76 \div 19 = 4$ Remainder 0

$\therefore 456 \div 19 = 24$

As the final remainder is 0, we know that 19 divides 'evenly' into 456 (24 times).

x^2 Worked Example 1.22

Divide $(6x^2 + 13x + 5)$ by $2x + 1$.

Solution

$$
\begin{array}{r}
3x + 5 \\
2x + 1 \overline{\smash{\big)}\ 6x^2 + 13x + 5} \\
-\ (6x^2 +\ 3x) \\
\hline
10x + 5 \\
-\ (10x + 5) \\
\hline
0
\end{array}
$$

Divide $6x^2$ by $2x$ to get $3x$.

Multiply $(2x + 1)$ by $3x$ to get $6x^2 + 3x$ and subtract to get $10x$.

Bring down the next term, which is 5. Divide $10x$ by $2x$ to get 5.

Multiply $(2x + 1)$ by 5 to get $10x + 5$ and subtract to get 0.

As the final remainder is 0, we know that $2x + 1$ divides 'evenly' into $6x^2 + 13x + 5$.

∴ Answer $= 3x + 5$

Note: It is good practice to check your work by expanding.

∴ $(2x + 1)(3x + 5) = 6x^2 + 13x + 5$

x^2 Worked Example 1.23

Simplify $\dfrac{12x^2 - 40x + 25}{6x - 5}$ using long division.

Solution

$$
\begin{array}{r}
2x - 5 \\
6x - 5 \overline{\smash{\big)}\ 12x^2 - 40x + 25} \\
-(12x^2 - 10x) \\
\hline
-30x + 25 \\
-(-30x + 25) \\
\hline
0
\end{array}
$$

Divide $12x^2$ by $6x$ to get $2x$.

Multiply $(6x - 5)$ by $2x$ to get $12x^2 - 10x$ and subtract to get $-30x$.

Bring down the next term, which is 25. Divide $-30x$ by $6x$ to get -5.

Multiply $(6x - 5)$ by -5 to get $-30x + 25$ and subtract to get 0.

As the final remainder is 0, we know that $6x - 5$ divides 'evenly' into $12x^2 - 40x + 25$.

∴ Answer $= 2x - 5$

Note: It is good practice to check your work by expanding.

∴ $(6x - 5)(2x - 5) = 12x^2 - 40x + 25$

Exercise 1.9

Simplify each of the following algebraic fractions:

1. $\dfrac{a^7}{a^3}$

2. $\dfrac{a^{10}}{a^7}$

3. $\dfrac{a^{11}}{a^5}$

4. $\dfrac{a^{12}}{a^3}$

5. $\dfrac{14a^5}{2a^3}$

6. $\dfrac{6a^5}{2a^5}$

7. $\dfrac{20a^{12}}{4a^7}$

8. $\dfrac{16a^5}{2a^4}$

9. $\dfrac{6a^2}{2a}$

10. $\dfrac{10a^{10}}{5a^5}$

11. $\dfrac{6a^6}{2a^2}$

12. $\dfrac{15a^3b^2}{3ab}$

13. $\dfrac{25a^6b^3}{5ab^2}$

14. $\dfrac{18a^2b^2}{6ab}$

15. $\dfrac{21ab^2}{3ab}$

16. $\dfrac{27b^2}{3b}$

17. $\dfrac{-21x^{11}}{7x^7}$

18. $\dfrac{-24x^7}{8x^7}$

19. $\dfrac{-12x^3}{-4x}$

20. $\dfrac{-2x^2}{x}$

21. $\dfrac{-6x^2}{-2x}$

22. $\dfrac{-2x^2y^3}{-xy}$

23. $\dfrac{-22x^2y}{-11x}$

24. $\dfrac{42x^7y^6}{6x^3y^4}$

25. $\dfrac{54x^{11}y^3}{6x^9y^2}$

26. $\dfrac{64x^4y^5z^7}{8x^3y^2z^5}$

27. $\dfrac{x^2-4x}{x-4}$

28. $\dfrac{x^2-64}{x-8}$

29. $\dfrac{x^2+7x+10}{x+2}$

30. $\dfrac{x^2+6x+8}{x+4}$

31. $\dfrac{x^2-14x+48}{x-8}$

32. $\dfrac{2x^2+15x+27}{2x+9}$

33. $\dfrac{10x^2+19x-15}{2x^2+13x+20}$

34. $\dfrac{6x^2-13x-28}{2x^2-3x-14}$

35. $\dfrac{6x^2-7x+2}{2x^2+3x-2}$

Divide the following expressions using long division:

36. $\dfrac{4x^2+8x+3}{2x+1}$

37. $\dfrac{9x^2+18x+5}{3x+5}$

38. $\dfrac{2x^2-13x+18}{2x-9}$

39. $\dfrac{16x^2-14x-15}{8x+5}$

40. $\dfrac{8x^2-34x+35}{4x-7}$

41. $\dfrac{60x^2+83x-45}{5x+9}$

42. $\dfrac{25x^2-169}{5x-13}$ = add 0x

43. $\dfrac{-6x^2+11x-4}{3x-4}$

44. $\dfrac{10x^2+61x+91}{-2x-7}$

1.11 ALGEBRAIC FRACTIONS II

x^2 Worked Example 1.24

Express as a single fraction in its simplest form:

$$\frac{5}{x}+\frac{2}{5x-1}, x\neq 0, \frac{1}{5}$$

Solution

$\dfrac{5}{x}+\dfrac{2}{5x-1}$

The LCD is $(x)(5x-1)$.

$\therefore \dfrac{5}{x}+\dfrac{2}{5x-1}=\dfrac{5(5x-1)+2(x)}{(x)(5x-1)}$

$=\dfrac{25x-5+2x}{(x)(5x-1)}$

$=\dfrac{27x-5}{(x)(5x-1)}$

We do not expand the denominator unless required to do so.

x^2 Worked Example 1.25

Write as a single fraction in its simplest form:

$$\frac{2}{2x+1}-\frac{3}{x-4}, x\neq -\frac{1}{2}, 4$$

Solution

$\dfrac{2}{2x+1}-\dfrac{3}{x-4}$

The LCD is $(2x+1)(x-4)$.

$\therefore \dfrac{2}{2x+1}-\dfrac{3}{x-4}=\dfrac{2(x-4)-3(2x+1)}{(2x+1)(x-4)}$

$=\dfrac{2x-8-6x-3}{(2x+1)(x-4)}$

$=\dfrac{-4x-11}{(2x+1)(x-4)}$

Exercise 1.10

Express as single fractions in their simplest form:

1. $\dfrac{4}{x} + \dfrac{2}{3x}$, $x \neq 0$

2. $\dfrac{5}{2x} - \dfrac{1}{4x}$, $x \neq 0$

3. $\dfrac{11}{2x - 1} - \dfrac{3}{x}$, $x \neq \dfrac{1}{2}, 0$

4. $\dfrac{1}{x + 2} + \dfrac{1}{x}$, $x \neq -2, 0$

5. $\dfrac{2}{x} + \dfrac{1}{x - 2}$, $x \neq 0, 2$

6. $\dfrac{2}{x - 3} + \dfrac{4}{x + 2}$, $x \neq 3, -2$

7. $\dfrac{2}{x - 8} - \dfrac{3}{x + 4}$, $x \neq 8, -4$

8. $\dfrac{5}{2x + 1} - \dfrac{3}{x + 4}$, $x \neq -\dfrac{1}{2}, -4$

9. $\dfrac{1}{3x - 1} - \dfrac{4}{2x - 3}$, $x \neq \dfrac{1}{3}, \dfrac{3}{2}$

10. $\dfrac{7}{2x - 1} - \dfrac{3}{1 + 2x}$, $x \neq \dfrac{1}{2}, -\dfrac{1}{2}$

11. $\dfrac{8}{2x + 5} - \dfrac{1}{3}$, $x \neq -\dfrac{5}{2}$

12. $\dfrac{5}{4x - 3} + \dfrac{4}{3 - 4x}$, $x \neq \dfrac{3}{4}$

13. $\dfrac{2}{4x + 1} - \dfrac{3}{2x - 3}$, $x \neq -\dfrac{1}{4}, \dfrac{3}{2}$

14. $\dfrac{5}{3x - 2} - \dfrac{2}{4 - 6x}$, $x \neq \dfrac{2}{3}$

 ## Revision Exercises

1. (a) If $p = -2$ and $q = 3$, evaluate:

    (i) $p + q$ (iv) pq

    (ii) $p - q$ (v) $-pq$

    (iii) $q - p$ (vi) $q^2 + pq - q$

(b) If $x = -5$ and $y = 2$, evaluate:

    (i) $x + y$ (iv) $x^2 + xy + 3x$

    (ii) $x - y$ (v) $(x + 2y)^2$

    (iii) $y^2 + 2y^2$ (vi) $y^2 + y^3$

(c) (i) If $b = -3$, evaluate:

$$\dfrac{5b - 1}{b - 1}$$

    (ii) If $k = -7$, find the value of:

$$\dfrac{k^2 - 1}{k - 1}$$

    (iii) If $x = 8$, find the value of:

$$\sqrt{\dfrac{3x + 1}{2x}}$$

    (iv) If $y = -3$, evaluate:

$$\sqrt{\dfrac{10 - 2y}{1 - y}}$$

    (v) If $x = 5$ and $y = -2$, evaluate:

$$\sqrt{\dfrac{x - 2y}{2(2x + y)}}$$

2. Simplify the following:

(a) (i) $11a + b - 2a - 3b + 3a$

    (ii) $3x + 2xy + 4x + 10xy$

    (iii) $a + 8a^2 + 2a + 3a^2$

    (iv) $9x^2 + x + 3x^2 + 10x$

    (v) $3y - 4 + 9y + 10$

    (vi) $12x + 5 - 2x - 25$

(b) (i) $11ab + 6 + 4ab - 2$

    (ii) $9x^2 + xy + 7 + 3x^2 + 10xy - 5$

    (iii) $12x^2 + 5x - 8 - x^2 - 2x - 5$

    (iv) $x^2 + 4x - 5 + 17x + x^2 - 11$

    (v) $3x^2 - 4x + 13 - x^2 - 15 + 11x$

    (vi) $y^2 + 11x^2 - 2xy - 13x^2 + 8xy + y^2$

(c) (i) $6xy + y^2 + 3xy - y - y^2$

    (ii) $y^2 + 3x^2 - x^2 - y^2$

    (iii) $6y^2 - y^2 + 3xy - xy + 5y^2$

    (iv) $x^2 + x^3 + 4x^2 + x^3$

    (v) $a - a^2 + 2a + 2a^2$

    (vi) $3a^3 - a^2 + 12a + 12a^2 + 5$

3. Multiply these terms:

(a) (i) $(2a)(7a^2)$ (iv) $(10d)(6d^2)$

   (ii) $(16b^5)(2b^6)$ (v) $(4e)(11e)(e)$

  (iii) $(5c)(3c)(2c)$

(b) (i) $(2ab)(10a^2b)$ (iv) $(2xy)(6xy^2)$

   (ii) $(6a^3b^5)(2a^2b^6)$ (v) $(4pq^3)(2pq)$

  (iii) $(5ac)(3a^5c^2)$

(c) (i) $(-2a)(-a)$ (iv) $(4d)(-9d^2)$

   (ii) $(-b^5)(-2b^6)$ (v) $(-e)(-2e)(-3e)$

  (iii) $(-c)(-c)(-c)(-c)$

4. Multiply out the following:

(a) (i) $(11a)^2$ (iv) $(10d)^3$

   (ii) $(2b)^3$ (v) $(3e)^3$

  (iii) $(5c)^3$

(b) (i) $(2a)^4$ (iv) $(10d)^4$

   (ii) $(-2b)^3$ (v) $(3e)^4$

  (iii) $(4c)^3$

(c) (i) $(-2a)^5$ (iv) $(3m^2)^3$

   (ii) $(-4b)^3$ (v) $(-2k^2)^2$

  (iii) $(4x)^3(2y)^2$

5. Multiply out the brackets and simplify where possible:

(a) (i) $2(3a + 4b)$ (iv) $-2(2x + 5y)$

   (ii) $3(4a + 10b)$ (v) $-3(10x - 2y)$

  (iii) $6(x + 2y + 3z)$ (vi) $3a(5a - 2b)$

(b) (i) $2(x + 3y) + 3(2x + y)$

   (ii) $6(m + 3n) + 7(m + n)$

  (iii) $2(4x^2 + x + 3) + 3(x^2 - 4x - 7)$

  (iv) $3(x + 2y - 6) - 2(x - 10y - 7)$

   (v) $4(2x^2 - x - 1) - 3(x^2 + 3x - 5)$

  (vi) $2x(x - 8) + x(x - 7)$

(c) (i) $(3a + 6b) - (2a + b)$

   (ii) $(a - 11b) - (6a - 2b)$

  (iii) $2(10a - 3b - 1) - (15a - 6b + 20)$

  (iv) $x(3x - 1) - (3x^2 - x - 11)$

   (v) $a(4a - 7b) - 2a(2a - 3b)$

  (vi) $2x(3x^2 + x + 1) - x(5x^2 + x - 3)$

6. Express each of the following as single fractions in their simplest form:

(i) $\dfrac{x + 1}{3} + \dfrac{x}{5} + 4$

(ii) $\dfrac{2x - 1}{2} + \dfrac{3x + 9}{5} - \dfrac{3}{10}$

(iii) $x + \dfrac{2x + 3}{7}$

(iv) $\dfrac{5x - 1}{2} - \dfrac{x - 1}{3}$

(v) $\dfrac{7x - 2}{10} - \dfrac{2x - 1}{5} + \dfrac{x + 3}{2}$

(vi) $\dfrac{5x - 3}{4} + \dfrac{2x - 1}{2} - \dfrac{4 - x}{8}$

7. Express each of the following as single fractions in their simplest form:

(i) $\dfrac{2}{x + 1} + \dfrac{3}{x + 7}, x \neq -1, -7$

(ii) $\dfrac{1}{x + 5} + \dfrac{2}{x + 6}, x \neq -5, -6$

(iii) $\dfrac{6}{x + 1} + \dfrac{3}{x - 7}, x \neq -1, 7$

(iv) $\dfrac{1}{x + 10} - \dfrac{3}{6x + 8}, x \neq -10, -\dfrac{4}{3}$

(v) $\dfrac{2}{2x + 1} - \dfrac{3}{5x - 1}, x \neq -\dfrac{1}{2}, \dfrac{1}{5}$

(vi) $\dfrac{12}{4x + 1} - \dfrac{3}{x - 7}, x \neq -\dfrac{1}{4}, 7$

(vii) $\dfrac{3}{2x + 1} - \dfrac{4}{2x - 1}, x \neq \pm\dfrac{1}{2}$

(viii) $\dfrac{1}{x - 9} - \dfrac{1}{x + 7}, x \neq 9, -7$

8. Expand the following and simplify:

(a) (i) $(x + 1)(x + 5)$ (iv) $(a + 2)^2$

   (ii) $(x + 2)(x + 4)$ (v) $(a + 5)(a - 8)$

  (iii) $(y + 2)(y + 7)$ (vi) $(k + 1)(k - 7)$

(b) (i) $(x - 2)(x - 3)$

   (ii) $(x - 9)(x - 2)$

  (iii) $(2x + 1)(3x + 5)$

  (iv) $(2a + 4)(2a + 4)$

   (v) $(3y + 2)^2$

  (vi) $(4y - 1)^2$

(c) (i) $x(x + 2)(x + 3)$

   (ii) $2x(x + 1)(x + 5)$

  (iii) $(x + 1)(x - 1)(x + 2)$

  (iv) $(x - 2)(x^2 + 2x + 4)$

   (v) $(2x + 3)(4x^2 - 6x + 9)$

  (vi) $(2x - 3)^3$

ACTIVE MATHS

9. Factorise fully the following expressions:

(a) (i) $x^2 - x - 20$

(ii) $y^2 - 36$

(iii) $x^2 - 50x$

(iv) $x^2 - 81$

(v) $x^2 - 7x + 12$

(vi) $x^2 + 3x - 10$

(vii) $x^2 + 4x - 12$

(viii) $x^2 - 6x + 5$

(ix) $x^2 - 5x + 6$

(x) $x^2 - 21x - 100$

(b) (i) $2x^2 - 3x + 1$

(ii) $5x^2 + 13x - 6$

(iii) $64y^2 - 16$

(iv) $12x^2 + 15x$

(v) $8x^2 - 11x$

(vi) $4x^2 + 4x + 1$

(vii) $6x^2 - x - 1$

(viii) $14x^2 + 3x - 2$

(ix) $15x^2 + 13x + 2$

(x) $18x^2 - 9x + 1$

(c) (i) $2x^2 - 13x + 20$

(ii) $2x^2 - 30x + 108$

(iii) $5x^2 + 34x - 7$

(iv) $2x^2 - 9x + 7$

(v) $10x^2 + 5x - 5$

(vi) $4x^2 - 17x + 13$

(vii) $7x^2 + 25x + 12$

(viii) $2x^2 - 20x + 42$

(ix) $4x^2 - 21x + 20$

(x) $6x^2 - 26x + 8$

10. Simplify the following:

(a) (i) $\dfrac{144xy^4z^5}{12xy^2z^5}$

(ii) $\dfrac{(3xy)(12x^2)}{6xy}$

(iii) $\dfrac{(12x^4y)(4xy^3)}{(2xy)^3}$

(iv) $\dfrac{(3p^4q^2)^2(10pq)}{(5pq)(3pq^2)}$

(b) (i) $\dfrac{x^2 + 8x + 15}{x + 5}$

(ii) $\dfrac{x^2 + 10x + 21}{x + 3}$

(iii) $\dfrac{3x^2 + 19x + 28}{x + 4}$

(iv) $\dfrac{4x^2 + 12x + 5}{2x + 1}$

(c) (i) $\dfrac{4x^2 + 18x}{2x}$

(iii) $\dfrac{x^2 - 9}{x^2 - 4x + 3}$

(v) $\dfrac{2x^2 + 9x + 4}{2x^2 + 11x + 5}$

(ii) $\dfrac{x^2 - 2x - 35}{x - 7}$

(iv) $\dfrac{x^2 - 2x}{x^2 - 4}$

(vi) $\dfrac{x^2 + x - 6}{x^2 + 3x - 10}$

(d) Using long division, simplify each of the following.

(i) $\dfrac{x^2 + 11x + 30}{x + 6}$

(iii) $\dfrac{15x^2 - 26x + 8}{5x - 2}$

(v) $\dfrac{40x^2 + 14x - 45}{4x + 5}$

(ii) $\dfrac{8x^2 + 2x - 3}{4x + 3}$

(iv) $\dfrac{14x^2 - 67x + 18}{7x - 2}$

(vi) $\dfrac{45x^2 + 92x + 32}{-9x - 4}$

11. (a) The area of a trapezoid can be found using the formula:

Work out the area of each of the following trapezoids.

Trapezoid	h	a	b
1	2 m	3 m	1 m
2	3 cm	10 cm	3.5 cm
3	20 mm	12 mm	40 mm
4	1.5 m	1 m	50 cm
5	20 cm	400 mm	0.30 m

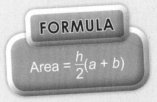

FORMULA

Area $= \dfrac{h}{2}(a + b)$

(b) The approximate time (t in seconds) taken for an object to fall from a height of h metres is given by the formula:

FORMULA

$$t = \sqrt{\dfrac{2h}{g}}$$

where $g = 9.81$.

(i) Calculate the time taken for each object to fall from the given height. Give your answer in seconds correct to two decimal places.

Object	h
1	30 m
2	3,000 m
3	4,000 m
4	1 km
5	0.75 km

An archaeologist wishes to determine how deep the water level is in a well.

To ensure an accurate measurement, she drops 10 stones into the well and records the time taken for the stones to hit the water.

Her results are as shown.

Add then ÷ by 10

Stone number	1	2	3	4	5	6	7	8	8	10
Time (secs)	2.0	2.1	1.9	1.8	2.1	2.1	1.9	2.0	2.1	1.8

(ii) What was the average time taken for the stone to hit the water?

(iii) Using this value for t, calculate the depth of water in the well to the nearest metre.

chapter 2

Real Numbers

Learning Outcomes

In this chapter you will learn about:

- ⊃ Factors, multiples and prime factors
- ⊃ Highest common factor and lowest common multiple
- ⊃ Addition, subtraction, multiplication and division of integers
- ⊃ Rational numbers
- ⊃ Irrational numbers
- ⊃ Real numbers
- ⊃ Rounding
- ⊃ Scientific notation
- ⊃ Orders of magnitude
- ⊃ Order of operations

2.1 NATURAL NUMBERS

The **natural numbers** are the ordinary counting numbers. The set of natural numbers is an **infinite** set. This means that the set is never-ending. The letter N is used to label the set of natural numbers.

$$N = \{1, 2, 3, 4...\}$$

The natural numbers are often represented on a numberline:

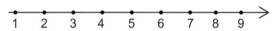

```
 •   •   •   •   •   •   •   •   •  ⟶
 1   2   3   4   5   6   7   8   9
```

2.2 FACTORS, MULTIPLES AND PRIME FACTORS

- Natural number
- Factor
- Multiple
- Prime factor
- LCM
- HCF
- Integers
- Rational number
- Irrational number
- Reciprocal
- Real number
- Recurring decimal
- Terminating decimal
- Scientific notation

Factors

A **factor** of a natural number is any natural number that divides evenly into the given number.

For example, all the factors of 16 are $\{1, 2, 4, 8, 16\}$.

As you can see, 1 is a factor of 16, and 16 is a factor of 16.

Every factor is part of a pair.

The number 16 has three factor pairs:

1 × 16 = 16
2 × 8 = 16
4 × 4 = 16

⇒ Factor pairs are: 1 and 16
2 and 8
4 and 4

- 1 is a factor of every natural number.
- Every natural number is a factor of itself.

Ⓡ Worked Example 2.1

List the factors of 24.

Solution

The factors of 24 are $\{1, 2, 3, 4, 6, 8, 12, 24\}$.

Ⓡ Worked Example 2.2

List the pairs of factors of 40.

Solution

The pairs of factors of 40 are
$1 \times 40, 2 \times 20, 4 \times 10, 5 \times 8$.

Multiples

A **multiple** of a natural number is itself a natural number into which the natural number divides, leaving no remainder.

The multiples of 6 are $\{6, 12, 18, 24, 30, 36...\}$ because:

$6 \times 1 = 6$
$6 \times 2 = 12$
$6 \times 3 = 18$
$6 \times 4 = 24$
$6 \times 5 = 30$, and so on.

As you can see, the set of multiples is an infinite set, i.e. it goes on forever.

R Worked Example 2.3

List the first six multiples of 4.

Solution

$4 \times 1 = 4$	$4 \times 4 = 16$
$4 \times 2 = 8$	$4 \times 5 = 20$
$4 \times 3 = 12$	$4 \times 6 = 24$

The first six multiples of 4 are
$\{4, 8, 12, 16, 20, 24\}$.

If five 2s are multiplied together, i.e. $2 \times 2 \times 2 \times 2 \times 2$, it is written as 2^5 (pronounced '2 to the power of 5').

Similarly, $3 \times 3 \times 3 \times 3 \times 3 \times 3 = 3^6$ ('3 to the power of 6').

In these examples, the ^{5} and the ^{6} are called **indices** or **powers**.

As you can see, 2 is a factor of 2^5, and 3 is a factor of 3^6.

In general, 2 is always a factor of 2^n and 3 is always a factor of 3^n, where n is a natural number.

> The singular of indices is index.

> a is a factor of a^n, where $a \in R$, $n \in N$.

R Worked Example 2.4

Write out all the factors of 7^4.
Where possible, give the factors in the form 7^a, where a is a natural number.

Solution

$7^4 = 7 \times 7 \times 7 \times 7$

Therefore, the factors of 7^4 are $\{1, 7^1, 7^2, 7^3, 7^4\}$.

Prime Numbers

> **Prime numbers** are natural numbers that have **two** factors only.

- 7 is a prime number, as it has two factors only: 1 and 7.
- 2 is the only even prime number. Its two factors are 1 and 2.
- 11 is the first two-digit prime. Its two factors are 1 and 11.
- 1 is **not** a prime, as it has one factor only: itself.
- 0 is **not** a prime, as it has an infinite number of factors and it is not a natural number.

Euclid (c. 365 BC–275 BC)

> The Greek mathematician Euclid proved that the number of primes is infinite.

> Natural numbers greather than 1 that are not prime are called **composite numbers**.
>
> The first five composite numbers are 4, 6, 8, 9 and 10.

ACTIVITY 2.1

Worked Example 2.5

List all the prime numbers between 10 and 20.

Solution

The prime numbers between 10 and 20 are {11, 13, 17, 19}.

Highest Common Factor (HCF)

The **highest common factor** of two natural numbers, n_1 and n_2, is the largest natural number that divides evenly into both n_1 and n_2.

The highest common factor of 12 and 20 is 4, as 4 is the largest natural number that divides evenly into both 12 and 20.

Worked Example 2.6

What is the HCF of 8 and 26?

Solution

Factors of 8 = {1, 2, 4, 8}.

Factors of 26 = {1, 2, 13, 26}.

∴ HCF = 2

Lowest Common Multiple (LCM)

The **lowest common multiple** of two numbers is the smallest multiple that both numbers share.

The lowest common multiple of 3 and 4 is 12, as 12 is the smallest number that both 3 and 4 divide evenly into.

Worked Example 2.7

What is the LCM of 6 and 15?

Solution

The multiples of 6 are {6, 12, 18, 24, (30), 36...}.

The multiples of 15 are {15, (30), 45, 60, 75...}.

∴ LCM = 30

The Greek mathematician Euclid discovered more than 2,000 years ago that every composite number could be written as a unique product of prime numbers. For example:

$30 = 2 \times 3 \times 5$

$36 = 2 \times 2 \times 3 \times 3 = 2^2 \times 3^2$

This fact is useful for finding HCFs and LCMs.

R Worked Example 2.8

Find the HCF of 80 and 48.

Solution

Divide using prime numbers, starting with the smallest possible prime that is a factor.

2	80
2	40
2	20
2	10
5	5
	1

2	48
2	24
2	12
2	6
3	3
	1

■ 2^4 is the highest common factor of 80 and 48.

∴ HCF = 2^4

HCF = 16

$80 = 2^4 \times 5$

$48 = 2^4 \times 3$

R Worked Example 2.9

Find the LCM of 60 and 42.

Solution

Write each number as a product of prime factors.

2	60
2	30
3	15
5	5
	1

2	42
3	21
7	7
	1

■ 2^2 is the bigger of the factors 2 and 2^2.

■ 3 is a common factor of both 60 and 42.

■ 5 and 7 are the non-common factors.

∴ LCM = $2^2 \times 3 \times 5 \times 7$

LCM = 420

$60 = 2^2 \times 3 \times 5$

$42 = 2 \times 3 \times 7$

 ACTIVITIES 2.2, 2.3, 2.4

This gives us a method of finding the prime factors and also of showing that each number is a product of primes.

Exercise 2.1

1. Represent the following natural numbers on a numberline:

    (i) 2   (ii) 4   (iii) 7   (iv) 11

2. Write down all the factors of each of the following natural numbers:

    (i) 40   (iii) 28   (v) 96

    (ii) 64   (iv) 35   (vi) 48

3. List the first six multiples of each of the following natural numbers:

    (i) 4   (iii) 8   (v) 12

    (ii) 6   (iv) 9   (vi) 14

4. Represent on a numberline the prime numbers between 10 and 20.

5. By finding all the factors of each number, write down the HCF of each of the following:

(i) 6 and 14   (v) 12 and 36   (viii) 15, 25 and 50

(ii) 20 and 45   (vi) 45 and 60   (ix) 16, 12 and 80

(iii) 18 and 24   (vii) 3, 9 and 30   (x) 9, 30 and 45

(iv) 37 and 19

6. By writing out the first six multiples, write down the LCM of each of the following:

(i) 4 and 6   (v) 15 and 18   (viii) 4, 5 and 20

(ii) 8 and 12   (vi) 16 and 20   (ix) 8, 10 and 20

(iii) 10 and 12   (vii) 2, 3 and 4   (x) 15, 18 and 30

(iv) 9 and 15

7. Write the following numbers as products of prime factors:

(i) 64   (v) 102   (viii) 374

(ii) 184   (vi) 368   (ix) 273

(iii) 2,310   (vii) 5,250   (x) 170

(iv) 1870

8. (a) Express each of the following pairs of numbers as the product of prime factors.

(b) Hence, find the LCM and HCF for each pair.

(i) 136 and 102   (v) 60 and 765

(ii) 117 and 130   (vi) 123 and 615

(iii) 368 and 621   (vii) 69 and 123

(iv) 58 and 174   (viii) 102 and 170

9. Write down the following:

(i) A natural number between 55 and 57   (v) The HCF of 14 and 30

(ii) A prime number between 14 and 18   (vi) The LCM of 4 and 6

(iii) A factor of 91 between 10 and 20   (vii) The product of the first five prime numbers.

(iv) A multiple of 7 between 20 and 30

10. 294 red pens, 252 green pens and 210 blue pens are distributed equally among some students (i.e. each student gets equal numbers of each colour).
What is the largest possible number of students in the group?

11. Alice, Bob and Carl are jumping up a large flight of stairs. Alice jumps two steps at a time, Bob jumps four steps at a time, while Carl jumps five steps at a time.
On which step will all three land together for the first time? (Assume they all begin on the same step.)

12. John looks out to sea and sees two lighthouses flash at the same time. One lighthouse flashes every 20 seconds, the other every 30 seconds.
How long will John have to wait before the lighthouses flash at the same time again?

13. A town planner has been assigned the task of dividing a large field into square allotments. The field is rectangular, and its dimensions are 168 m by 196 m. The allotments need to be as large as possible.

(i) What is the length of a side of each allotment?

(ii) How many allotments will the field contain?

(iii) What is the area of each allotment?

14. A group of girls bought 72 multi-coloured bracelets, 144 red and brown bracelets and 216 pink and yellow bracelets. If each girl buys the same number of each type, then what is the largest possible number of girls in the group?

15. The organisers of an outdoor pursuits camp are organising activities for the day ahead. The table shows the planned activities and the number of people in each team.

Activity	No. of people
Kayaking	5
Paintballing	20
Tennis	2
Soccer	11

The organisers divide the participants into groups, such that each group can be divided evenly into teams for each event.

(i) If each group has to be as small as possible, what is the size of each group?

(ii) If the camp can cater for 700 people, then what is the maximum number of participants it can take on this particular day?

2.3 INTEGERS

The integers are made up of zero and all the positive and negative whole numbers. Mathematicians use the letter Z to represent the set of integers.

$$Z = \{...-6, -5, -4, -3, -2, -1, 0, 1, 2, 3, 4, 5, 6, 7...\}$$

Multiplication and Division of Integers

In your Junior Cert course you met with the rules for multiplication/division of integers and addition/subtraction of integers. Here is a summary of the rules:

Addition/Subtraction	Multiplication/Division
Think of going up and down a lift, starting at the ground floor: zero. Plus is up; minus is down.	Like signs give plus; unlike signs give minus.
−8 + 2 = −6 [down 8, up 2 is −6]	−8 × −2 = 16 [like signs give plus]
−8 − 2 = −10 [down 8, down 2 is −10]	−8 ÷ 2 = −4 [unlike signs give minus]

Ⓡ Worked Example 2.10

Evaluate the following:

(i) 6 + 9

(ii) 8 − 10

(iii) −12 − 15

Solution

(i) 6 + 9 = 15

(ii) 8 − 10 = −2

(iii) −12 − 15 = −27

ACTIVITIES 2.5, 2.6, 2.7

In Activities 2.5 to 2.7 you derived the following rules of signs for multiplication and division:

Rules for Multiplication	Rules for Division
(i) positive × positive = positive	(i) positive ÷ positive = positive
(ii) positive × negative = negative	(ii) positive ÷ negative = negative
(iii) negative × positive = negative	(iii) negative ÷ positive = negative
(iv) negative × negative = positive	(iv) negative ÷ negative = positive

Note that division by 0 is **undefined**. For example, 8 ÷ 0 is undefined (math error on calculator).

Ⓡ Worked Example 2.11

Evaluate the following:

(i) 3×-12

(ii) $(-5)(-11)$

(iii) $60 \div -30$

(iv) $(-5)^3$

Solution

(i) $3 \times -12 = -36$ (positive × negative = negative)

(ii) $(-5)(-11) = 55$ (negative × negative = positive)

(iii) $60 \div -30 = -2$ (positive ÷ negative = negative)

(iv) $(-5)^3 = (-5)(-5)(-5) = (25)(-5) = -125$

📖 Exercise 2.2

1. Evaluate each of the following:

   (i) 5 − 2

   (ii) 9 − 4

   (iii) 6 − 10

   (iv) 17 − 22

   (v) −7 − 4

   (vi) −8 − 7

2. Evaluate each of the following:

   (i) −3 − 9

   (ii) 8 − 1

   (iii) 2 − 12

   (iv) −5 − 10

   (v) −10 − 50

   (vi) 12 − 15

3. Evaluate each of the following:

   (i) 3 − 2 + 1

   (ii) 3 − 8 − 2

   (iii) 5 − 6 − 2 + 3

   (iv) 8 − 2 + 1 − 5

   (v) −7 − 4 − 3 − 4

   (vi) −3 + 4 − 1 + 2

4. Evaluate each of the following:

   (i) −5 − 2 + 5 + 8

   (ii) 5 − 5 − 4 + 4

   (iii) −5 − 8 − 3 + 2

   (iv) −2 + 5 − 8 + 3

   (v) 8 − 7 + 7 − 8

   (vi) 6 − 9 − 4 + 2

5. On Sunday evening, Seán has €1,500 in his credit union account. The following week Seán visits his bank four times.

   (a) On Monday, he withdraws €700 from his account.

   (b) On Tuesday, he lodges €800 to his account.

   (c) On Thursday, he withdraws a further €700.

   (d) On Friday morning, he lodges €100.

   What is the balance in Seán's credit union account on Friday evening?

6. There are 10 questions on a multiple choice test. A correct answer is worth 5 marks. An incorrect answer incurs a penalty of –2 marks and an unanswered question is worth 1 mark. Alice, Bob and Kylie take the test.

(a) Alice answers four questions correctly, leaves two unanswered and gets the rest wrong.

(b) Bob answers seven questions correctly and answers one incorrectly. He leaves the rest unanswered.

(c) Kylie answers three questions incorrectly and leaves one unanswered. She gets the rest correct.

How many marks did Alice, Bob and Kylie each get on the test?

7. Evaluate the following without using a calculator:

(i) $(4)(5)$ (iii) $(5)(-4)$

(ii) $(-5)(4)$ (iv) $(-5)(-4)$

8. Evaluate, without using a calculator, each of the following:

(i) $(10)(4)$ (iv) $(-15)(-6)$

(ii) $(-2)(16)$ (v) $(-5)(6)(-3)$

(iii) $(7)(-8)$ (vi) $(-15)(-2)(-5)$

9. Evaluate the following, without using a calculator:

(i) $15 \div 3$ (iv) $21 \div -7$

(ii) $-24 \div 6$ (v) $16 \div 4$

(iii) $-39 \div -13$ (vi) $96 \div -8$

10. Evaluate each of the following:

(i) $-99 \div -33$ (iv) $-16 \div -8$

(ii) $-66 \div 11$ (v) $121 \div -11$

(iii) $144 \div -12$ (vi) $-72 \div 9$

11. Match the items in column A with those in column B:

A	B
The product of a positive integer and a negative integer	0
The population of Dublin multiplied by zero	$-y$
The product of two negative integers	A negative integer
x multiplied by 1, where x is any integer	8
The sum of this integer and y is zero	A positive integer
The opposite of –8	x

12. Evaluate the following without the use of a calculator:

(i) $(-2)^2$ (iii) $(-4)^2$ (v) $(1)^3$

(ii) $(3)^2$ (iv) $(-1)^3$

13. Evaluate each of the following without the use of a calculator:

(i) $(2)^3$ (iii) $(5)^2$ (v) $(4)^3$

(ii) $(-3)^3$ (iv) $(-6)^2$ (vi) $(-10)^3$

2.4 RATIONAL NUMBERS

The letter Q is used to represent the set of rational numbers.

$Q = \{$any number that can be written in the form $\frac{a}{b}$, where $a, b \in Z, b \neq 0\}$

Rational numbers are also called fractions.

There are two parts to every fraction: the **numerator** (the top) and the **denominator** (the bottom).

R Worked Example 2.12

Which is bigger: $\frac{2}{5}$ or $\frac{5}{12}$?

Solution

Step 1

Find a common denominator. This means find an equivalent fraction for $\frac{2}{5}$ and $\frac{5}{12}$ so that both equivalent fractions have the same denominator.

The lowest common denominator will be the LCM of 5 and 12, which is 60.

Step 2

$$\frac{2}{5} = \frac{24}{60} \quad \text{and} \quad \frac{5}{12} = \frac{25}{60}$$

$$\frac{25}{60} > \frac{24}{60}$$

Therefore, $\frac{5}{12} > \frac{2}{5}$.

R Worked Example 2.13

Mary and Aisling are painting a wall. At the end of the week, Mary measures the area she has painted and declares that she has painted half the wall in one week. Aisling measures the area she has painted and says she has painted a third of the wall.

What fraction of the wall has been painted in the week?

Solution

We need to add the fractions $\frac{1}{3} + \frac{1}{2}$.

Step 1

Find the LCM of 3 and 2.

LCM(3, 2) = 6

Step 2

Change $\frac{1}{3}$ and $\frac{1}{2}$ to equivalent fractions that have a denominator of 6.

$$\frac{1}{3} = \frac{2}{6} \quad \text{and} \quad \frac{1}{2} = \frac{3}{6}$$

It is now clear that:

$$\frac{1}{3} + \frac{1}{2} = \frac{2}{6} + \frac{3}{6} = \frac{5}{6}$$

So $\frac{5}{6}$ of the wall is painted at the end of the week.

R Worked Example 2.14

Evaluate the following:

(i) $\frac{1}{5} \times \frac{2}{3}$ (ii) $\frac{3}{5}$ of $\frac{3}{4}$

Solution

(i) $\frac{1}{5} \times \frac{2}{3} = \frac{1 \times 2}{5 \times 3}$

$$= \frac{2}{15}$$

$$\frac{\text{Numerator} \times \text{numerator}}{\text{Denominator} \times \text{denominator}}$$

(ii) $\frac{3}{5}$ of $\frac{4}{3} = \frac{3}{5} \times \frac{3}{4} = \frac{3 \times 3}{5 \times 4} = \frac{9}{20}$

(multiplying numerator by numerator and denominator by denominator)

R Worked Example 2.15

How many strips of ribbon, each $2\frac{1}{2}$ cm long, can be cut from a roll of ribbon $32\frac{1}{2}$ cm in length?

Solution

We need to find the number of $2\frac{1}{2}$ cm lengths in $32\frac{1}{2}$ cm, i.e. $32\frac{1}{2} \div 2\frac{1}{2}$.

Step 1

Find the reciprocal of the fraction by which you are dividing:

$$2\frac{1}{2} = \frac{5}{2}$$

The reciprocal of $\frac{5}{2}$ is $\frac{2}{5}$.

> The reciprocal of a fraction is found by turning the fraction upside down. For example, the reciprocal of $\frac{11}{12}$ is $\frac{12}{11}$.

Step 2

To divide by a fraction, we multiply by its reciprocal:

Therefore, $32\frac{1}{2} \div 2\frac{1}{2} = \frac{65}{2} \div \frac{5}{2} = \frac{65}{2} \times \frac{2}{5} = \frac{65 \times 2}{2 \times 5}$

$$= \frac{130}{10}$$

$$= 13$$

There are 13 strips.

Exercise 2.3

1. Evaluate each of the following, without using a calculator:

   (i) $\frac{2}{3} + \frac{5}{12}$

   (ii) $\frac{3}{4} - \frac{1}{8}$

   (iii) $\frac{3}{5} - \frac{1}{10}$

   (iv) $\frac{2}{9} + \frac{7}{12}$

   (v) $\frac{3}{4} - \frac{1}{2}$

   (vi) $2\frac{1}{2} + 3\frac{1}{4}$

   (vii) $5\frac{3}{4} - 3\frac{1}{8}$

   (viii) $5\frac{1}{6} + 6\frac{3}{8}$

   (ix) $9\frac{7}{8} - 3\frac{7}{12}$

   (x) $3\frac{1}{2} - 1\frac{3}{4}$

2. Express each of the following as a single fraction in its simplest form:

   (i) $\frac{1}{5} \times \frac{2}{3}$

   (ii) $\frac{1}{2} \times \frac{1}{3}$

   (iii) $\frac{5}{6} \times \frac{1}{4}$

   (iv) $\frac{4}{5} \times \frac{4}{9}$

   (v) $\frac{3}{5} \times \frac{3}{4}$

   (vi) $2\frac{3}{7} \times \frac{7}{15}$

   (vii) $1\frac{1}{2} \times 4\frac{2}{3}$

   (viii) $5\frac{1}{4} \times 1\frac{3}{7}$

   (ix) $3\frac{1}{2} \times 8\frac{1}{4}$

   (x) $2\frac{5}{8} \times 1\frac{1}{6}$

3. Evaluate each of the following and write the answer as a single fraction in its simplest form:

   (i) $\frac{1}{6} \div \frac{2}{3}$

   (ii) $\frac{1}{3} \div \frac{1}{3}$

   (iii) $\frac{1}{4} \div \frac{2}{3}$

   (iv) $3\frac{1}{9} \div 2\frac{1}{3}$

   (v) $\frac{3}{5} \div \frac{1}{4}$

   (vi) $12\frac{2}{5} \div 3\frac{1}{10}$

   (vii) $\frac{6}{25} \div \frac{9}{10}$

   (viii) $28\frac{1}{2} \div 2\frac{3}{8}$

   (ix) $\frac{7}{8} \div \frac{3}{4}$

   (x) $4\frac{4}{5} \div 1\frac{1}{7}$

4. Thomas is training for a 10 km road race. On Monday of last week, he ran $4\frac{2}{5}$ km. On Thursday he ran $5\frac{3}{8}$ km and on Sunday he ran $5\frac{1}{2}$ km.

   How many kilometres did Thomas run last week?

5. A ball bearing weighs $1\frac{1}{4}$ g. How many ball bearings weigh a total of 35 g?

6. A householder burns $17\frac{3}{4}$ kg of coal every week during the winter months.

   (i) How much coal will he burn during the month of December?

   (ii) How many weeks does it take to burn $97\frac{5}{8}$ kg of coal?

7. Caoimhe has bought 12 bars of chocolate.

   How many pieces will she have if she breaks the bars into:

   (i) Halves   (ii) Quarters   (iii) Thirds

REAL NUMBERS

ACTIVE MATHS   39

8. Kevin is trying to negotiate an increase in his pocket money.

His parents are offering him the following two options:

(i) An increase of $\frac{3}{10}$ this year, which is then increased by $\frac{2}{5}$ the next year

OR

(ii) An increase of $\frac{2}{5}$ this year, which is then increased by $\frac{3}{10}$ the next year

Which option should Kevin choose and why?

9. John was given $\frac{1}{3}$ of the 84 bars in a jar.

He ate $\frac{3}{4}$ of the bars that he was given.

How many bars did John eat?

10. Marie went to the fair with €100.

She spent $\frac{1}{4}$ of her €100 on rollercoasters and $\frac{1}{10}$ of her €100 on snacks.

How much money did she spend?

11. Jenny has finished the third day of a six day hike. If she has completed $\frac{3}{7}$ of the hike's total distance of 336 km, how many kilometres per day must she average for the remainder of her trip?

12. Nessa is 120 cm tall.

If John is $\frac{4}{3}$ of the height of Nessa and Paul is $\frac{5}{4}$ of the height of John, how tall is Paul?

2.5 DECIMALS AND IRRATIONAL NUMBERS

Consider the decimal 0.352. This number is the sum of the fractions $\frac{3}{10} + \frac{5}{100} + \frac{2}{1,000}$.

Consider two types of decimal: terminating decimals and recurring decimals.

Terminating Decimals

A number such as 0.3456 is called a **terminating decimal**. It is called terminating because it terminates (or ends) after four decimal places. This number can be written as the sum $\frac{3}{10} + \frac{4}{100} + \frac{5}{1,000} + \frac{6}{10,000}$.

As you can see, all the denominators are powers of 10.

Examples of fractions that are terminating decimals are $\frac{2}{5}, \frac{3}{4}$ and $\frac{5}{16}$.

$\frac{2}{5} = 0.4$ $\qquad\qquad$ $\frac{3}{4} = 0.75$ $\qquad\qquad$ $\frac{5}{16} = 0.3125$

R Worked Example 2.16

Write 0.8154 as the sum of four fractions.

Solution

$$0.8154 = \frac{8}{10} + \frac{1}{100} + \frac{5}{1,000} + \frac{4}{10,000}$$

Recurring Decimals

A decimal such as 0.353535..., which contains an infinite number of digits and where the digits form a pattern, is called a **recurring** or **repeating decimal**.

Any fraction whose denominator's prime factors are not just 2 and/or 5 are **recurring** decimals.

Examples of fractions that are recurring decimals are $\frac{1}{3}, \frac{2}{9}$ and $\frac{5}{13}$.

$\frac{1}{3} = 0.333333...$ $\qquad$ $\frac{2}{9} = 0.222222...$ $\qquad$ $\frac{5}{13} = 0.384615384615...$

The **dot notation** is often used to represent a recurring decimal. For example, 0.222... can be written as $0.\dot{2}$.

The dots go over the first digit of the block to be repeated and the last digit of the block to be repeated. For example, $0.8\dot{9}1\dot{7} = 0.8917917...$

All fractions are either recurring decimals or terminating decimals. You can use your calculator to convert fractions to decimals: simply divide the numerator by the denominator.

Examples: $\frac{7}{8} = 7 \div 8 = 0.875$ $\qquad\qquad \frac{8}{15} = 8 \div 15 = 0.5333... = 0.5\dot{3}$

R Worked Example 2.17

Find the prime factors of 50 and 9 and hence decide whether the fractions $\frac{3}{50}$ and $\frac{1}{9}$ recur or terminate.

Solution

$50 = 5^2 \times 2$

As the only prime factors are 2 and 5, the fraction $\frac{3}{50}$ will terminate.

Checking on the calculator reveals that $\frac{3}{50} = 0.6$.

$9 = 3^2$. As the prime factors are not 2 and/or 5, the fraction $\frac{1}{9}$ will recur.

Checking on the calculator reveals $\frac{1}{9} = 0.11111...$ (or $0.\dot{1}$)

Rounding

R Worked Example 2.18

Write, correct to the nearest whole number:

    (i) 12.56   (ii) 9.48

Solution

    (i) 12.56

        When rounding to the **nearest whole number**, we look at the **first number after the decimal point**.

        ■ If this number is 5 or greater, then we round up to 13.

        ■ If this number is less than 5, then the corrected answer is 12.

        As 5 is the first number after the decimal point, 12.56 rounded to the nearest whole number is 13.

                         12.56

            12   12.5   13   Answer = 13

        On the numberline above, it is clear that 12.56 is nearer to 13 than to 12.

    (ii) 9.48

        Here, the first number after the decimal point is 4, which is less than 5. Therefore, the corrected answer is 9.

              9.48

        9   9.5   10   Answer = 9

        On the numberline, 9.48 is closer to 9 than to 10.

Write, correct to one decimal place:

    (i) 2.57

    (ii) 39.32

Solution

    (i) 2.57

When rounding to **one decimal place,** we look at the **second number after the decimal point**. Again, if this number is 5 or greater, we round up to 2.6. Otherwise, the corrected answer is 2.5. As 7 is the second number after the decimal point, we round up to 2.6.

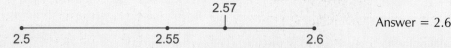

Answer = 2.6

    (ii) 39.32

Here, the second number after the decimal point is 2, which is less than 5. Therefore, the number rounded to one decimal place is 39.3.

Answer = 39.3

Irrational Numbers

In the right-angled triangle shown, the value for x can be found using the theorem of Pythagoras. Here is the solution:

$$x^2 = 1^2 + 1^2$$
$$x^2 = 1 + 1$$
$$x^2 = 2$$
$$x = \sqrt{2} \quad (\text{as } x > 0)$$

Can $\sqrt{2}$ be written as a fraction? This problem preoccupied the ancient Greek mathematicians for many years. Around 500 BC Hippasus, a follower of Pythagoras, proved that $\sqrt{2}$ could **not** be written as a fraction. Legend has it that Pythagoras disagreed to such an extent that he threw Hippasus overboard from a ship, causing him to drown. Numbers that cannot be written as fractions are called **irrational numbers**. $\sqrt{2}$ was the first known irrational number.

- A **rational number** is a number that can be written in the form $\frac{a}{b}$, where a is an integer and b is a non-zero integer.

- An **irrational number** is a number that **cannot** be written as a fraction, i.e. it is a non-terminating, non-recurring decimal.

While $\sqrt{2}$ cannot be written as a fraction, it is possible to find an approximation for $\sqrt{2}$. A calculator gives the approximation $\sqrt{2} = 1.414213562$, but this decimal goes on forever with no pattern or repetition.

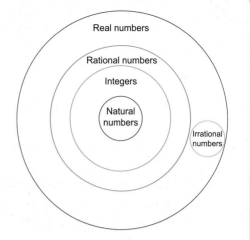

> The rational numbers together with the irrational numbers make up the **Real Number System.**

$\sqrt{2}$ on the Numberline

Consider the diagram.

$|PQ|^2 = |OP|^2 + |OQ|^2$ (theorem of Pythagoras)

$|PQ|^2 = 1^2 + 1^2$

$|PQ|^2 = 2$

$|PQ| = \sqrt{2}$ (as $|PQ| > 0$)

Using a compass, we can now construct a segment of length $\sqrt{2}$ on the x-axis.

(i) Place the compass point at P and the pencil at Q. The compass is now set to a width of $\sqrt{2}$.

(ii) Place the compass point at O and swing an arc to intersect the x-axis at R.

$|OR| = \sqrt{2}$.

R Worked Example 2.20

1. Using a calculator, evaluate the following to four decimal places:

   (i) $\sqrt{3}$

   (ii) $\sqrt{14}$

2. Evaluate, without the use of a calculator:

   (i) $(\sqrt{6})^2$

   (ii) $(\sqrt{10})^2$

Solution

1. (i) $\sqrt{3} = 1.7320508... \approx 1.7321$

   (ii) $\sqrt{14} = 3.741657... \approx 3.7417$

2. (i) $(\sqrt{6})^2 = (\sqrt{6})(\sqrt{6}) = \sqrt{36} = 6$

   (ii) $(\sqrt{10})^2 = (\sqrt{10})(\sqrt{10}) = \sqrt{100} = 10$

Significant Figures

Significant figures are different from decimal places. When counting siginificant figures, we count **all** digits except zeros at the beginning and end.

> The **significant figures** of a number are all digits except zeros at the start and end.

R **Worked Example 2.21**

Correct the following numbers to two **significant figures**:

    (i) 5.82265   (ii) 72,471   (iii) 0.00456

Solution

    (i) 5.82265

The **first significant figure** in a number is the **first non-zero digit in the number**. In this number, 5 is the first significant figure in the number. We need to correct to two significant figures, so we look at the third significant digit. If this number is 5 or greater, we round up the second digit. The third digit is 2, so the corrected number is 5.8.

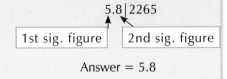

Answer = 5.8

    (ii) 72,471

Here, the third digit is 4, which is less than 5. Therefore, the rounded number is 72,000.

Note that all other digits after the rounded digit change to zero.

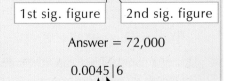

Answer = 72,000

    (iii) 0.00456

The third significant digit is 6. Therefore, the rounded number is 0.0046.

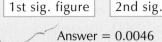

Answer = 0.0046

- Leading zeros are not significant figures. For example, 0.0053 has two significant figures, 5 and 3.
- Zeros that appear between two non-zero digits **are** significant. For example, 503.25 has five significant figures.

R **Worked Example 2.22**

By rounding appropriately, estimate the value of the following expression:

$$\frac{\sqrt{85} \times 5.276}{1.01 \times 14.79}$$

Use your calculator to find the value of the expression to two decimal places.

Solution

$$\frac{\sqrt{85} \times 5.276}{1.01 \times 14.79} \approx \frac{\sqrt{81} \times 5}{1 \times 15}$$

$$= \frac{9 \times 5}{15}$$

$$= \frac{45}{15}$$

∴ Estimate = 3

The answer 3.2563... is displayed ≈ 3.26   Note: Individual calculators may differ.

Exercise 2.4

1. If $\sqrt{71}$ is approximately 8.426149773, write $\sqrt{71}$:

   (i) Correct to one decimal place

   (ii) Correct to two decimal places

   (iii) Correct to three decimal places

   If $\sqrt{38}$ is approximately 6.164414003, write $\sqrt{38}$:

   (iv) Correct to one decimal place

   (v) Correct to two decimal places

   (vi) Correct to three decimal places

   If $\sqrt{57}$ is approximately 7.549834435, write $\sqrt{57}$:

   (vii) Correct to one decimal place

   (viii) Correct to two decimal places

   (ix) Correct to three decimal places

2. (i) Find the prime factors of each of the following numbers:

   40, 2, 5, 50, 400

   (ii) Hence, decide whether the following fractions can be converted into recurring decimals:

   $\dfrac{7}{40}, \dfrac{1}{2}, \dfrac{2}{5}, \dfrac{7}{50}, \dfrac{13}{400}$

   (iii) Use your calculator to check that your answers to part (ii) are correct.

3. Using a calculator, evaluate the following to four decimal places:

   (i) $\sqrt{5}$ (iii) $\sqrt{17}$

   (ii) $\sqrt{8}$ (iv) $\sqrt{19}$

4. Evaluate, without the use of a calculator:

   (i) $(\sqrt{2})^2$ (iv) $(\sqrt{15})^2$

   (ii) $(\sqrt{11})^2$ (v) $(\sqrt{5})^2$

   (iii) $(\sqrt{3})^2$ (vi) $(\sqrt{13})^2$

5. Write each of the following correct to three decimal places:

   (i) $3 + \sqrt{2}$ (iii) $2\sqrt{7}$

   (ii) $5 - \sqrt{5}$ (iv) $8 - 3\sqrt{3}$

6. Write these numbers correct to one significant figure:

   (i) 45.28   (iv) 6,981

   (ii) 7.587   (v) 5,965

   (iii) 18,254   (vi) 9,987

7. Write these numbers correct to two significant figures:

   (i) 0.00894   (vi) 0.000048

   (ii) 0.0215   (vii) 957,444

   (iii) 0.0023   (viii) 0.238

   (iv) 0.000000852   (ix) 0.000912

   (v) 2.000045   (x) 0.00000008

8. (i) Write 4.78 correct to the nearest whole number.

   (ii) Write 6.19 correct to the nearest whole number.

   (iii) Write 10.31 correct to the nearest whole number.

   (iv) Using your answers from parts (i) to (iii), estimate the value of:

   $\dfrac{4.78 \times 6.19}{10.31}$

   (v) Calculate to four decimal places (using your calculator):

   $\dfrac{4.78 \times 6.19}{10.31}$

9. By rounding appropriately estimate:

   (i) $\dfrac{\sqrt{68} \times 15.2}{12.54}$

   (ii) $\dfrac{9.3 \times 2.6 \times 8.7}{\sqrt{10} \times \sqrt{15.8}}$

   (iii) $\dfrac{\sqrt{38} \times 5.2}{\sqrt{3.9} \times 15.34}$

10. Using your calculator, evaluate parts (i) to (iii) in Q. 9 to four decimal places.

11. Estimate the following expressions and then use your calculator to evaluate to four decimal places:

   (i) $\sqrt[3]{(2.78 + 3.9 + 0.5)^2}$

   (ii) $\sqrt{\dfrac{(4.12)^3 - 1}{(1.99)^3 - 1}}$

   (iii) $\sqrt{\dfrac{(2.9)^3 + (2.6)^2}{(3.21)^2 - 2.74}}$

   (iv) $\sqrt[3]{(4.41)^2 + (2.8)^2 + 1.62}$

   (v) $\sqrt[3]{(9.8)^2 + (4.7)^2}$

12. A carpenter measures the length and width of a room. He measures the length as 5.28 m and the width as 3.52 m.

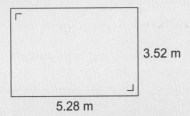

3.52 m

5.28 m

   (i) Calculate the area of the room.

   (ii) Calculate the perimeter of the room.

The carpenter decides to round the measurements to the nearest metre.

   (iii) Calculate the area and perimeter with the rounded measurements.

   (iv) Write down the difference in area and perimeter caused by rounding.

13. Three towns A, B and C are connected by three roads [AB], [BC] and [AC]. Their positions are shown in the diagram below.

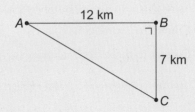

   (i) Use the theorem of Pythagoras to find |AC| correct to the nearest metre.

   (ii) Find the area of the triangle ABC.

2.6 SCIENTIFIC NOTATION

When doing calculations, scientists often use very large numbers or very small numbers. For example, the speed of light is about 300,000,000 metres per second.

Very large or very small numbers can be awkward to write down. So scientists use scientific notation to write down these numbers.

A number is written in **scientific notation** if it is of the form $a \times 10^n$, where $1 \leqslant a < 10$ and n is an integer.

Another name for scientific notation is **standard form**.

R Worked Example 2.23

Write the following numbers in scientific notation:

   (i) 725,000,000,000

   (ii) 980,000

   (iii) 0.0000056

   (iv) 0.000000034

Solution

(i) First, note that dividing a number P by 10^n, where $n \in N$, moves the decimal point n places to the left.

For example, $\dfrac{144.25}{10^2} = 1.4425$ (Decimal point moves two places to the left)

$\therefore 725{,}000{,}000{,}000 = \dfrac{725{,}000{,}000{,}000}{10^{11}} \times 10^{11}$

$\qquad\qquad\qquad\qquad = 7.25 \times 10^{11}$

(ii) $980{,}000 = \dfrac{980{,}000}{10^5} \times 10^5$

$\qquad\qquad = 9.8 \times 10^5$

(iii) Note that dividing a number P by 10^n, where n is a negative integer, moves the decimal n places to the right.

For example, $\dfrac{0.00146}{10^{-3}} = 0.00146 \times \dfrac{1}{10^{-3}}$

$\qquad\qquad\qquad\quad = 0.00146 \times 10^3$ (Rules of indices)

$\qquad\qquad\qquad\quad = 1.46$ (Decimal point moves three places to the right)

$\therefore 0.0000056 = \dfrac{0.0000056}{10^{-6}} \times 10^{-6}$

$\qquad\qquad\qquad = 5.6 \times 10^{-6}$

(iv) $0.000000034 = \dfrac{0.000000034}{10^{-8}} \times 10^{-8}$

$\qquad\qquad\qquad = 3.4 \times 10^{-8}$

Orders of Magnitude

Orders of magnitude are generally used to make very approximate comparisons. If two numbers differ by one order of magnitude, one is about 10 times larger than the other.

> A number rounded to the nearest power of 10 is called an **order of magnitude.**

R Worked Example 2.24

By how many orders of magnitude does 345,632 differ from 567,123,423?

Solution

Write both numbers in scientific notation:

$345{,}632 = 3.45632 \times 10^5$ $\qquad\qquad\qquad\qquad$ $567{,}123{,}423 = 5.67123423 \times 10^8$

> ■ If the decimal number is less than 5, round to 1.
> ■ If the decimal number is 5 or greater, round to 10.

$\approx 1 \times 10^5$ $\qquad\qquad\qquad\qquad\qquad\qquad\qquad$ $\approx 10 \times 10^8$

$= 10^0 \times 10^5$ Note: $1 = 10^0$ $\qquad\qquad\qquad\qquad$ $= 10^1 \times 10^8$

$= 10^5$ $\qquad\qquad\qquad\qquad\qquad\qquad\qquad\qquad$ $= 10^9$

$\dfrac{10^9}{10^5} = 10^{9-5} = 10^4$

Therefore, both numbers differ by four orders of magnitude.

Exercise 2.5

1. Write these numbers in scientific notation:

(i) 3,800

(ii) 75,000

(iii) 240

(iv) 848,000

(v) 5,376,000

(vi) 0.01

(vii) 0.001

(viii) 0.0001

(ix) 0.0012

(x) 0.00003

2. Write these as decimal numbers:

(i) 5×10^3

(ii) 8×10^2

(iii) 2.4×10^3

(iv) 6.2×10^7

(v) 8.4×10^2

(vi) 1.9×10^{-3}

(vii) 3.64×10^{-4}

(viii) 2.6×10^{-2}

(ix) 2.6×10^{-1}

(x) 5.06×10^{-6}

3. Write these numbers in scientific notation:

(i) 34,000,000

(ii) 0.25

(iii) 4,570

(iv) 0.0001258

(v) 7,206

(vi) 0.000032

(vii) 5,000,000

(viii) 0.6464

(ix) 532,600

(x) 5,000

4. Write these as decimal numbers:

(i) 2.65×10^2

(ii) 4.53×10^{-3}

(iii) 7.2×10^6

(iv) 1.7×10^{-5}

(v) 3×10^2

(vi) 4×10^{-2}

(vii) 2.64×10^7

(viii) 7.612×10^3

(ix) 2.76×10^8

(x) 3.02×10^{-9}

5. The following numbers are written in scientific notation. Rewrite the numbers in ordinary form.

(i) 2×10^6

(ii) 1.69×10^4

(iii) 2.48×10^3

(iv) 6.47×10^5

(v) 6.12×10^1

(vi) 7.93×10^4

6. Write the following numbers in the form $a \times 10^n$, where $1 \leqslant a < 10$:

(i) 0.000036   (ii) 0.0005613   (iii) 0.0345   (iv) 0.00063   (v) 0.0078

7. Write the following numbers in the form $a \times 10^n$, where $1 \leqslant a < 10$:

(i) 0.00068   (ii) 0.0000328   (iii) 0.0657   (iv) 0.0000000097   (v) 0.00000056

8. The following numbers are written in scientific notation. Rewrite the numbers in ordinary form.

(i) 1.5×10^{-3} (ii) 2.54×10^{-4} (iii) 3.5×10^{-5} (iv) 6.67×10^{-6} (v) 8.15×10^{-2}

9. By how many orders of magnitude do the following numbers differ?

(i) 1,239,868 and 345

(ii) 345,789,213 and 4,538

(iii) 767,894,567,000 and 23,000,000

(iv) 23 and 234,678

(v) 1.8 and 234

10. The radius of the Milky Way galaxy is 3.9×10^{20} m. The solar system has a radius of 5.9×10^{12} m. By how many orders of magnitude do the two radii differ?

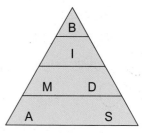

11. The speed of light is 3×10^8 m s^{-1}. If the sun is 1.5×10^{11} m from the earth, how many seconds does it take light to reach the earth? Express your answer in scientific notation.

12. One of the closest stars to our solar system is Alpha Centauri. It is 4.047×10^{13} km from Earth. A light year is the distance that light travels in one year, which is approximately 9.5×10^{12} km. How many light years from Earth is Alpha Centauri?

13. A computer is able to process 803,000 bits of data in 0.00000525 seconds. Find the rate of processing the data in bits/sec. Give your answer in scientific notation.

14. Using the following data, find the density of the earth in kilograms per square metre (kg m^{-1}). Density $= \frac{\text{Mass}}{\text{Volume}}$.

   ■ Volume of a sphere $= \frac{4}{3}\pi r^3$

   ■ Radius of the earth $= 6.3 \times 10^6$ m

   ■ Mass of the earth $= 5.9742 \times 10^{24}$ kg

   Take $\pi = 3.14$ (give your answer correct to one decimal place).

15. The earth is almost spherical. Scientists approximate the earth to a sphere when the diameter, volume or surface area of the earth need to be calculated.

   ■ The earth has a diameter of 1.276×10^7 m.

   ■ A plant cell has a diameter of 1.276×10^{-6} m.

   How many times bigger than the diameter of a plant cell is the diameter of the earth?

2.7 ORDER OF OPERATIONS

In maths, the order of operations is the order in which things are done. It is important to have order, otherwise answers will differ.

BIMDAS

We can use the guide shown to help us remember the order in which operations are carried out.

These letters stand for **B**rackets, **I**ndex, **M**ultiplication, **D**ivision, **A**ddition, and **S**ubtraction. We start at the top of the triangle and work down. Therefore, **B**rackets come first, then **I**ndices (powers), **M**ultiplication/**D**ivision and finally **A**ddition/**S**ubtraction:

$$\boxed{B} \rightarrow \boxed{I} \rightarrow \boxed{MD} \rightarrow \boxed{AS}.$$

For $\boxed{MD}$ and $\boxed{AS}$, read left to right.

R Worked Example 2.25

Find the value of each of the following:

(i) $\left(2\frac{1}{3} + \frac{1}{6}\right)^2 - \frac{1}{2} \div \frac{3}{4} + \frac{5}{6} \times \frac{2}{3}$

(ii) $\dfrac{12 \times \frac{1}{3} + 7.2 - 6.4}{2\frac{1}{5} \times \frac{3}{4} - \frac{2}{7}}$

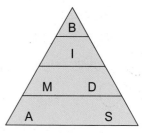

Solution

(i) $\left(2\frac{1}{3} + \frac{1}{6}\right)^2 - \frac{1}{2} \div \frac{3}{4} + \frac{5}{6} \times \frac{2}{3}$

$\left(2\frac{1}{2}\right)^2 - \frac{1}{2} \times \frac{4}{3} + \frac{5}{6} \times \frac{2}{3}$ (Brackets)

$= \frac{25}{4} - \frac{1}{2} \times \frac{4}{3} + \frac{5}{6} \times \frac{2}{3}$ (Indices)

$= \frac{25}{4} - \frac{2}{3} + \frac{5}{9}$ (Multiplication/ Division)

$= \frac{225}{36} - \frac{24}{36} + \frac{20}{36}$

$= \frac{221}{36}$

$= 6\frac{5}{36}$

(ii) $\dfrac{12 \times \frac{1}{3} + 7.2 - 6.4}{2\frac{1}{5} \times \frac{3}{4} - \frac{2}{7}}$

$= \dfrac{4 + 7.2 - 6.4}{\frac{33}{20} - \frac{2}{7}}$ (Multiplication)

$= \dfrac{4.8}{\frac{191}{140}}$ (Addition/ Subtraction)

$= 4.8 \div \frac{191}{140}$

$= 4\frac{4}{5} \times \frac{140}{191}$

$= \frac{672}{191}$ $\left(\text{or } 3\frac{99}{191}\right)$

Exercise 2.6

1. Calculate each of the following:

  (i) $5 + 5$ (iv) $5 \div 5$

  (ii) $5 - 5$ (v) 5^3

  (iii) 5×5

2. Calculate each of the following:

  (i) $12^2 + 13^2$ (iii) $13^2 + 14^2$

  (ii) $12^3 + 13^2$ (iv) $1^2 + 1^{10}$

3. Calculate each of the following:

  (i) $1^2 \times 3^2$ (iii) $5^3 \div 5^2$

  (ii) $5^2 \times 2^2$ (iv) $4^3 - 2^2$

4. Calculate each of the following:

  (i) $2\left(\frac{7}{9} - \frac{2}{3}\right)$

  (ii) $5\left(\frac{3}{4} + \frac{4}{9}\right) + 3\left(\frac{2}{7} + \frac{5}{9}\right)$

  (iii) $3\left(\frac{7}{4} - \frac{5}{12}\right)^2 + 5(5 - 2)^3$

  (iv) $2(5 - 2)^2 - 3\left(1\frac{1}{3} - \frac{2}{9}\right)^2$

5. Calculate each of the following:

  (i) $98 \div \left(2\frac{1}{2} + 4\frac{1}{2}\right)^2$

  (ii) $12 \times \frac{3}{4} + 24 \div 2^2$

  (iii) $3(4)^2 + 2(4) + 10$

  (iv) $(500 \div 10 - 42)^2$

6. Calculate each of the following:

  (i) $3\left(\frac{5}{7} - \frac{2}{3}\right)^2 - 4\left(\frac{1}{4} \div \frac{1}{2}\right)^2 + 5\left(\frac{1}{3}\right)^3$

  (ii) $2\left(\frac{3}{4}\right)^3 + 5\left(6\frac{1}{4} - 2\frac{3}{4}\right)^2 - 10 \div \frac{1}{2}$

  (iii) $\frac{5}{7}(47 + 2)^2 - 3(3 \times 2)^2 + 12(1)^{49}$

  (iv) $6(1,112 \div 1,112)^{50} + 7 \times 3 - 27$

7. Calculate each of the following:

  (i) $\dfrac{2 \times 4 + 3}{(6 + 5)}$

  (ii) $\dfrac{4 + 8 \times 3}{12 - 5}$

  (iii) $\dfrac{3(5 - 2)^2 - 3(4 \div 2)^2 + 5(3)^3}{(5 - 2)^2}$

  (iv) $\dfrac{7(6 - 2)^2 + 3(10 \div 2)^2 + 3}{(8 - 3)^2}$

8. Evaluate to two decimal places:

  (i) $5.2(3.4 - 6) + 12(17.6 - 12.4)$

  (ii) $\dfrac{8.4(19.6 - 12.2)^2}{(14.5 - 12.2)^3}$

9. Evaluate to two decimal places:

  (i) $\dfrac{5 \times 10^3 - 6 \times 10^2}{2.1 \times 10^1}$

  (ii) $\dfrac{5 \times 10^3(2 \times 10^4 - 3 \times 10^3) + 2 \times 10^9}{(2 \times 10^3)^2}$

  (iii) $\dfrac{(6.67 \times 10^{-11})\,(6.0 \times 10^{24})\,(7.36 \times 10^{22})}{(3.84 \times 10^{16})^2}$

2

ACTIVE MATHS

1. (a) List the first six multiples of each of the following:

   (i) 5   (iv) 12
   (ii) 2   (v) 13
   (iii) 10   (vi) 25

   (b) Write down all the factors of each of the following:

   (i) 70   (iv) 128
   (ii) 80   (v) 256
   (iii) 56   (vi) 100

   (c) Write the following numbers as products of prime factors:

   (i) 128   (iv) 748
   (ii) 204   (v) 1,860
   (iii) 170 (vi) 2,652

2. Express each of the following numbers as the product of prime factors, and hence, find the LCM and HCF of each pair.

   (i) 68 and 102   (iii) 104 and 351
   (ii) 69 and 123   (iv) 123 and 615

3. Estimate the following expressions and then use your calculator to evaluate each expression correct to four decimal places.

   (i) $\dfrac{3.76 \times 7.21}{27.92}$

   (ii) $\dfrac{\sqrt{26} \times 5.2 + 7}{(1.8)^5}$

   (iii) $\dfrac{8.7 \times 3.21 \times 9.4}{\sqrt{8} \times \sqrt{17.4}}$

   (iv) $\dfrac{\sqrt{37} \times (3.8 + 0.98)}{\sqrt{4.1} \times 15.34}$

4. Write these numbers correct to two significant figures.

   (i) 852,233   (iv) 0.000054
   (ii) 0.134   (v) 652,494
   (iii) 2.00062 (vi) 0.000814

5. (a) Calculate the value of the following expression and write your answer correct to three decimal places:

   $$\dfrac{72.45 + 90.44}{2.4 \times 10^3}$$

   (b) Express 286 and 910 as products of prime factors and, hence, find the HCF of 286 and 910.

   (c) The table below shows the fraction by which the population of a particular town increased each year over a three-year period.

Year	Fractional increase
2007	$\frac{1}{10}$
2008	$\frac{1}{25}$
2009	$\frac{1}{50}$

   At the start of the year 2007, the population of the town was 50,000.

   (i) Find the population of the town at the end of the year 2009.

   (ii) By what fraction did the population of the town increase over the period 2007–2009?

6. (a) (i) Find the values of the primes p and q, if $p^3 \times 13 \times q = 1{,}768$.

   (ii) Find the values of the primes m and n, if $24 \times m \times n = 3{,}192$.

   (iii) Using your answers to parts (i) and (ii), find the HCF and LCM of 1,768 and 3,192.

   (b) Evaluate the following, giving your answer in scientific notation:

   $$\dfrac{3\frac{3}{7} \times \left(2\frac{2}{5} + 1\frac{1}{10}\right)}{3 \times 10^4}$$

7. (a) A palindromic number is a number that reads the same forwards and backwards. For example, 52,325 is a palindromic number. All four-digit palindromic numbers have 11 as a prime factor.

   (i) Find the prime factorisations of the palindromic numbers 2,332 and 6,776.

   (ii) Hence, find the HCF and LCM of 2,332 and 6,776.

(b) Members of a club had two weeks to raise money for their club. The president of the club agreed to contribute an extra 5 cents for every euro raised by the members.

    (i) In the first week, the members raised €2,700. How much did the president add to this in the first week?

    (ii) In the second week, the total raised by the members and the president was €3,675. How much did the members raise in the second week?

8. (a) Write down four fractions that are greater than 0.4 and less than 0.6. Give your answers as fractions in their simplest form.

  (b) Choose any integer greater than 1.

    (i) Write down its reciprocal and subtract it from 1.

    (ii) Write down the reciprocal of your result from part (i) and subtract from 1.

    (iii) Write down the reciprocal of your result from part (ii) and subtract from 1.

    (iv) Repeat the process three more times. What happens?

9. (a) A single-celled protozoa is about one-tenth of a millimetre in diameter. Write down its diameter in metres, giving your answer in scientific notation.

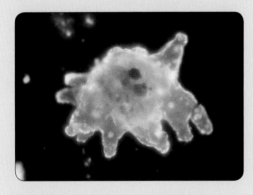

  (b) A bag contains 350 disks. Seán takes four-fifths of the disks out of the bag and divides them into seven equal groups. How many disks are in each group?

10. (i) The odometer on a car reads 83,038 km. This is a palindromic number because it reads the same backwards as forwards. What will be the next palindromic number to appear on the odometer?

    (ii) Write down a decimal that lies between $\frac{3}{5}$ and $\frac{5}{8}$.

    (iii) Marie has filled a bucket with sand. She has worked out that the bucket contains 6×10^8 grains of sand. Marie estimates that the sand on a small beach would fill 100,000,000 buckets. Approximately how many grains of sand are on the beach? Give your answer in scientific notation.

11. (a) What fraction when added to $\frac{1}{4}$ gives $\frac{1}{3}$?

  (b) A mathematician states that her children's ages are all prime numbers that multiply together to give 7,429. She also says that two of her children are teenagers.

    (i) How many children does she have?

    (ii) What are their ages?

12. (a) Write $\frac{5}{22}$ as a recurring decimal.

  (b) If Aoife works eight hours' overtime, she is allowed an extra day's holiday. She works Monday to Friday. She earned a day's holiday after working overtime each day for four weeks. On average, how many extra minutes did she work each day to earn the extra day's holiday?

13. (i) *P* represents a pointer on a gauge. What is the decimal value shown by the pointer?

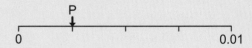

    (ii) A computer shop buys a batch of iPod nanos for €99 each and marks the price up by $\frac{1}{3}$. The goods fail to sell so they are included in the next sale where all prices are reduced by $\frac{1}{4}$. What price would you pay for an iPod nano in the sale?

    (iii) John calculates correctly $85 \times 142 = 12,070$. **Using this information**, what should his answer be for $12,070 \div 850$?

14. (i) In 1742 the German mathematician Christian Goldbach conjectured that every even integer greater than 2 can be written as the sum of two prime numbers (e.g. $18 = 5 + 13$). Find the five different ways in which 54 can be written as the sum of two primes.

(ii) Approximate the irrational number $\sqrt{13}$ to two decimal places.

(iii) Find the four prime factors of 2,010.

(iv) What is the natural number n if the fraction $\frac{19}{n}$ has a value between 4 and 5?

(v) A shepherd loses three-fifths of her sheep and then finds three-fifths of those she lost. What fraction of her flock is still missing?

3 chapter

Indices

Learning Outcomes

In this chapter you will learn about:

⮩ **The laws of indices**

(1) $a^p \times a^q = a^{p+q}$

(2) $a^p \div a^q = a^{p-q}$

(3) $(a^p)^q = a^{pq}$

(4) $a^0 = 1$

(5) $a^{\frac{1}{q}} = \sqrt[q]{a}$

(6) $a^{\frac{p}{q}} = \sqrt[q]{a^p}$

(7) $a^{-p} = \dfrac{1}{a^p}$

(8) $(ab)^p = a^p b^p$

(9) $\left(\dfrac{a}{b}\right)^p = \dfrac{a^p}{b^p}$

⮩ **How to solve equations with x as an index**

⮩ **The laws of surds**

(1) $\sqrt{a}\ \sqrt{b} = \sqrt{ab}$

(2) $\dfrac{\sqrt{a}}{\sqrt{b}} = \sqrt{\dfrac{a}{b}}$

3.1 NUMBERS IN INDEX FORM

Historians believe that the game of chess originated in India around the sixth century AD. There is an interesting fable from that time about the invention of the game.

KEY WORDS

■ **Index**

■ **Power**

■ **Exponent**

■ **Base**

■ **Surd**

The story goes that the inventor of the game was asked by the emperor to name his prize. The inventor told his master that he would like just one grain of rice on the first square of the chessboard, double the number of grains on the second square, double the number of grains on the second square to be placed on the third square, and so on.

This seemed to the emperor to be a modest request, so he called for his servants to bring the rice. How surprised he was to find that the rice quickly covered the chessboard and then filled the palace!

The table below shows the number of grains on the first 10 squares.

Square	1	2	3	4	5	6	7	8	9	10
Number of rice grains	1	2	4	8	16	32	64	128	256	512
Index form	2^0	2^1	2^2	2^3	2^4	2^5	2^6	2^7	2^8	2^9

How many grains of rice would be on the last square? In index form, there would be 2^{63} grains on the last square. This number contains 19 digits, so it is simpler to write it in index form.

A number in index form is of the form b^n. We call b the **base** and n the **index**, **power** or **exponent**.

Negative Bases to Even and Odd Powers

Consider the number $(-2)^3$. Is this a positive or a negative number?

$$(-2)^3 = (-2) \times (-2) \times (-2) = -8 \quad \text{(a negative number)}$$

Is $(-2)^4$ positive or negative?

$$(-2)^4 = (-2) \times (-2) \times (-2) \times (-2) = 16 \quad \text{(a positive number)}$$

In general:

■ A negative number raised to an odd power is negative.

■ A negative number raised to an even power is positive.

3.2 LAWS 1–4 OF INDICES

ACTIVITIES 3.1, 3.2, 3.3, 3.4

In Activities 3.1 to 3.4, you derived the first four laws of indices.

These formulae appear on page 21 of *Formulae and Tables*.

FORMULA

Law 1: $a^p \times a^q = a^{p+q}$
Law 2: $\dfrac{a^p}{a^q} = a^{p-q}$
Law 3: $(a^p)^q = a^{pq}$
Law 4: $a^0 = 1$

a^{pq} Worked Example 3.1

Simplify the following, giving the answer in index notation:

(i) $(-2)^3$

(ii) $(-3)^4$

Solution

(i) $(-2)^3 = -2^3$ $[(-)^{\text{odd power}} = -]$

(ii) $(-3)^4 = 3^4$ $[(-)^{\text{even power}} = +]$

a^{pq} Worked Example 3.2

Use the laws of indices to write each of the following in the form a^m, where a and $m \in N$.

(i) $3^4 \times 3^6$

(ii) $5^8 \div 5^3$

(iii) $(2^2)^5$

Solution

(i) $3^4 \times 3^6 = 3^{4+6}$ (Law 1)

             $= 3^{10}$

(ii) $5^8 \div 5^3 = 5^{8-3}$ (Law 2)

             $= 5^5$

(iii) $(2^2)^5 = 2^{10}$ (Law 3)

a^{pq} Worked Example 3.3

Using the laws of indices, write each of the following in index notation.

(i) $(-3)^4 \times (-3)^3$

(ii) $\dfrac{(-6)^7}{(-6)^3}$

(iii) $((-9)^6)^5$

Solution

(i) $(-3)^4 \times (-3)^3 = (-3)^7$ (Law 1)

               $= -3^7$

(ii) $\dfrac{(-6)^7}{(-6)^3} = (-6)^4$ (Law 2)

          $= 6^4$

(iii) $((-9)^6)^5 = (-9)^{30}$ (Law 3)

             $= 9^{30}$

INDICES

Exercise 3.1

1. Without using a calculator, evaluate each of the following:

(i) 5^2 (v) $(-2)^4$

(ii) 2^3 (vi) $(-3)^1$

(iii) $(-5)^2$ (vii) $(-4)^2$

(iv) $(-6)^3$ (viii) $(8)^0$

2. Simplify the following, giving your answer in index notation:

(i) $(-3)^3$ (v) $(-4)^{12}$

(ii) $(-2)^{20}$ (vi) $-(-1)^{100}$

(iii) $(-5)^{19}$ (vii) $-(6)^3$

(iv) $(3)^3$ (viii) $-(-6)^3$

3. Show that $-(-3)^5 = 3^5$.

4. In the table below, match the numbers in Column A with the corresponding answer in Column B.

Column A	Column B
3^4	-4^4
$(-2)^8$	-6^8
$(-6)^8$	-125
$-(-4)^4$	27
$-(6)^8$	6^8
$(-4)^4$	16
$-(-3)^3$	81
$(-5)^3$	4^4
$(-2)^4$	256

5. Copy and complete the following tables:

(i)

Index notation	2	2^2	2^3	2^4	2^5	2^6	2^7
Whole number	2	4	8	16	32	64	128

(ii)

Index notation	3	3^2	3^3	3^4	3^5	3^6
Whole number	3	9	27	81	243	729

(iii)

Index notation	4	4^2	4^3	4^4	4^5	4^6
Whole number	4	16	64	256	1024	4046

(iv)

Index notation	9	9^2	9^3	9^4	9^5	9^6
Whole number	9	81	729	6561	59049	531441

Using the tables above, find a value for x and a value for y in each of the following equations:

(a) $2^x = 4^y$ (b) $9^x = 3^y$

6. If $a^n = b$, find the values of a, b and n in each of the following cases:

(i) a is the first odd prime number and n is the number of faces on a die.

(ii) a is the only even prime number and b is the number of squares on a chessboard.

(iii) b is the number of metres in a kilometre and n is the number of divisors of 4.

7. Use the law $a^p \times a^q = a^{p+q}$ to write the following in index notation:

(i) $5^3 \times 5^2$ (vii) $\left(\frac{1}{4}\right)^6 \times \left(\frac{1}{4}\right)^5$

(ii) $8^7 \times 8^3$ (viii) $\left(\frac{2}{7}\right)^4 \times \left(\frac{2}{7}\right)^4$

(iii) 6×6^2

(iv) $4^3 \times 4^5$ (ix) $(0.2)^3 \times (0.2)^2$

(v) $2^9 \times 2^{12}$ (x) $(2.4)^5 \times (2.4)^8$

(vi) $\left(\frac{1}{2}\right)^7 \times \left(\frac{1}{2}\right)^5$

8. Use the law $a^p \times a^q = a^{p+q}$ to write the following in index notation. Simplify your answer.

(i) $(-5)^3 \times (-5)^7$ (vi) $\left(-\frac{1}{6}\right)^2 \times \left(-\frac{1}{6}\right)^3$

(ii) $(-2)^6 \times (-2)^3$ (vii) $\left(-\frac{3}{8}\right)^3 \times \left(-\frac{3}{8}\right)^5$

(iii) $(-3)^4 \times (-3)^3$ (viii) $\left(-\frac{3}{2}\right)^8 \times \left(-\frac{3}{2}\right)^{10}$

(iv) $(-5)^3 \times (-5)^2$ (ix) $\left(-\frac{3}{5}\right)^3 \times \left(-\frac{3}{5}\right)^4$

(v) $(-7)^3 \times (-7)^5$ (x) $(-2.7)^4 \times (-2.7)^3$

9. Use the law $\frac{a^p}{a^q} = a^{p-q}$ to write the following in index notation:

(i) $\frac{3^7}{3^6}$　　　　　　(vi) $\frac{4}{4^6}$

(ii) $\frac{2^9}{2^3}$　　　　　　(vii) $\frac{4}{4}$

(iii) $\frac{10^5}{10^2}$　　　　　(viii) $\frac{8^3}{8^9}$

(iv) $\frac{7^{12}}{7^5}$　　　　　(ix) $\frac{5}{5}$

(v) $\frac{10^2}{10^8}$　　　　　(x) $\frac{7^2}{7^4}$

10. Use the law $\frac{a^p}{a^q} = a^{p-q}$ to write the following in index notation:

(i) $(-8)^{22} \div (-8)^{18}$　　(vi) $\frac{(-12)^9}{(-12)^4}$

(ii) $(-6)^{13} \div (-6)^{10}$　　(vii) $\frac{(-2)^6}{(-2)^3}$

(iii) $(-4)^6 \div (-4)^2$　　(viii) $\frac{\left(-\frac{1}{2}\right)^{17}}{\left(-\frac{1}{2}\right)^{13}}$

(iv) $(-2)^7 \div (-2)^3$　　(ix) $\frac{\left(-\frac{3}{5}\right)^3}{\left(-\frac{3}{5}\right)^{10}}$

(v) $(-10)^8 \div (-10)^3$　　(x) $\frac{\left(-\frac{3}{4}\right)^4}{\left(-\frac{3}{4}\right)^4}$

11. Use the law $(a^p)^q = a^{pq}$ to simplify the following, giving your answer in index notation:

(i) $(3^3)^5$　　　　　(vi) $(8^5)^3$

(ii) $(6^4)^5$　　　　　(vii) $(16^2)^3$

(iii) $(10^5)^5$　　　　(viii) $(10^4)^9$

(iv) $(4^5)^6$　　　　　(ix) $(2^2)^2$

(v) $(7^6)^7$　　　　　(x) $(13^9)^3$

12. Use the law $(a^p)^q = a^{pq}$ to simplify the following, giving your answer in index notation:

(i) $((-8)^3)^4$　　　　(vi) $\left(\left(-\frac{3}{2}\right)^5\right)^5$

(ii) $((-7)^9)^5$　　　　(vii) $\left(\left(-\frac{3}{2}\right)^6\right)^6$

(iii) $((-18)^5)^8$　　　(viii) $\left(\left(-\frac{3}{4}\right)^7\right)^6$

(iv) $((-10)^4)^5$　　　(ix) $((-2.3)^2)^3$

(v) $((-12)^7)^5$　　　(x) $\left(\left(-\frac{3}{5}\right)^3\right)^6$

13. Copy and complete the following table:

Index notation	5	5^2	5^3	5^4	5^5	5^6
					3125	
Whole number			125			

Using the table write the following in the form 5^n, where $n \in N$.

(i) 25×125　　　　(iv) $15{,}625^{11}$

(ii) $3{,}125 \times 15{,}625$　(v) $25^3 \times 625^5$

(iii) $625 \div 25$　　　　(vi) $\frac{15{,}625^4}{125^3}$

14. Copy and complete the following multiplication pyramid:

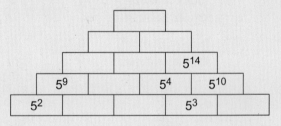

3.3 LAWS 5–9 OF INDICES

ACTIVITIES 3.5, 3.6, 3.7

In Activities 3.5 to 3.7, you derived laws 5 to 7 of indices.

> $\sqrt[q]{a}$ is called the qth root of a.
>
> b is the qth root of a if $b^q = a$.

$\sqrt[3]{27} = 3$, as $3^3 = 27$. Similarly, $\sqrt[6]{64} = 2$, as $2^6 = 64$.

These formulae appear on page 21 of *Formulae and Tables*.

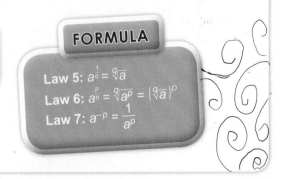

FORMULA

Law 5: $a^{\frac{1}{q}} = \sqrt[q]{a}$

Law 6: $a^{\frac{p}{q}} = \sqrt[q]{a^p} = (\sqrt[q]{a})^p$

Law 7: $a^{-p} = \frac{1}{a^p}$

Worked Example 3.4

Using the law $a^{-p} = \frac{1}{a^p}$, write each of the following in the form $\frac{1}{a^n}$, where $n \in N$.

(i) 2^{-5} (ii) 3^{-6} (iii) 4^{-2}

Solution

(i) $2^{-5} = \frac{1}{2^5}$ (ii) $3^{-6} = \frac{1}{3^6}$ (iii) $4^{-2} = \frac{1}{4^2}$

Worked Example 3.5

Evaluate each of the following without the use of a calculator:

(i) $\sqrt{25}$ (ii) $\sqrt[5]{32}$ (iii) $\sqrt[3]{1{,}000}$

Solution

(i) Let $b = \sqrt{25}$, where $b > 0$ (note that $\sqrt{a} = \sqrt[2]{a}$).

$\Rightarrow b^2 = 25$

$b^2 = 5^2$

$\therefore b = 5$

(ii) Let $b = \sqrt[5]{32}$

$\Rightarrow b^5 = 32$

$b^5 = 2^5$

$\therefore b = 2$

(iii) Let $b = \sqrt[3]{1{,}000}$

$\Rightarrow b^3 = 1{,}000$

$b^3 = 10^3$

$\therefore b = 10$

Worked Example 3.6

Evaluate each of the following using the law $a^{\frac{p}{q}} = \sqrt[q]{a^p} = \left(\sqrt[q]{a}\right)^p$

(i) $32^{\frac{4}{5}}$ (ii) $81^{\frac{5}{4}}$ (iii) $125^{\frac{2}{3}}$

Solution

(i) $32^{\frac{4}{5}} = \left(\sqrt[5]{32}\right)^4$

$= (2)^4$

$= 16$

(ii) $81^{\frac{5}{4}} = \left(\sqrt[4]{81}\right)^5$

$= (3)^5$

$= 243$

(iii) $125^{\frac{2}{3}} = \left(\sqrt[3]{125}\right)^2$

$= (5)^2$

$= 25$

Worked Example 3.7

Evaluate each of the following:

(i) $64^{-\frac{4}{3}}$

(ii) $27^{-\frac{5}{3}}$

Solution

(i) $64^{-\frac{4}{3}} = \frac{1}{64^{\frac{4}{3}}}$ (Law 7)

$= \frac{1}{\left(\sqrt[3]{64}\right)^4}$

$= \frac{1}{(4)^4}$

$= \frac{1}{256}$

(ii) $27^{-\frac{5}{3}} = \frac{1}{27^{\frac{5}{3}}}$

$= \frac{1}{\left(\sqrt[3]{27}\right)^5}$

$= \frac{1}{(3)^5}$

$= \frac{1}{243}$

a^{pq} Worked Example 3.8

Use your calculator to evaluate each of the following correct to two decimal places:

(i) $\sqrt[5]{122}$ (ii) $\sqrt[4]{17}$ (iii) $16^{\frac{2}{3}}$ (iv) $17^{-\frac{5}{3}}$

Solution

(i)

The answer 2.613797668 is displayed.

Answer = 2.61

(ii)

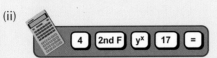

The answer 2.030543185 is displayed.

Answer = 2.03

(iii)

The answer 6.349604208 is displayed.

Answer = 6.35

(iv)

The answer 0.008897168 is displayed.

Answer = 0.01

Note that individual calculators may differ.

 **ACTIVITIES 3.8, 3.9**

In Activities 3.8 and 3.9, you derived laws 8 and 9 of indices.

FORMULA

Law 8: $(ab)^p = a^p b^p$

Law 9: $\left(\dfrac{a}{b}\right)^p = \dfrac{a^p}{b^p}$

These formulae appear on page 21 of *Formulae and Tables*.

a^{pq} Worked Example 3.9

Use the law $(ab)^p = a^p b^p$ to show that $12^8 = 3^8 4^8$.

Solution

$12^8 = ((3)(4))^8$
$= 3^8 4^8$ (Law 8)

---

a^{pq} Worked Example 3.10

(i) Use the law $\left(\dfrac{a}{b}\right)^p = \dfrac{a^p}{b^p}$ to show that $(0.75)^9 = \dfrac{3^9}{4^9}$.

(ii) Evaluate $\left(\dfrac{27}{1,000}\right)^{-\frac{2}{3}}$.

Solution

(i) $0.75 = \dfrac{3}{4}$

$(0.75)^9 = \left(\dfrac{3}{4}\right)^9$

$= \dfrac{3^9}{4^9}$ (Law 9)

(ii) $\left(\dfrac{27}{1,000}\right)^{-\frac{2}{3}} = \dfrac{1}{\left(\dfrac{27}{1,000}\right)^{\frac{2}{3}}}$ (Law 7)

$= \dfrac{1}{\left(\sqrt[3]{\dfrac{27}{1,000}}\right)^2}$ (Law 6)

$= \dfrac{1}{\left(\dfrac{\sqrt[3]{27}}{\sqrt[3]{1,000}}\right)^2}$ (Law 9)

$= \dfrac{1}{\left(\dfrac{3}{10}\right)^2}$

$= \dfrac{1}{\dfrac{9}{100}} = \dfrac{100}{9}$

Exercise 3.2

1. Using the law $a^{-p} = \frac{1}{a^p}$, write the following as fractions:

(i) 2^{-3} (ii) 4^{-2} (iii) 9^{-3} (iv) 5^{-3} (v) 6^{-2}

(vi) 7^{-2} (vii) 3^{-4} (viii) 8^{-2} (ix) 4^{-3} (x) 5^{-2}

2. Using the law $a^{-p} = \frac{1}{a^p}$, write the following as fractions in their simplest form:

(i) $2(5^{-3})$ (ii) $3(8^{-2})$ (iii) $5(4^{-2})$ (iv) $4(3^{-4})$ (v) $2(8^{-2})$

(vi) $3(7^{-2})$ (vii) $4(2^{-4})$ (viii) $3(6^{-2})$ (ix) $2(4^{-2})$ (x) $5(10^{-3})$

3. Without using a calculator, evaluate each of the following:

(i) $\sqrt{25}$ (ii) $\sqrt{49}$ (iii) $\sqrt[3]{27}$ (iv) $\sqrt[4]{16}$ (v) $\sqrt[5]{32}$

(vi) $\sqrt[10]{1}$ (vii) $\sqrt{36}$ (viii) $\sqrt[4]{81}$ (ix) $\sqrt[6]{64}$ (x) $\sqrt{121}$

4. Copy and complete the following tables:

x	1	2	3	4	5	6	7	8	9	10
x^2			9						81	

x	1	4	9	16	25	36	49	64	81	100
$\sqrt{x}$						6				

5. Copy and complete the following tables:

x	1	2	3	4	5	6	7	8	9	10
x^3		27								1,000

x	1	8	27	64	125	216	343	512	729	1,000
$\sqrt[3]{x}$							7			

6. Using the law $a^{\frac{1}{q}} = \sqrt[q]{a}$ and the completed tables from Questions 4 and 5, evaluate each of the following:

(i) $100^{\frac{1}{2}}$ (v) $16^{\frac{1}{2}}$ (viii) $1000^{\frac{1}{3}}$

(ii) $64^{\frac{1}{2}}$ (vi) $8^{\frac{1}{3}}$ (ix) $64^{\frac{1}{3}}$

(iii) $216^{\frac{1}{3}}$ (vii) $9^{\frac{1}{2}}$ (x) $36^{\frac{1}{2}}$

(iv) $512^{\frac{1}{3}}$

7. Using the law $a^{\frac{p}{q}} = \left(\sqrt[q]{a}\right)^p$, evaluate each of the following:

(i) $16^{\frac{1}{4}}$ (v) $100^{\frac{3}{2}}$ (viii) $81^{\frac{3}{4}}$

(ii) $27^{\frac{2}{3}}$ (vi) $125^{\frac{2}{3}}$ (ix) $9^{\frac{3}{2}}$

(iii) $64^{\frac{2}{3}}$ (vii) $16^{\frac{5}{4}}$ (x) $64^{\frac{4}{3}}$

(iv) $16^{\frac{3}{4}}$

8. Using the laws $a^{-p} = \frac{1}{a^p}$ and $a^{\frac{p}{q}} = \left(\sqrt[q]{a}\right)^p$, evaluate each of the following. Write your answer in the form $\frac{1}{m}$, $m \in N$.

(i) $100^{-\frac{1}{2}}$ (v) $81^{-\frac{3}{4}}$ (viii) $125^{-\frac{2}{3}}$

(ii) $36^{-\frac{1}{2}}$ (vi) $8^{-\frac{2}{3}}$ (ix) $16^{-\frac{5}{4}}$

(iii) $16^{-\frac{1}{4}}$ (vii) $9^{-\frac{5}{2}}$ (x) $100^{-\frac{5}{2}}$

(iv) $9^{-\frac{3}{2}}$

9. Using the law $(ab)^p = a^p b^p$, verify that each of the following is true:

(i) $20^4 = 5^4 4^4$ (iii) $36^{\frac{1}{2}} = 9^{\frac{1}{2}} 4^{\frac{1}{2}}$

(ii) $15^6 = 3^6 5^6$ (iv) $216^{\frac{1}{3}} = 8^{\frac{1}{3}} 27^{\frac{1}{3}}$

10. Using the law $\left(\frac{a}{b}\right)^p = \left(\frac{a^p}{b^p}\right)$, verify that each of the following is true:

(i) $\left(\frac{3}{4}\right)^8 = \frac{6^8}{8^8}$ (iii) $\left(\frac{9}{16}\right)^{\frac{1}{2}} = \frac{18^{\frac{1}{2}}}{32^{\frac{1}{2}}}$

(ii) $\left(\frac{3}{5}\right)^9 = \frac{9^9}{15^9}$ (iv) $\left(\frac{25}{64}\right)^{-\frac{1}{2}} = \frac{75^{-\frac{1}{2}}}{192^{-\frac{1}{2}}}$

$\frac{1}{100}$ ½
$\left(\frac{1}{\sqrt{100}}\right)^1$
$\frac{1}{10}$

3

INDICES

ACTIVE MATHS   **61**

11. Evaluate each of the following without using a calculator:

   (i) $\left(\frac{1}{4}\right)^{\frac{1}{2}}$ (iv) $\left(\frac{81}{25}\right)^{\frac{1}{2}}$ (vii) $\left(\frac{16}{81}\right)^{\frac{3}{4}}$

   (ii) $\left(\frac{1}{25}\right)^{\frac{1}{2}}$ (v) $\left(\frac{8}{27}\right)^{\frac{1}{3}}$ (viii) $\left(\frac{27}{64}\right)^{\frac{2}{3}}$

   (iii) $\left(\frac{4}{9}\right)^{\frac{1}{2}}$ (vi) $\left(\frac{8}{125}\right)^{\frac{1}{3}}$

12. Use your calculator to evaluate each of the following:

   (i) $\left(\frac{36}{25}\right)^{-\frac{1}{2}}$ (iv) $\left(\frac{27}{1000}\right)^{-\frac{2}{3}}$ (vii) $\left(\frac{4}{9}\right)^{-\frac{3}{2}}$

   (ii) $\left(\frac{4}{121}\right)^{-\frac{1}{2}}$ (v) $\left(\frac{125}{27}\right)^{-\frac{2}{3}}$ (viii) $\left(\frac{27}{64}\right)^{-\frac{2}{3}}$

   (iii) $\left(\frac{8}{125}\right)^{-\frac{1}{3}}$ (vi) $\left(\frac{8}{125}\right)^{-\frac{2}{3}}$

13. The law $(ab)^p = a^p b^p$ can be used to find the prime factors of numbers of the form q^n, where q and $n \in N$.

   (i) Write 15 as a product of prime numbers.

   (ii) Hence find the prime factors of 15^9.

14. Write 36 as a product of prime factors and hence find the prime factors of $36^{2,011}$.

15. Write 100 as a product of prime factors and hence find the prime factors of $100^{1,601}$.

16. Use your calculator to evaluate each of the following to two decimal places:

   (i) $\sqrt{19}$ (iii) $\sqrt[3]{28}$ (v) $39^{\frac{3}{4}}$

   (ii) 2.75^4 (iv) $13^{\frac{1}{4}}$ (vi) 3.42^{-3}

   (vii) $26^{\frac{3}{4}}$ (ix) $\sqrt[5]{34}$

   (viii) $42^{-\frac{7}{8}}$ (x) $\sqrt[6]{100}$

17. Write each of the following in the form 2^p:

   (i) 4   (iv) 32   (vii) $\sqrt{2}$

   (ii) 8   (v) $\frac{1}{2}$ (viii) $\sqrt[3]{2}$

   (iii) 16   (vi) $\frac{1}{4}$ (ix) $\frac{1}{\sqrt{2}}$

18. Write each of the following in the form 3^p:

   (i) 1   (iv) 81   (vii) $\sqrt{3}$

   (ii) 9   (v) $\frac{1}{3}$ (viii) $\sqrt{27}$

   (iii) 27   (vi) $\frac{1}{9}$ (ix) $\frac{1}{\sqrt{3}}$

19. Write each of the following in the form 5^p:

   (i) 25   (iv) 1   (vii) $\sqrt{5}$

   (ii) 125   (v) $\frac{1}{25}$ (viii) $\sqrt[5]{5}$

   (iii) $\frac{1}{5}$ (vi) $\frac{1}{125}$ (ix) $\frac{1}{\sqrt{5}}$

20. Write each of the following in the form 10^p:

   (i) 100   (v) $\frac{1}{10}$ (ix) $\frac{1}{\sqrt{10}}$

   (ii) 1,000   (vi) $\frac{1}{1,000}$ (x) $\frac{\sqrt{10}}{\sqrt[3]{10}}$

   (iii) 0.01   (vii) $\sqrt{10}$ (xi) $\sqrt{1,000}$

   (iv) 10,000   (viii) $\sqrt[100]{10}$ (xii) $\frac{100}{\sqrt{10}}$

3.4 EQUATIONS WITH X AS AN INDEX

$2^x = 64$ is an example of an equation where the unknown quantity x is an index or power. The laws of indices will help us to solve many equations where the unknown quantity is an index.

> If $a^x = a^y$, then $x = y$, $a \neq 0, \pm 1$.

a^{pq} Worked Example 3.11

Solve each of the following equations:

   (i) $2^x = 2^5$ (ii) $3^y = 3^{-2}$ (iii) $\left(\frac{1}{2}\right)^z = \left(\frac{1}{2}\right)^{\frac{1}{4}}$

Solution

   (i) $2^x = 2^5$ (ii) $3^y = 3^{-2}$ (iii) $\left(\frac{1}{2}\right)^z = \left(\frac{1}{2}\right)^{\frac{1}{4}}$

         $\therefore x = 5$ $\therefore y = -2$ $\therefore z = \frac{1}{4}$

a^{pq} Worked Example 3.12

Solve each of the following equations:

(i) $2^x = 16$

(ii) $3^x = 27$

Solution

(i) $2^x = 16$

$2^x = 2^4$ (express 16 as a power of 2)

$\therefore x = 4$

(ii) $3^x = 27$

$3^x = 3^3$ (express 27 as a power of 3)

$\therefore x = 3$

a^{pq} Worked Example 3.13

Solve $4^x = \dfrac{8}{\sqrt{2}}$, where $x \in Q$.

Solution

All numbers in the equation can be written as powers of 2.

$2 = 2^1$

$4 = 2^2$

$8 = 2^3$

The equation can now be written as:

$(2^2)^x = \dfrac{2^3}{\sqrt{2}}$

$2^{2x} = \dfrac{2^3}{2^{\frac{1}{2}}}$ — subtracting powers

$2^{2x} = 2^{2\frac{1}{2}}$

$\Rightarrow 2x = 2\frac{1}{2}$ $\dfrac{2x}{2} = \dfrac{5}{2} \div 2$

$x = \dfrac{2\frac{1}{2}}{2}$

$\therefore x = 1\frac{1}{4} \left(\text{or } \frac{5}{4}\right)$

Note that $\sqrt{2} = 2^{\frac{1}{2}}$.

Exercise 3.3

1. Solve the following equations:

(i) $2^x = 4$ (vi) $3^x = 81$

(ii) $3^x = 27$ (vii) $10^x = 10{,}000$

(iii) $5^x = 125$ (viii) $6^x = 216$

(iv) $10^x = 1{,}000$ (ix) $7^x = 49$

(v) $4^x = 64$ (x) $3^x = 729$

2. Solve the following equations:

(i) $9^x = 3^4$ (vi) $2^x = 16^5$

(ii) $4^x = 8^2$ (vii) $4^{2x} = 8^3$

(iii) $5^x = 25^2$ (viii) $3^{3x} = 27^2$

(iv) $10^x = 100^3$ (ix) $4^{5x} = 8^5$

(v) $11^x = 121^5$ (x) $a^{2x} = (a^2)^3$

3. Write the following in the form 2^k, where $k \in Q$.

(i) 16   (iii) $\sqrt{8}$

(ii) 8   (iv) $\dfrac{16}{\sqrt{8}}$

Hence, solve the equation $2^{2x-1} = \left(\dfrac{16}{\sqrt{8}}\right)^3$.

4. Write the following in the form 3^k, where $k \in Q$.

(i) 27   (ii) $\sqrt{3}$

Hence, solve the equation $3^{3x-1} = \left(\dfrac{27}{\sqrt{3}}\right)^5$.

5. Write the following in the form 5^p, where $p \in Q$.

(i) 25   (ii) $\sqrt{125}$ (iii) $\sqrt[3]{5}$

Hence, solve the equation $25^x = \left(\dfrac{\sqrt{125}}{\sqrt[3]{5}}\right)^{12}$.

INDICES

6. Write the following in the form 7^p, where $p \in Q$.

   (i)   49   (ii) $\sqrt[3]{7}$ (iii) $\sqrt{343}$

   Hence, solve the equation $49^{x-4} = \left(\dfrac{\sqrt{343}}{\sqrt[3]{7}}\right)^{2x}$.

7. (i) Evaluate $8^{\frac{1}{3}}$.

   (ii) Express $4^{\frac{1}{4}}$ in the form 2^k, $k \in Q$.

   (iii) Solve the equation:
$$\left(8^{\frac{1}{3}}\right)\left(4^{\frac{1}{4}}\right) = 2^{5-x}$$

8. Find the prime factors of 75 and, hence, solve the equation:
$$\frac{5^x}{3} = \frac{5^6}{75}.$$

9. Using the laws of indices, solve the following equations:

   (i) $2^x = 2^7\sqrt{2}$ (v) $10^{x-3} = \dfrac{\sqrt{10}}{100}$

   (ii) $2^x = \dfrac{2^7}{4}$ (vi) $7^x = \dfrac{49}{\sqrt[3]{7}}$

   (iii) $5^x = \dfrac{125}{\sqrt{5}}$ (vii) $10^{2x-1} = \dfrac{\sqrt{1{,}000}}{10}$

   (iv) $3^{x+1} = \dfrac{9}{\sqrt{3}}$ (viii) $4^x = \dfrac{32\sqrt{2}}{2}$

10. Solve the equation $\left(a^{\frac{1}{3}}\right)\left(b^{\frac{1}{3}}\right) = c^{5-x}$ if:

   (i) $a = 8$, $b = 4$ and $c = 2$

   (ii) $a = 27$, $b = 9$ and $c = 3$

11. Copy and complete the table below. Answers in the second row must be in index form.

$2^2 - 2$	$2^3 - 2^2$	$2^4 - 2^3$	$2^5 - 2^4$	$2^6 - 2^5$	$2^7 - 2^6$
2	2^2	8	16	32	64

   Hence, write $2^{p+1} - 2^p$ as a power of 2.

12. Using the results from Question 11, solve for x:
$$\left(\frac{2^{12}}{16}\right) = 2^{x+1} - 2^x$$

13. Solve each of the following equations for p.

   (i) $9^p = \dfrac{1}{\sqrt{3}}$ (ii) $2^{3p-7} = 2^6 - 2^5$

14. Solve for y:
$$\left(\frac{2^{16}}{8}\right) = 2^y - 2^{y-1}$$

3.5 SURDS

ACTIVITIES 3.10, 3.11

$\sqrt{2}$ and $\sqrt{3}$ are examples of surds.

> $\sqrt{a}$ is called a surd if it cannot be written as a rational number.

In Activities 3.10 and 3.11, you derived two laws of surds.

FORMULA

Law 1: $\sqrt{a}\sqrt{b} = \sqrt{ab}$

Law 2: $\dfrac{\sqrt{a}}{\sqrt{b}} = \sqrt{\dfrac{a}{b}}$

> The word 'surd' comes from the Latin word *surdus* (meaning 'deaf' or 'mute'). Arabic mathematicians liked to think of rational numbers as being audible and irrational numbers as being inaudible.

Worked Example 3.14

What is $\sqrt{a^2}$?

Solution

$\sqrt{a^2} = (a^2)^{\frac{1}{2}}$

    $= a^1$ (Law 3 of Indices)

    $= a$

Worked Example 3.15

What is $\sqrt{a}\sqrt{a}$?

Solution

$\sqrt{a}\sqrt{a} = \sqrt{(a)(a)}$ (Law 1 of Surds)

    $= \sqrt{a^2}$

    $= a$

INDICES

Reducing Surds

Surds can be reduced or simplified if the number under the radical sign (square root sign) has a perfect square number as a factor. Perfect squares are 4, 9, 16, 25, 36 ... etc.

Example: $\sqrt{300} = \sqrt{100 \times 3} = \sqrt{100} \times \sqrt{3} = 10\sqrt{3}$

a^pq Worked Example 3.16

Simplify $\sqrt{32}$.

Solution

Step 1

Find the largest square number that is a factor of 32. Sixteen is the largest square number that is a factor of 32.

Step 2

$\sqrt{32} = \sqrt{16 \times 2}$

$\quad = \sqrt{16}\,\sqrt{2}$ (Law 1 of Surds)

$\quad = 4\sqrt{2}$

a^pq Worked Example 3.17

Simplify $\sqrt{50} + \sqrt{8} + \sqrt{32}$.

Solution

$\sqrt{50} + \sqrt{8} + \sqrt{32} = \sqrt{25}\sqrt{2} + \sqrt{4}\sqrt{2} + \sqrt{16}\sqrt{2}$

$\qquad\qquad\qquad\quad = 5\sqrt{2} + 2\sqrt{2} + 4\sqrt{2}$

$\qquad\qquad\qquad\quad = 11\sqrt{2}$

Exercise 3.4

1. Evaluate each of the following (no calculators allowed):

   (i) $(\sqrt{3})^2$
   (ii) $(\sqrt{6})^2$
   (iii) $(\sqrt{17})^2$
   (iv) $(\sqrt{19})^2$
   (v) $(\sqrt{30})^2$
   (vi) $(2\sqrt{7})^2$
   (vii) $(5\sqrt{10})^2$
   (viii) $(2\sqrt{5})^2$
   (ix) $(10\sqrt{2})^2$
   (x) $(3\sqrt{15})^2$

2. Say if each of the following is true or false:

   (i) $\sqrt{3} + \sqrt{5} = \sqrt{8}$
   (ii) $\sqrt{5} - \sqrt{3} = \sqrt{2}$
   (iii) $\sqrt{5}\sqrt{3} = \sqrt{15}$
   (iv) $\dfrac{\sqrt{35}}{\sqrt{5}} = \sqrt{7}$

3. Evaluate each of the following, without the use of a calculator:

   (i) $\sqrt{12}\sqrt{3}$
   (ii) $\sqrt{20}\sqrt{5}$
   (iii) $\sqrt{2}\sqrt{8}$
   (iv) $\sqrt{2}\sqrt{32}$

   (v) $\sqrt{50}\sqrt{2}$
   (vi) $\dfrac{\sqrt{27}}{\sqrt{3}}$
   (vii) $\dfrac{\sqrt{50}}{\sqrt{2}}$
   (viii) $\dfrac{\sqrt{28}}{\sqrt{7}}$
   (ix) $\dfrac{\sqrt{72}}{\sqrt{8}}$
   (x) $\dfrac{\sqrt{200}}{\sqrt{8}}$

4. Simplify these surds:

   (i) $\sqrt{8}$
   (ii) $\sqrt{45}$
   (iii) $\sqrt{300}$
   (iv) $\sqrt{12}$
   (v) $\sqrt{32}$
   (vi) $\sqrt{500}$
   (vii) $\sqrt{27}$
   (viii) $\sqrt{54}$
   (ix) $\sqrt{75}$
   (x) $\sqrt{98}$

5. Write $\sqrt{50} + \sqrt{8}$ in the form $k\sqrt{2}$, where $k \in Q$.

6. Write $\sqrt{27} + \sqrt{12}$ in the form $k\sqrt{3}$, where $k \in Q$.

7. Write $\sqrt{125} + \sqrt{20}$ in the form $k\sqrt{5}$, where $k \in Q$.

8. If $\sqrt{44} + \sqrt{99} = n\sqrt{11}$, then find n where $n \in N$.

1. Use Laws 1 to 4 of indices to write the following in index notation:

   (i) $5^3 \times 5^8$ (iii) $(3^2)^3$

   (ii) $\dfrac{8^7}{8^7}$ (iv) $\dfrac{16^9}{16^5}$

2. Use Laws 5 to 7 of indices to write the following in the form a^p, where $p \in Q$:

   (i) $\dfrac{1}{7^5}$ (iii) $\sqrt[5]{17^3}$

   (ii) $\sqrt[8]{15}$ (iv) $\dfrac{5^3}{\sqrt{5^5}}$

3. Use the laws of indices to simplify each of the following. Leave your answer in index notation.

   (i) $((2^3)(2^5))^2$ (iii) $\left(\dfrac{2^9}{2^5}\right)^6$

   (ii) $((7^6)(7^5))^2$ (iv) $\left(\dfrac{5^8}{5^3}\right)^7$

4. Use the laws of surds to simplify each of the following:

   (i) $\sqrt{125}$ (iii) $\sqrt{128}$

   (ii) $\sqrt{98}$ (iv) $\sqrt{18}$

5. Write these in the form a^n:

   (i) $a^4 \times a^6$ (iii) $\sqrt[4]{a^6}$

   (ii) $(a^4)^6$ (iv) $\sqrt[5]{a^3 \times a^7}$

6. Use the laws of surds to simplify each of the following:

   (i) $\sqrt{8} + \sqrt{98} + \sqrt{128}$

   (ii) $\sqrt{80} + \sqrt{245} + \sqrt{405}$

7. (i) Evaluate $25^{\frac{1}{2}}$.

   (ii) Write 9 and $\sqrt{3}$ as powers of 3, and hence, solve the equation $3^x = \dfrac{9}{\sqrt{3}}$.

   (iii) If $\sqrt{8} + \sqrt{50} - \sqrt{2} = n\sqrt{2}$, find n.

8. (i) Evaluate $64^{-\frac{1}{2}}$.

   (ii) Write 128 and $\sqrt{2}$ as a power of 2. Hence, solve the equation:

   $$2^{2x+1} = \dfrac{128}{\sqrt{2}}$$

9. (i) Evaluate $\left(\dfrac{4}{81}\right)^{-\frac{1}{2}}$.

   (ii) Write as a power of 7:

   (a) 343

   (b) $\sqrt{7}$

   Hence, solve the equation:

   $$7^{2x+1} = \dfrac{343}{(\sqrt{7})^3}$$

10. (i) Simplify $a^4 + a^4 + a^4 + a^4$.

    Hence, write $2^4 + 2^4 + 2^4 + 2^4$ as a power of 2.

    (ii) Write $2^{\frac{1}{4}} + 2^{\frac{1}{4}} + 2^{\frac{1}{4}} + 2^{\frac{1}{4}}$ as a power of 2.

    (iii) Simplify $3a^5 + 6a^5$.

    Hence, write $3(3^5) + 6(3^5)$ as a power of 3.

    (iv) Write $20(3^8) + 7(3^8)$ as a power of 3.

chapter 4

Number Patterns

Learning Outcomes

In this chapter you will learn about:

- ➲ Patterns in mathematics

- ➲ Linear sequences

- ➲ Graphing linear sequences (arithmetic sequences)

- ➲ Finding the general term of a linear sequence (arithmetic sequence)

- ➲ Summing a linear series

- ➲ Quadratic sequences

- ➲ Exponential sequences

- ➲ Cubic sequences

4

'We live in a universe of patterns.'

Ian Stewart, popular science writer and Professor of Mathematics, University of Warwick.

Mathematics is the study of patterns. Mathematicians seek out patterns and from these patterns formulate new conjectures. They then try to establish the truth of the conjectures by rigorous deduction from axioms, definitions and theorems.

4.1 PATTERNS

A **pattern** is a set of numbers, objects or diagrams that repeat in a predictable manner

Here are some examples of **patterns**.

(a)

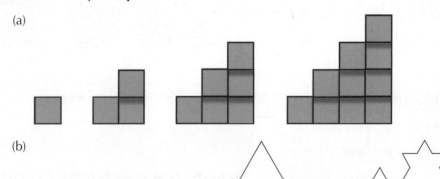

(b)

We call each distinct object, number or diagram in a pattern a **term** of the pattern.

The first term of a pattern is called T_1, the second term T_2, and so on.

ACTIVITY 4.1

(c) 2, 4, 6, 8, 10... $\Rightarrow T_1 = 2, T_2 = 4, T_3 = 6$, etc.

(d) 101, 1001, 10001, 100001, 1000001... $\Rightarrow T_1 = 101, T_2 = 1001, T_3 = 10001$, etc.

To predict what will come next in a pattern, we must find a rule that links one number or diagram with the next.

NUMBER PATTERNS

Worked Example 4.1

The pattern below begins with the integer 101. Each successive term is found by inserting an extra 0 immediately to the left of the units digit of the previous term:

101, 1001, 10001, 100001, 1000001, 10000001...

    (i) Write down T_7 and T_8, the next two terms of the pattern.

    (ii) How many zeros are in T_{12}, the 12th term?

    (iii) How many zeros are in T_n, the nth term?

Solution

    (i) $T_7 = 100,000,001$ and $T_8 = 1,000,000,001$

    (ii) The number of zeros in each term is equal to the number of the term.

        ∴ There are 12 zeros in T_{12}, the 12th term.

    (iii) The number of zeros in each term is equal to the number of the term.

        ∴ There are n zeros in the nth term.

 Worked Example 4.2

A four-tile repeating pattern is made up of the shapes shown.

    (i) Draw the next two shapes in the pattern.

    (ii) What is the shape of T_{100}, the 100th tile?

    (iii) What is the shape of T_{4n}, $n \in N$?

Solution

    (i)   (As the pattern repeats every four tiles, the fifth and sixth tiles will be the same as the first and second tiles.)

    (ii) We can draw a table to help us:

Tile	Shape
1	Triangle
2	Square
3	Pentagon
4	Hexagon
5	Triangle
6	Square
7	Pentagon
8	Hexagon
9	Triangle

We can see that the pattern repeats itself every four tiles.

$100 \div 4 = 25$, with a remainder of 0 (25 repeating blocks of four tiles).

∴ 100 is a multiple of 4.

If we consider our table, we see that every multiple of 4 will be a hexagon.

∴ The 100th tile is a hexagon.

    (iii) If $n \in N$, then T_{4n} is the set of tiles $\{T_4, T_8, T_{12}, T_{16}...\}$. This set consists of every fourth tile. From part (ii), we know that every fourth tile is a hexagon. Therefore, the shape of T_{4n} is a hexagon.

Exercise 4.1

1. Find the next shape in each of the following patterns:

   (i) □◆♥□◆♥□   (repeats every three)

   (ii) ÷ ≠ ≡ ≈ ÷ ≠ ≡ ≈   (repeats every four)

   (iii) ∠ ∇ ® © ∠ ∇ ® ©   (repeats every four)

   (iv) ◁ ▷ ▲ ▼ ◁ ▷ ▲ ▼ ◁   (repeats every four)

   (v) ⬤ ℞ ⊞ ⬤ ⤸ ✳ ▪ ℞ ✳ ⬤ ℞   (repeats every nine)

2. A coloured pattern is shown. In each case, after the last block shown, the pattern repeats. Identify the colour of the next three blocks.

   (i)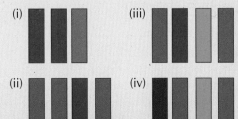

   (iii)

   (ii)

   (iv)

3. A coloured pattern is shown. In each case, after the last block shown, the pattern repeats. Identify:

   (a) The colours of the next three blocks

   (b) The colours of the 50th block, the 100th block and the 150th block

   (i)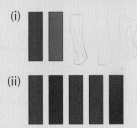

   (ii)

(iii)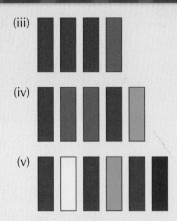

(iv)

(v)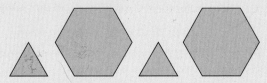

4. A two-tile repeating pattern consisting of a triangle and a hexagon is shown.

   (i) What is the shape of the 50th tile?

   (ii) What is the shape of the 93rd tile?

   (iii) What is the shape of the nth tile if n is an even number?

5. A three-tile repeating pattern is shown.

   (i) What the shape of the 40th tile?

   (ii) What is the shape of the 30th tile?

   (iii) If T_1 is the shape of the first tile, T_2 the shape of the second and so on, then explain why T_{3n}, $n \in N$, is always a square.

6. A four-tile repeating pattern is shown.

   (i) What is the shape of the 15th tile?

   (ii) What is the shape of the 94th tile?

   (iii) What colour is the 100th tile?

   (iv) Copy and complete the following sentence:

   If n is even, then T_n will always be a _____ -shaped tile, whereas if n is odd, T_n will always

   be a _____ -shaped tile.

7. Consider the pattern shown below.

Identify the colours of the next nine squares. Explain your reasoning.

8. To predict what will come next in a pattern, we must find a rule that will link one number or diagram with the next.

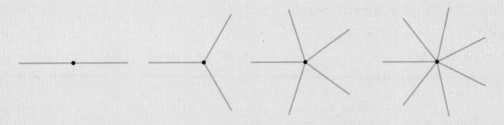

(i) Identify two different rules for the above pattern.

(ii) For each of the rules, draw the next two diagrams in the pattern.

4.2 ARITHMETIC SEQUENCES

> A **sequence** is a set of terms, in a definite order, where the terms are obtained by some rule.

> A **number sequence** is an ordered set of numbers with a rule to find every number in the sequence.

2, 5, 8, 11, 14... is an example of a **number sequence**. The first term is 2 ($T_1 = 2$).
The rule for finding a particular term is add 3 to the previous term.

> In an **arithmetic (linear) sequence**, the difference or change between one term and the next is always the same number. This means that the change in an arithmetic sequence is always constant.

2, 5, 8, 11, 14... is an example of an **arithmetic sequence**. The difference between consecutive terms is 3.

> The difference, $T_n - T_{n-1}$, between consecutive terms in any sequence is referred to as the **first difference**.

> The difference between each term in an arithmetic sequence can also be referred to as the **common difference**. The letter d is used to represent the common difference.

	T_1	T_2	T_3	T_4	T_5	T_6
Term value:	2	5	8	11	14	17
First difference:	+3	+3	+3	+3	+3	

Note: **First difference** is also known as **first change**.

The first differences in any arithmetic sequence are always constant (same number).

Graphing Arithmetic Sequences

When we graph the terms of an arithmetic sequence against the term number, we find that the points can be joined with a straight line, hence the name 'linear sequence'.

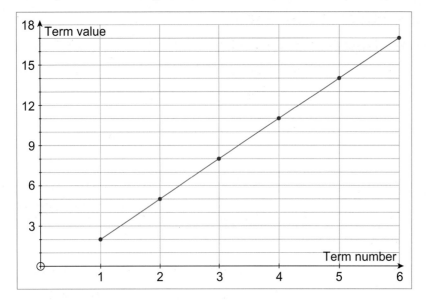

The first six terms of the arithmetic sequence 2, 5, 8, 11, 14, 17... are graphed above.

Worked Example 4.3

The first three terms of a pattern are shown.

$T_1 = \bullet$ $T_2 = \bullet$ $T_3 = \bullet$

(i) Draw the next two terms of the pattern.

(ii) Count the number of dots in each of the first five terms and display the results in a table.

(iii) Describe the sequence of numbers generated by the pattern.

(iv) How many dots are there in T_7, the seventh term?

(v) How many dots are there in T_n, the nth term?

Solution

(i) $T_4 = \bullet$ $T_5 = \bullet$

(ii)

T_1	T_2	T_3	T_4	T_5
6	8	10	12	14

(iii) The sequence is arithmetic, with first term 6 and common difference 2.

(iv)

T_1	T_2	T_3	T_4	T_5	T_6	T_7
6	8	10	12	14	16	18

+2 +2 +2 +2 +2 +2

From the diagram, it is clear that $T_7 = 6 + (6)2 = 18$.

(v) Using the same reasoning as in part (iv), $T_n = 6 + (n - 1)2$

$$= 6 + 2n - 2$$

$$= 4 + 2n$$

$$\therefore T_n = 4 + 2n$$

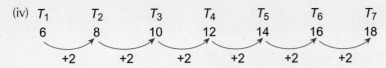

Worked Example 4.4

For each of the following arithmetic sequences, write down:

(a) T_1, the first term of the sequence

(b) d, the common difference

(c) The next three terms

    (i) 1, 5, 9, 13,...   (ii) 3, 1, –1, –3,...

Solution

(i) 1, 5, 9, 13,...   (ii) 3, 1, –1, –3,...

(a) $T_1 = 1$ (a) $T_1 = 3$

(b) $d = T_2 - T_1$ (b) $d = T_2 - T_1$

      $= 5 - 1$ $= 1 - 3$

$\therefore d = 4$ $\therefore d = -2$

(c) 17, 21, 25   (c) –5, –7, –9

Worked Example 4.5

x, $2x + 1$ and $5x - 4$ are the first three terms of an arithmetic sequence. Find:

(i) The value of x

(ii) The fourth term of the sequence

Solution

(i) Since the sequence is arithmetic, the difference between any two consecutive terms is a constant.

$$T_2 - T_1 = T_3 - T_2$$

$$\therefore (2x + 1) - x = (5x - 4) - (2x + 1)$$

$$2x + 1 - x = 5x - 4 - 2x - 1$$

$$x + 1 = 3x - 5$$

$$-2x = -6$$

$$\Rightarrow x = 3$$

(ii) If $x = 3$, then the sequence is 3, 2(3) + 1, 5(3) – 4...

This gives the sequence 3, 7, 11... The common difference is 4.

$$\therefore T_4 = 11 + 4 = 15.$$

Exercise 4.2

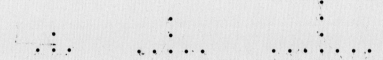

Remember: In an arithmetic (linear) sequence, the first difference is a non-zero constant

1. The first three terms of a pattern are shown.

   $T_1 = \bullet$ $T_2 = \bullet$ $T_3 = \bullet$

   (i) Draw the next two terms of the pattern.
   (ii) Count the number of dots in each of the first five terms and display the results in a table.
   (iii) Describe the sequence of numbers generated by the pattern.
   (iv) How many dots are there in T_8, the eighth term?
   (v) How many dots are there in T_n, the nth term?

2. The first three terms of a pattern are shown.

   (i) Draw the next two terms of the pattern.
   (ii) Count the number of dots in each of the first five terms and display the results in a table.
   (iii) Describe the sequence of numbers generated by the pattern.
   (iv) How many dots are there in T_9, the ninth term?
   (v) How many dots are there in T_n, the nth term?

3. The first three terms of a pattern are shown.

   (i) Draw the next two terms of the pattern.
   (ii) Count the number of red squares in each of the first five terms and display the results in a table.

   (iii) Describe the sequence of numbers generated by the pattern.
   (iv) How many red squares are there in T_7, the seventh term?
   (v) How many red squares are there in T_n, the nth term?
   (vi) How many white squares are there in T_n, the nth term?

4. The first three terms of a pattern are shown.

   (i) Draw the next two terms of the pattern.
   (ii) Count the number of red squares in each of the first five terms and display the results in a table.

(iii) Describe the sequence of numbers generated by the pattern.

(iv) How many red squares are there in T_7, the seventh term?

(v) How many red squares are there in T_n, the nth term?

5. State, giving a reason, whether or not the following sequences are arithmetic:

(i) 3, 5, 7, 9...

(vi) 2, 2.5, 3, 3.5, 4...

(ii) 2, 4, 6, 8, 10...

(vii) 12, 15, 18, 21...

(iii) 1, 2, 4, 8, 16...

(viii) $\frac{1}{2}, \frac{1}{3}, \frac{1}{4}, \frac{1}{5}, \frac{1}{6}\cdots$

(iv) 1, 1, 2, 3, 5, 8...

(ix) −5, −1, 3, 7, 11...

(v) 5, 10, 15, 20, 25...

(x) 20, 21, 22, 23...

6. For each of the following arithmetic sequences, write down:

(a) T_1, the first term of the sequence   (b) d, the common difference   (c) The next three terms

(i) 2, 6, 10...

(vi) −5, −3, −1...

(ii) 5, 7, 9, 11...

(vii) 5.5, 6, 6.5...

(iii) 19, 16, 13...

(viii) 1, $1\frac{1}{4}$, $1\frac{1}{2}$...

(iv) 100, 90, 80...

(ix) 72, 61, 50...

(v) 13, 20, 27...

(x) $\frac{1}{6}, \frac{1}{3}, \frac{1}{2}$...

7. For each of these arithmetic sequences, write down:

(a) The value of d, the common difference   (b) The next three terms

(i) −6, −9...

(vi) $15\frac{1}{2}$, 14...

(ii) 100, 90...

(vii) 11, $13\frac{3}{4}$, $16\frac{1}{2}$...

(iii) 4.4, 6, 7.6...

(viii) −5.4, −1...

(iv) −4, 0...

(ix) $\frac{1}{10}, \frac{1}{5}\cdots$

(v) −10, $-7\frac{1}{2}$...

(x) $\frac{7}{8}, \frac{3}{4},\cdots$

8. For each of the following graphs of arithmetic sequences, identify:

(a) T_1, the first term   (b) d, the common difference   (c) T_4 the fourth term

5 16

(i)

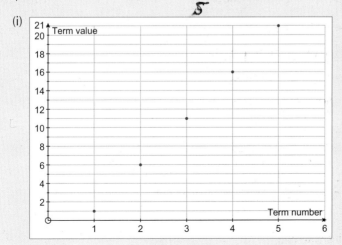

(ii)

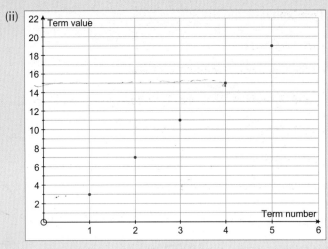

(iii)

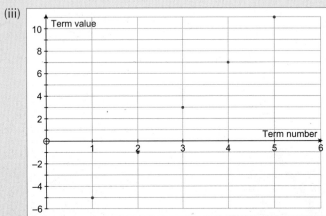

(iv)

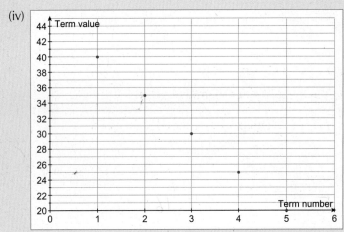

(v)

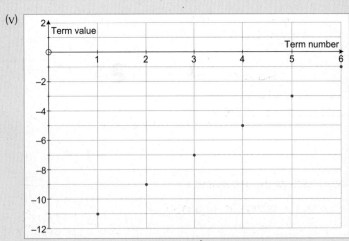

9. The nth term of some sequences are given below.

    (a) Write down the first four terms of each sequence.

    (b) By drawing a graph, decide whether the sequence is arithmetic or not.

      (i) $T_n = 2n + 1$ (ii) $T_n = 3n - 1$ (iii) $T_n = n^2 + 3$ (iv) $T_n = 12 - 2n$ (v) $T_n = \frac{1}{n}$

10. The nth term of some sequences are given below.

    (a) Write down the first four terms of each sequence.

    (b) By drawing a graph, decide whether the sequence is arithmetic or not.

      (i) $T_n = 4n + 1$ (ii) $T_n = 13 - 3n$ (iii) $T_n = 2n^2 + 3$ (iv) $T_n = 10 - 3n$ (v) $T_n = 4^n$

11. The graphs of three sequences are shown. Lines and curves are included for clarity.

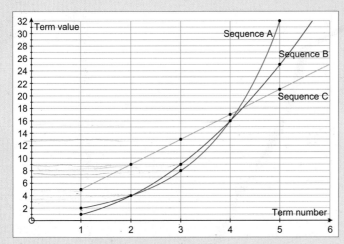

    (a) Identify the arithmetic sequence.

    (b) Write down the first three terms of each of the sequences.

    (c) What is d, the common difference, in the arithmetic sequence?

12. The graphs of three sequences are shown. Lines and curves are included for clarity.

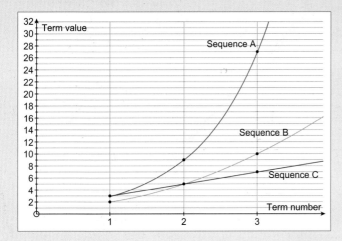

    (a) Identify the arithmetic sequence.

    (b) Write down the first three terms of each of the sequences.

    (c) What is d, the common difference, in the arithmetic sequence?

13. The graphs of three sequences are shown. Lines are included for clarity.

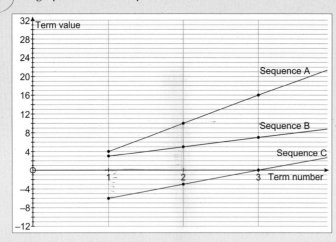

(i) Find the common differences, d_A, d_B and d_C, for each of the three sequences.

(ii) Find m_A, m_B and m_C, the slopes of each of the three lines associated with each sequence.

(iii) What is the connection between the common differences and the slopes?

14. $x + 3$, $3x - 1$ and $4x - 1$ are the first three terms of an arithmetic sequence. Solve for x.

15. $x + 1$, $3x$ and $2x + 8$ are the first three terms of an arithmetic sequence. Solve for x.

16. $3x + 2$, 20 and $2x + 3$ are the first three terms of an arithmetic sequence. Find:

(i) The value of x (ii) The value of d, the common difference   (iii) The fourth term, T_4

17. $3x - 2$, $2x + 1$ and $18 - x$ are the first three terms of an arithmetic sequence. Find:

(i) The value of x (ii) The value of d, the common difference   (iii) The fourth and fifth terms (T_4 and T_5)

4.3 THE GENERAL TERM OF AN ARITHMETIC SEQUENCE

Let a be the first term of an arithmetic sequence and d be the common difference.
The table below shows the first five terms of the sequence.

T_1	T_2	T_3	T_4	T_5
a	$a + d$	$a + 2d$	$a + 3d$	$a + 4d$

What is T_n, the nth term of the sequence?

Continuing the pattern, $T_n = a + (n - 1)d$.

FORMULA

The **general term** for any arithmetic sequence is $T_n = a + (n - 1)d$, where a is the first term and d is the common difference.

This formula appears on page 22 of *Formulae and Tables*.

Worked Example 4.6

For the arithmetic sequence 5, 15, 25, 35..., find the following:

(i) T_n, the nth term   (ii) The 20th term   (iii) The first term that is greater than 450

Solution

(i) $d = T_2 - T_1$

$ = 15 - 5$

$ \therefore d = 10 \qquad a = 5$

$T_n = a + (n-1)d$

$ = 5 + (n-1)10$

$ = 5 + 10n - 10$

$\therefore T_n = 10n - 5$

(ii) $T_{20} = 10(20) - 5$

$\therefore T_{20} = 195$

(iii) $T_n > 450$

$10n - 5 > 450$

$10n > 455$

$n > 45.5$

$\therefore$ The first term greater than 450 is the 46th term (as $n \in N$).

 ## Worked Example 4.7

How many terms of the arithmetic sequence 45, 43, 41... are positive?

Solution

$a = 45 \qquad\qquad d = 43 - 45 = -2$

We need to find the largest value of n, for which $T_n > 0$.

$T_n = a + (n-1)d$ $T_n > 0$

$T_n = 45 + (n-1)(-2)$ $\Rightarrow 47 - 2n > 0$

$ = 45 - 2n + 2$ $-2n > -47$

$\therefore T_n = 47 - 2n$ $2n < 47$ (change inequality sign)

$ n < 23.5$

$ \Rightarrow n = 23$ (n must be a whole number.)

$ \therefore$ 23 terms of the sequence are positive.

 ## Exercise 4.3

1. In each of the following arithmetic sequences, find:

     (a) The first term   (b) The common difference   (c) The nth term (general term)

         (i) 5, 7, 9, 11...   (vi) −12, −7, −2...

         (ii) 4, 7, 10, 13...   (vii) 43, 40, 37, 34...

         (iii) 1, 5, 9, 13...   (viii) −16, −20, −24...

         (iv) 13, 20, 27, 34...   (ix) 75, 84, 93...

         (v) 59, 57, 55...   (x) −20, −17, −14...

2. −11, −15, −19... is an arithmetic sequence.

  (i) Find the *n*th term of the sequence.

  (ii) Hence, write down the 55th term.

3. 10, 22, 34... is an arithmetic sequence.

  (i) Find the *n*th term of the sequence.

  (ii) Hence, write down the 64th term.

4. 0, 7, 14, 21, 28... is an arithmetic sequence.

  (i) Find the *n*th term of the sequence.

  (ii) Hence, write down the 85th term.

5. 7, 13, 19... is an arithmetic sequence.

  (i) Find the *n*th term of the sequence.

  (ii) Hence, write down the 33rd term.

6. 3, 11, 19... is an arithmetic sequence.

  (i) Find the *n*th term of the sequence.

  (ii) Hence, write down the 96th term.

7. 31, 25, 19... is an arithmetic sequence.

  (i) Find the *n*th term of the sequence.

  (ii) Hence, write down the 21st term.

8. 5, 9, 13... is an arithmetic sequence.

  (i) Find the *n*th term of the sequence.

  (ii) Hence, write down the 55th term.

9. 116 is the *n*th term of the arithmetic sequence 14, 17, 20...

  Find the value of *n*.

10. How many terms of the arithmetic sequence 91, 89, 87... are positive?

11. How many terms of the arithmetic sequence 17, 21, 25... are less than 100?

12. How many terms of the sequence 100, 97, 94... are positive?

13. The 19th term of an arithmetic sequence is 150. If T_1, the first term, is 6, then find *d*, the common difference.

14. The 51st term of an arithmetic sequence is 248. If *d*, the common difference, is 15, then find *a*, the first term.

15. The 40th term of an arithmetic sequence is 480. If the difference between T_{50} and T_{49} is 5, find *a*, the first term.

16. The natural numbers greater than 1 are arranged as shown in the following chart:

	A	B	C	D	E
Row 1			2	3	4
Row 2	7	6	5		
Row 3			8	9	10
Row 4	13	12	11		
Row 5			14	15	16
Row 6	19	18	17		
Row 7			20	21	22
Row 8	25	24	23		
Row 9			26	27	28

  (i) Copy and complete the pattern for rows 6 to 9.

  (ii) What number will appear in Row 100 of Column A?

  (iii) What number will appear in Row 99 of Column E?

  (iv) Determine the position of the integer 2,011.

17. As part of a new tree-planting initiative, Seán has to plant 30 trees on his farm in 2011, 35 in 2012, 40 in 2013, and so on until the year 2030.

(i) How many trees will Seán plant in 2024?

(ii) In what year will Seán plant 75 trees?

(iii) Draw a graph showing the number of trees that will be planted in each of the years from 2025 to 2030.

18. A person just fitted for contact lenses is told to wear the lenses for two hours the first day and to gradually increase the amount of time they wear the lenses by 15 minutes per day.

(i) Complete the table below.

Day	Number of hours wearing lenses
1	2
2	2.25
3	
4	
5	

(ii) On which day will the person be able to wear the contact lenses for 14 hours?

19. An architect is designing a skyscraper. He has been told that each floor must contain exactly 90 rooms. He has constructed a table showing the total number of rooms for each floor and all floors below it. Part of the table is shown below.

Floor number	Number of rooms on the floor and all floors below
1	90
2	180
3	270
4	360
5	450

(i) Construct the next five rows of the table.

(ii) All rooms on the first 20 floors will be equipped with a special security door. How many of these doors will be required?

(iii) The building must contain 9,090 rooms. How many floors will the skyscraper have?

4.4 THE SUM OF AN ARITHMETIC SERIES

An **arithmetic series** is the sum of all the terms in an arithmetic sequence.

Carl Friedrich Gauss (1777–1855) was a German mathematician who made significant contributions to many fields, including number theory, statistics, calculus, geometry and physics. He has been called 'the greatest mathematician since antiquity'.

Gauss was a child prodigy. When he was in primary school, he was punished by his teacher for misbehaviour. His punishment was to add all the whole numbers from 1 to 100. To the amazement of his teacher, he calculated the sum in a matter of seconds. How did he do it?

Carl Friedrich Gauss

Gauss's Method

It is most likely that the young Gauss employed the following method to sum the first 100 natural numbers.

Step 1

Write the series in ascending order from 1 to 100.

$1 + 2 + 3 + 4 + ... + 97 + 98 + 99 + 100$

Step 2

Write the series in descending order from 100 to 1.

$100 + 99 + 98 + 97 + ... + 4 + 3 + 2 + 1$

Step 3

Add together both representations of the series.

$$\begin{array}{r}1 + 2 + 3 + 4 + ... + 97 + 98 + 99 + 100 \\ 100 + 99 + 98 + 97 + ... + 4 + 3 + 2 + 1 \\ \hline 101 + 101 + 101 + 101 + ... + 101 + 101 + 101 + 101\end{array}$$

This gives $100(101) = 10{,}100$.

This is the sum of two series. Therefore, the sum of one series is $\frac{1}{2}(10{,}100) = 5{,}050$.

$1 + 2 + 3 + 4 + ... + 97 + 98 + 99 + 100 = 5{,}050$

ACTIVITY 4.3

FORMULA

The sum of the first n terms of an arithmetic series is given by the formula $S_n = \frac{n}{2}\{2a + (n-1)d\}$.

This formula appears on page 22 of *Formulae and Tables*.

- a is the first term.
- d is the common difference.

NUMBER PATTERNS

Worked Example 4.8

Find the sum of the first 100 terms of the arithmetic series $7 + 10 + 13 + ...$

Solution

$S_n = \dfrac{n}{2}\{2a + (n - 1)d\}$

$a = 7, \qquad d = 3, \qquad n = 100$

$S_{100} = \dfrac{100}{2}\{2(7) + (100 - 1)3\}$

$\qquad = 50\{14 + 99(3)\}$

$\qquad = 50\{311\}$

$\therefore S_{100} = 15{,}550$

Worked Example 4.9

Find the sum of the arithmetic series $11 + 13 + 15 + ... + 51$

Solution

Step 1

We need to know how many terms there are in the series.

Let n = the number of terms. Therefore $T_n = 51$.

$a = 11 \qquad d = 2$

$T_n = a + (n - 1)d$

$\therefore T_n = 11 + (n - 1)2$

$\qquad = 11 + 2n - 2$

$\Rightarrow T_n = 2n + 9$

$2n + 9 = 51$

$\qquad 2n = 51 - 9$

$\qquad 2n = 42$

$\therefore n = 21$

There are 21 terms.

Step 2

Next we must find the sum of these 21 terms.

$S_n = \dfrac{n}{2}\{2a + (n - 1)d\}$

$a = 11, \qquad d = 2, \qquad n = 21$

$S_{21} = \dfrac{21}{2}\{2(11) + (21 - 1)2\}$

$\qquad = 10.5\{22 + 20(2)\}$

$\qquad = 10.5\{62\}$

$\therefore S_{21} = 651$

$\Rightarrow 11 + 13 + 15 + ... + 51 = 651$

Worked Example 4.10

On 1 January 2010, Caitlin opened a bank account and deposited €200 in the account. On 1 February 2010, she deposited €210 in the account. She plans to make deposits on the first of every month, increasing the amount deposited by €10 each month.

    (i) How much will Caitlin deposit on 1 December 2015?

    (ii) In total, how much will Caitlin have deposited by the end of December 2015?

4

Solution

(i) Consider the first six deposits Caitlin makes:

200, 210, 220, 230, 240, 250

The deposits form an arithmetic sequence.

Now find the total number of deposits made:

There are 12 deposits made each year for six years. This gives a total of 72 deposits.

Therefore, the 72nd term of the sequence 200, 210, 220, 230... gives the amount that Caitlin deposited on 1 December, 2015.

$a = 200 \qquad d = 10$

$T_n = a + (n - 1)d$

$T_{72} = 200 + (72 - 1)10$

$\qquad = 200 + 710$

$\qquad = 910$

Caitlin deposits €910 on 1 December 2015.

(ii) We need to sum 72 terms of the series
200 + 210 + 220 + ...

$S_n = \dfrac{n}{2}\{2a + (n - 1)d\}$

$a = 200, \qquad d = 10, \qquad n = 72$

$S_{72} = \dfrac{72}{2}\{2(200) + (72 - 1)10\}$

$\qquad = 36\{400 + 710\}$

$\qquad = 36\{1110\}$

$\qquad = 39960$

Caitlin will have deposited €39,960 by the end of December 2015.

Exercise 4.4

1. Find the sum of the first 20 terms of each of the following arithmetic series:

   (i) 11 + 22 + 33 + ...

   (ii) 5 + 7 + 9 + ...

   (iii) 43 + 40 + 37 + ...

   (iv) 1 + 5 + 9 + ...

   (v) 13 + 20 + 27 + ...

2. Find the sum of the first 30 terms of each of the following arithmetic series:

   (i) 4 + 7 + 10 + ...

   (ii) 3 + 8 + 13 + ...

   (iii) −5 + 2 + 9 + ...

   (iv) 35 + 33 + 31 + ...

   (v) 20 + 19 + 18 + ...

3. Find the sum of the first 10 terms of each of the following series:

   (i) −11 + 1 + 13 + ...

   (ii) −8 − 2 + 4 + ...

   (iii) 4 − 2 − 8 − ...

   (iv) −8 − 10 − 12 − ...

   (v) −4 − 2 − 0 + ...

4. $S_{80} = 1 + 2 + 3 + 4 + ... + 79 + 80$ is the sum of the first 80 natural numbers. Find S_{80}.

5. Find the sum of the first 30 odd natural numbers: 1 + 3 + 5 + ... + 59.

6. How many terms are there in the arithmetic series 2 + 4 + 6 + ... + 80? Find their sum.

7. Given the arithmetic series
1 + 7 + 13 + 19 + ...:

   (i) Find the sum of the first 10 terms.

   (ii) Find the sum of the first 20 terms.

   (iii) Hence, find the sum of the second 10 terms.

8. Given the arithmetic series $2 + 10 + 18 + \ldots$:

   (i) Find the sum of the first 20 terms.

   (ii) Find the sum of the first 40 terms.

   (iii) Hence, find the sum of the second 20 terms.

9. Given the arithmetic series $-1 + 7 + 15 + \ldots$:

   (i) Find the sum of the first 10 terms.

   (ii) Find the sum of the first 20 terms.

   (iii) Hence, find the sum of the second 10 terms.

10. Find the sum of the following arithmetic series:

   (i) $2 + 5 + 8 + \ldots + 65$

   (ii) $11 + 22 + 33 + \ldots + 319$

   (iii) $88 + 86 + 84 + \ldots + 8$

   (iv) $55 + 51 + \ldots + 11$

   (v) $3 + 6 + 9 + \ldots + 99$

11. $5, 9, 13 \ldots$ is an arithmetic sequence.

   (i) Find the nth term of the sequence.

   (ii) Hence, write down the 55th term.

   (iii) Find S_{50}, the sum of the first 50 terms.

12. On 1 January 2010, Fergal opened a bank account and deposited €100 in the account. On 1 February 2010, he deposited €105 in the account. He plans to make deposits on the first of every month, increasing the amount deposited by €5 each month.

   (i) How much will Fergal deposit on 1 December 2014?

   (ii) In total, how much will Fergal have deposited by the end of December 2014?

13. An athlete begins a training programme for a 10 km road race, 50 weeks before the event. He plans to train each day for 49 weeks and rest on the week before the race. In the first week he runs 2 km each day, in the second week he runs 2.25 km, in the third 2.5 km and so on, increasing his distance by 0.25 km each successive week.

   (i) How many kilometres will he run each day in the 30th week?

   (ii) During which week will he run the race distance?

   (iii) How many kilometres in total will he run on the training programme, assuming he trains seven days a week?

14. A snail is crawling up a wall. The first hour it climbs 20 cm, the second hour it climbs 18 cm, the third hour 16 cm and so on.

   (i) After how many hours will it have stopped climbing?

   (ii) Assuming that the snail reaches the top of the wall just as it stops climbing, how high is the wall?

15. A football stadium has a section of red seating in one of its stands (see the diagram below).

The first and second rows contain two red seats each. The third and fourth rows contain three red seats each. This pattern continues for all other rows in the section. There are 100 rows in the section. The table below gives the pattern for the first nine rows.

Row number	1	2	3	4	5	6	7	8	9
Number of red seats	2	2	3	3	4	4	5	5	6

   (i) How many red seats are in the 51st row?

   (ii) How many red seats are in the 98th row?

   (iii) How many red seats in total are in the section?

4.5 NON-LINEAR SEQUENCES

In arithmetic (linear) sequences, the difference between consecutive terms, also called the first difference, is always constant. If the difference between consecutive terms is **not** constant, then we say that the sequence is **non-linear**.

> In **non-linear sequences**, the difference changes between each pair of consecutive terms.

The sequence 1, 8, 27, 64... is non-linear.

 **ACTIVITY 4.4**

Quadratic Sequences

Consider the non-linear sequence 2, 5, 10, 17...

We can see that the first difference between each term is **not** the same.

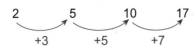

When we look at the second difference, i.e. the difference between the differences, we may be able to spot a pattern.

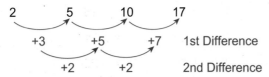

> A **quadratic sequence** is a sequence where the nth term is of the form $T_n = an^2 + bn + c,\ a, b, c \in R,\ a \neq 0$.
>
> The second difference is constant. It is also known as the second change.

The second difference is the same value each time.

In this case, the pattern is referred to as a **quadratic pattern**.

A quadratic pattern graphed will be a **curve** and **not** a straight line.

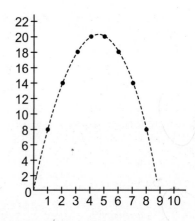

Worked Example 4.11

Show that the sequence 1, 6, 15, 28, 45... is quadratic.

Solution

Term:	T_1	T_2	T_3	T_4	T_5
Sequence:	1	6	15	28	45
1st difference:		5	9	13	17
2nd difference:			4	4	4

We see that the second difference is constant. Therefore, the sequence is quadratic.

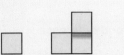 Worked Example 4.12

The first three terms of a pattern are shown.

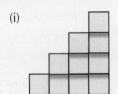

(i) Draw the next term of the pattern.

(ii) Count the number of squares in each of the first four terms and display the results in a table.

(iii) Describe the sequence of numbers generated by the pattern.

(iv) How many squares are there in T_7, the seventh term?

Solution

(i)

(ii)

Term	Number of squares
1	1
2	3
3	6
4	10

(iii)

Term	Number of squares	First difference	Second difference
1	1		
2	3	2	
3	6	3	1
4	10	4	1

The sequence is quadratic, as the second differences are all 1, a constant.

(iv) The second difference is a constant of 1.

Therefore, the first difference will increase by 1 each term.

Use a table to help find T_7.

T_1	=	1				
T_2	=	1	+	2	=	3
T_3	=	3	+	3	=	6
T_4	=	6	+	4	=	10
T_5	=	10	+	5	=	15
T_6	=	15	+	6	=	21
T_7	=	21	+	7	=	28

$\therefore T_7$ has 28 squares.

Worked Example 4.13

The first three terms of a pattern are shown:

(i) Draw the next term in the pattern.

(ii) Count the number of squares in each of the first four terms and display the results in a table.

(iii) Describe the sequence of numbers generated by the pattern.

(iv) How many squares are in T_n, the nth pattern?

Solution

(i)

(ii)

Term	Number of squares
1	4
2	12
3	24
4	40

(iii)

Term	Number of squares	First difference	Second difference
1	4		
2	12	8	
3	24	12	4
4	40	16	4

The sequence is quadratic as the second differences are all 4, a constant.

(iv) When we study the rectangles we see that the length of the rectangle grows by 2 units and the height of the rectangles grows by 1 unit. The area of each rectangle gives the number of squares in each rectangle. The table shows the lengths, heights and areas of the first five rectangles.

Length	2	4	6	8	10
Height	2	3	4	5	6
Area	4	12	24	40	60

The lengths form an arithmetic sequence with start term 2 and common difference 2.

The heights form an arithmetic sequence with start term 2 and common difference 1.

Let L_n and H_n be the respective length and height of the nth term.

Then $T_n = L_n \times H_n$

$$L_n = 2 + (n-1)(2) \qquad\qquad H_n = 2 + (n-1)(1)$$
$$= 2 + 2n - 2 \qquad\qquad\qquad = 2 + n - 1$$
$$= 2n \qquad\qquad\qquad\qquad = n + 1$$

$$\therefore T_n = 2n(n+1)$$
$$= 2n^2 + 2n$$

Graphing Quadratic Sequences

When we graph the terms of a quadratic sequence against the term number, we find that the points can be joined with a curve.

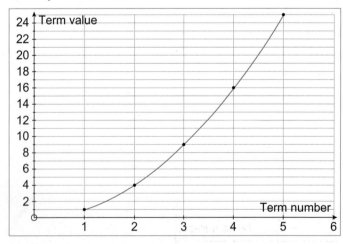

The first five terms of the quadratic sequence 1, 4, 9, 16, 25... are graphed above.

Exponential Sequences

Another example of a non-linear pattern is 4, 8, 16, 32... In this sequence each term is double the previous term. This type of sequence is called an **exponential sequence**.

> Sequences that involve doubling, tripling, halving, etc., are referred to as exponential sequences.

Worked Example 4.14

Orla is 8 m away from a wall. She moves towards the wall and, with each move, she halves the distance between herself and the wall.

    (i) Construct a table showing Orla's distance from the wall after each of her first six moves.

    (ii) Plot a graph of Orla's distance from the wall against move number towards the wall.

    (iii) Find a formula for Orla's distance from the wall after n moves.

    (iv) Hence, find Orla's distance from the wall after 10 moves.
        Give your answer in centimetres, correct to the nearest centimetre.

Solution

(i)

Move	Distance from the wall (metres)
0	8
1	4
2	2
3	1
4	$\frac{1}{2}$
5	$\frac{1}{4}$
6	$\frac{1}{8}$

(ii)

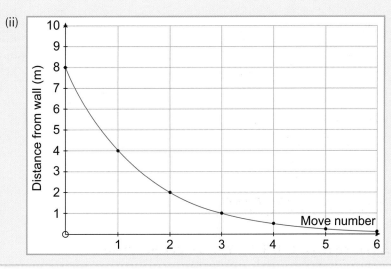

(iii)

Move	Distance from the wall
0	8
1	$8 \times \frac{1}{2}$
2	$8 \times \frac{1}{2} \times \frac{1}{2} = 8 \times \left(\frac{1}{2}\right)^2$
3	$8 \times \frac{1}{2} \times \frac{1}{2} \times \frac{1}{2} = 8 \times \left(\frac{1}{2}\right)^3$
4	$8 \times \frac{1}{2} \times \frac{1}{2} \times \frac{1}{2} \times \frac{1}{2} = 8 \times \left(\frac{1}{2}\right)^4$
5	$8 \times \frac{1}{2} \times \frac{1}{2} \times \frac{1}{2} \times \frac{1}{2} \times \frac{1}{2} = 8 \times \left(\frac{1}{2}\right)^5$
6	$8 \times \frac{1}{2} \times \frac{1}{2} \times \frac{1}{2} \times \frac{1}{2} \times \frac{1}{2} \times \frac{1}{2} = 8 \times \left(\frac{1}{2}\right)^6$

Following the pattern in the table, we can see that:

$T_n = 8 \times \left(\frac{1}{2}\right)^n$, where n represents the step number.

(iv) $T_{10} = 8\left(\frac{1}{2}\right)^{10} = 0.0078125$ m $= 0.78125$ cm $= 1$ cm to the nearest centimetre.

Cubic Sequences

> A **cubic sequence** is a sequence of the form
> $T_n = an^3 + bn^2 + cn + d, \, a, b, c, d \in R, a \neq 0$.

For a cubic sequence, the **third difference** is always constant.

Worked Example 4.15

Show that the sequence 2, 10, 30, 68, 130, 222... is cubic.

Solution

Sequence	First difference	Second difference	Third difference
2			
10	8		
30	20	12	
68	38	18	6
130	62	24	6
222	92	30	6

The third difference is a constant. Therefore, the sequence is cubic.

Exercise 4.5

> Remember: Linear sequence ⇒ 1st difference is a non-zero constant
> Quadratic sequence ⇒ 2nd difference is a non-zero constant
> Cubic sequence ⇒ 3rd difference is a non-zero constant

1. The first four terms of a pattern are shown.

   (i) Construct the next two terms of the pattern.

   (ii) Count the number of dots in each of the first five terms and display the results in a table.

   (iii) Describe the sequence of numbers generated by the pattern.

   (iv) How many dots are there in T_7, the seventh term?

2. The first four terms of a pattern are shown.

   (i) Draw the next two terms of the pattern.

   (ii) Count the number of dots in each of the first five terms and display the results in a table.

   (iii) Describe the sequence of numbers generated by the pattern.

   (iv) How many red dots are there in T_8, the eighth term?

   (v) Find a formula for L_n, the number of dots on the base of the nth rectangle.

   (vi) Find a formula for H_n, the number of dots on the height of the nth rectangle.

   (vii) Hence, find a formula for T_n, the number of dots in the nth rectangle.

3. The first three terms of a pattern are shown.

 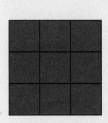 

   (i) Draw the next two terms of the pattern.

   (ii) Count the number of red squares in each of the first five terms and display the results in a table.

(iii) Describe the sequence of numbers generated by the pattern.

(iv) How many red squares are there in T_7, the seventh term?

(v) Find a formula for T_n, the number of squares in the nth pattern.

4. Determine whether the following sequences are arithmetic, quadratic or exponential. In each case give a reason for your answer.

    (i) –1, 2, 9, 20...   (ix) 5, 10, 20, 40...

    (ii) 2, 4, 8, 16...   (x) 4, 12, 36, 108...

    (iii) 1, 5, 11, 19...

    (iv) 5, 20, 45, 80...

    (v) 5, 10, 15, 20...

    (vi) 3, 9, 27, 81...

    (vii) 3, 6, 13, 24...

    (viii) 6, 8, 10 ,12...

5. For each of the following quadratic sequences, find:

    (a) a, the first term

    (b) The first and second differences

    (c) The next three terms

        (i) 8, 14, 24, 38...

        (ii) 1, 3, 6, 10...

        (iii) 7, 16, 31, 52...

        (iv) 3, 13, 27, 45...

        (v) 15, 23, 39, 63...

        (vi) 8, 12, 14, 14, 12...

        (vii) 5, 7, 5, –1, –11...

        (viii) 1, –2, –2, 1...

        (ix) 10, 4, 1, 1, 4...

6. For each exponential sequence:

    (a) Determine whether it doubles or triples.

    (b) Find the next three terms.

        (i) 8, 16, 32, 64, 128...

        (ii) 6, 18, 54, 162, 486...

        (iii) 33, 99, 297, 891...

        (iv) 13, 26, 52, 104, 208...

        (v) –5, –15, –45, –135, –405...

7. During a visit to a clinic, a patient receives a dose of radioactive medication. The active ingredient in the medication decays at a rate of 20% per hour. There are 150 micrograms (μg) of the radioactive ingredient in the medication.

    (i) Construct a table showing the amount of radioactive medication in the patient's body for the first six hours after the treatment.

    (ii) Plot a graph of micrograms of medication left in the patient's body against hours elapsed.

    (iii) Is it possible to reduce the amount of radioactive medication in the patient's body to 0?

8. The first four terms of a pattern are shown.

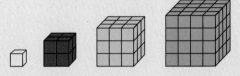

    (i) How many cubes in the next three terms of the pattern?

    (ii) Construct a table showing the first six terms of the sequence, the first difference, the second difference and the third difference.

    (iii) Hence, explain why the sequence is cubic.

9. The first six terms of a pattern are shown.

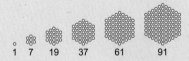

    1   7   19   37   61   91

    (i) Draw a table showing the first six terms of the corresponding number sequence, the first difference, second difference and third difference.

    (ii) Hence, explain why the sequence is cubic.

    (iii) How many circles are there in the seventh term?

10. The first three terms of a pattern are shown.

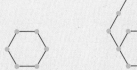

(i) Draw the next shape in the pattern.

(ii) How many dots are there in terms 5 and 6?

(iii) Construct a table showing the first six terms of the corresponding number sequence, the first difference, the second difference and the third difference.

(iv) What type of sequence is this? Give a reason for your answer.

Revision Exercises

1. The first three terms of a pattern are shown.

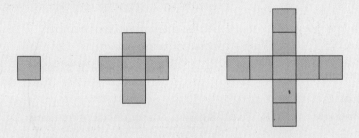

(i) Draw the fourth pattern.

(ii) How many squares are there in the nth term?

(iii) How many squares are there in the 50th term?

(iv) Which term has 237 squares?

2. A pattern of triangles is built up from matchsticks as follows:

   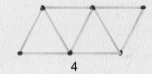

    1   2   3   4

(i) Draw the next set of triangles in the pattern.

(ii) How many matchsticks are needed for the nth set of triangles?

(iii) Using your result from part (ii), find the number of matchsticks needed to make the 50th set of triangles.

(iv) If there are only 200 matchsticks, which is the largest set of triangles that could be made?

3. The first three terms of a pattern are shown.

(i) Draw the next two terms of the pattern.

(ii) Count the number of dots in each of the first five terms and display the results in a table.

(iii) Describe the sequence of numbers generated by the pattern.

(iv) How many dots are there in T_n, the nth term?

(v) How many dots are there in T_8, the eighth term?

4. The *n*th term of an arithmetic sequence is given by $T_n = 5n + 1$.

   (i) Find the value of *a*, the first term.

   (ii) Find the value of *d*, the common difference.

   (iii) Find the value of *n* for which $T_n = 156$.

   (iv) Find the sum of the first 12 terms of the sequence.

5. Copy the pattern shown.

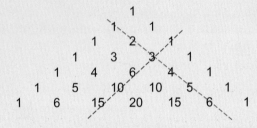

   (i) Draw the next two rows of the pattern.

   (ii) Identify the type of sequence along the diagonal marked with a broken red line and find its *n*th term.

   (iii) Identify the type of sequence along the diagonal marked with a broken blue line.

6. A bath contains 3 litres of water. A tap fills this bath at a rate of 500 ml per minute.

   (i) How many litres of water will be in the the bath after 10 minutes?

   (ii) If the capacity of the bath is 50 litres, how long will it take for the bath to overflow?

7. The first three terms of a pattern are shown.

   (i) Draw the next two terms of the pattern.

   (ii) Count the number of dots in each of the first five terms and display the results in a table.

   (iii) Describe the sequence of numbers generated by the pattern.

   (iv) How many dots are there in T_7, the seventh term?

8. 3, 12, 29, 54... is a sequence of numbers.

   (i) Determine whether the sequence is arithmetic, quadratic or exponential.

   (ii) Find T_5, the fifth term.

   (iii) Show the first five terms on a graph.

9. The graphs, A and B, of two sequences are shown. One sequence is linear and the other is quadratic.

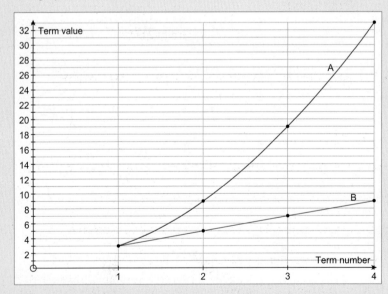

   (i) Identify the graph of the quadratic sequence and the graph of the linear sequence. Give a reason for your answer.

   (ii) Write down the first four terms of each sequence.

   (iii) What is the difference between T_6 of the arithmetic sequence and T_6 of the quadratic sequence?

10. Consider the pattern consisting of equilateral triangles shown below. The first pattern is constructed by joining together the midpoints of the sides and shading the resulting triangle. This creates a total of four triangles within the larger triangle.

The second pattern is constructed by carrying out the same process on the remaining non-shaded triangles. Each pattern is created by shading the middle third of the non-shaded triangles.

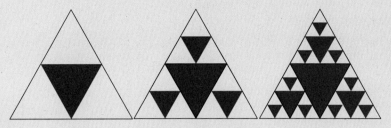

(i) How many triangles will be shaded in the fourth pattern?

(ii) What fraction of the area of the original triangle is shaded in the first pattern?

(iii) What fraction of the area of the original triangle is shaded in the third pattern?

11. Síle is investigating the number of square green tiles needed to make patterns in a sequence. The first three patterns are shown below, and the sequence continues in the same way. In each pattern, the tiles form a square and its two diagonals. There are no tiles in the white areas in the patterns – there are only the green tiles.

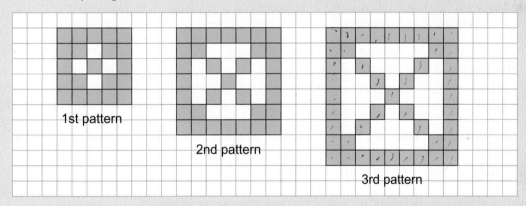

1st pattern

2nd pattern

3rd pattern

(a) In the table below, write the number of tiles needed for each of the first five patterns.

Pattern	1	2	3	4	5
No. of tiles	21	33	48	57	8769

(b) Find, in terms of n, a formula that gives the number of tiles needed to make the nth pattern.

(c) Using your formula, or otherwise, find the number of tiles in the 10th pattern.

(d) Síle has 399 tiles. What is the biggest pattern in the sequence that she can make?

(e) Find, in terms of n, a formula for the total number of tiles in the first n patterns.

(f) Síle starts at the beginning of the sequence and makes as many of the patterns as she can. She does not break up the earlier patterns to make the new ones. For example, after making the first two patterns, she has used up 54 tiles (21 + 33).
How many patterns can she make in total with her 399 tiles?

SEC Project Maths Paper 1 sample paper,
Leaving Certificate Ordinary Level, 2011

12. John is given two sunflower plants. One plant is 16 cm high and the other is 24 cm high. John measures the height of each plant at the same time every day for a week. He notes that the 16 cm plant grows 4 cm each day, and the 24 cm plant grows 3.5 cm each day.

(a) Draw up a table showing the heights of the two plants each day for the week, starting on the day that John got them.

(b) Write down two formulas – one for each plant – to represent the plant's height on any given day.
State clearly the meaning of any letters used in your formulas.

(c) John assumes that the plants will continue to grow at the same rates. Draw graphs to represent the heights of the two plants over the first four weeks.

(d) (i) From your diagram, write down the point of intersection of the two graphs.

(ii) Explain what the point of intersection means, with respect to the two plants. Your answer should refer to the meaning of both co-ordinates.

(e) Check your answer to part (d)(i) using your formulae from part (b).

(f) The point of intersection can be found either by reading the graph or by using algebra. State one advantage of finding it using algebra.

(g) John's model for the growth of the plants might not be correct.
State one limitation of the model that might affect the point of intersection and its interpretation.

SEC Project Maths Paper 1 sample paper,
Leaving Certificate Ordinary Level, 2011

13. The terms in an arithmetic sequence are given by the formula

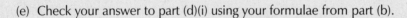

$T_n = 38 - 4n,$ for $n = 1, 2, 3, 4, \ldots$

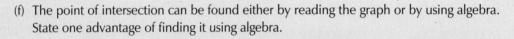

(a) Write out the first three terms in the sequence.

(b) What is the first negative term in the sequence?

(c) Find the sum of the first 15 terms of the sequence.

(d) Find the value of n for which the sum of the first n terms of the sequence is 0.

SEC Project Maths Paper 1
Leaving Certificate Ordinary Level, 2011

chapter 5

Arithmetic I

Learning Outcomes

In this chapter you will learn to:

- Solve problems involving:
    - Rates, income tax and PRSI
    - Value added tax (VAT)
    - Mark-up and margin
    - Finding compound interest
    - Finding depreciation (reducing-balance method)
- Perform calculations involving formulae for compound interest and depreciation (reducing-balance method)

5.1 INCOME TAX

Income and Deductions

Employees expect to earn money for the work they carry out.

- If you are paid according to the number of hours worked or goods produced, this is called a **wage**.

- If you are paid the same amount regardless of the number of hours worked or goods produced, this is called a **salary**.

Most people cannot keep all the money they earn. Employees have several **deductions** made to their earnings before they receive their money.

> **Gross pay** or **gross income** is money earned before deductions are made.

> **Net pay** or **net income** is money received after all deductions have been made.

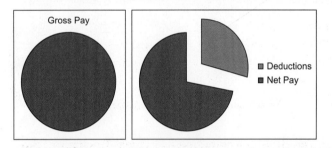

Gross Pay
■ Deductions
■ Net Pay

Statutory and Non-Statutory Deductions

Deductions can be **statutory** or **non-statutory**.

> **Statutory deductions** are payments that **must** be made to the government. They are taken from gross pay by the employer.

Statutory deduction	What is it used for?
Income tax (PAYE – Pay As You Earn)	Payment of public services, e.g. Gardaí, health care, education, etc.
Pay-Related Social Insurance (PRSI)	Old-age pensions, jobseeker's benefit, jobseeker's allowance, child benefit, etc
Universal social charge (USC)	Income for the state

YOU SHOULD REMEMBER...

- Calculation of percentages

KEY WORDS

- Gross income
- Net/take-home income
- Statutory deductions
- Non-statutory deductions
- Income tax (PAYE)
- Pay-related social insurance (PRSI)
- Universal social charge (USC)
- Standard rate of tax
- Standard rate cut-off point
- Tax credit
- Gross tax
- Tax payable
- VAT
- Compound interest
- Interest payable
- Investment interest
- Annual equivalent rate (AER)
- Depreciation

The rates for the universal social charge (USC) are as follows (figures accurate for 2011):

■ Zero, if total income is under €4,004

For people with an income of €4,004 or more, the rates will be:

Rate of USC	Charged on income from
2%	€0 to €10,036
4%	€10,036.01 to €16,016
7%	Above €16,016

People over the age of 70 have a maximum USC rate of of 4% (even on incomes over €16,016).

Medical card holders also have a top USC rate of 4%.

> **Non-statutory deductions are voluntary** deductions. They are taken from gross pay by the employer at the request of the employee.

Examples of voluntary deductions include healthcare payments, union fees, pension payments, etc.

Income Tax (PAYE)

There are two rates of income tax in Ireland.

> Note that these rates can vary from year to year.

■ The lower rate is called the **standard rate** of tax.

■ The higher rate is called the **higher rate** of tax.

For example, the first €32,800 that a single person earns is taxed at 20%, and any income above this amount is taxed at 41% (figures accurate for 2011).

> The amount up to which an employee is taxed at the standard rate is called the **standard rate cut-off point.**

For a married couple where both people are working, the first €65,600 is taxed at 20% and any additional income is taxed at 41%.

Every employee receives a **tax credit** certificate. This shows the employee's tax credit. This amount can change for individual employees.

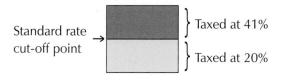

Standard rate cut-off point → } Taxed at 41% } Taxed at 20%

> **Gross tax** is the amount of tax owed to the state before tax credits are deducted.

> **Tax payable** is gross tax less the tax credit.

> The **tax credit** is a sum deducted from the total amount (gross tax) a taxpayer owes to the state.

 ## Worked Example 5.1

Albert earns €27,000 a year. He pays tax at a rate of 20%. He has instructed his employer to pay his annual health insurance premium of €550 directly from his salary. He has a tax credit of €1,950. Find Albert's:

(i) Tax payable   (iii) Net pay

(ii) Total deductions

ARITHMETIC I

Solution

(i) Gross tax = €27,000 × 20%

   = €27,000 × 0.20 = €5,400

Tax payable = gross tax – tax credit

   = €5,400 – €1,950 = €3,450

∴ The tax payable is €3,450.

(ii) Total deductions = tax payable + health insurance

   = €3,450 + €550 = €4,000

∴ The total deductions are €4,000.

(iii) Net pay = gross pay – total deductions

   = €27,000 – €4,000

   = €23,000

∴ The net pay is €23,000.

Worked Example 5.2

Sanabel earns €50,000 per annum.
Calculate the amount that will be deducted from her pay for the universal social charge.

Rate of USC	Charged on income from
2%	€0 to €10,036
4%	€10,036.01 to €16,016
7%	Above €16,016

Solution

Step 1

Break the salary down into the various threshold amounts.

€10,036 @ 2%

€16,016 – €10,036 = €5,980 @ 4%

€50,000 – €16,016 = €33,984 @ 7%

Step 2

Calculate the percentages.

First	Next	Remainder
€10,036	€5,980	€33,984
2%	4%	7%
€200.72	€239.2	€2,378.88

∴ The total USC = €200.72 + €239.20 + €2,378.88

   = €2,818.80.

Pay-Related Social Insurance (PRSI)

The amount of PRSI you pay depends on your earnings and the class under which you are insured.

For people in employment in Ireland, social insurance contributions are divided into different categories, known as classes or rates of contribution. The type of class and rate of contribution you pay is determined by the nature of your work.

There are 11 different classes of social insurance in Ireland. The majority of people fall into Class A. The other classes are B, C, D, E, H, J, K, M, P and S. If you are insured under one of these classes, you are paying insurance at a lower rate than Class A contributors, which means that you are not entitled to the full range of social insurance payments. This is because you are paying less towards social insurance than a Class A contributor.

Class A applies to people in industrial, commercial and service employment who are employed under a contract of service with a **reckonable pay** of €38 or more per week. It also includes civil servants and public servants recruited from 6 April 1995.

> **Reckonable pay** is the employee's gross pay plus notional pay (or benefit in kind), if applicable.

The PRSI contribution is made up of a number of different components, which include:

- Social insurance at the appropriate percentage rate for employees and employers, which varies according to the pay and PRSI class of the employee and benefits for which he or she is insured
- A health contribution, paid by the employee where applicable, which goes towards funding the health service
- The 0.70% National Training Fund Levy, which is included in the employers' contribution in classes A and H

PRSI is calculated on the employee's weekly or reckonable pay.

weekly

PRSI contribution rates from 1 January 2011					
Non-cumulative weekly earnings bands	PRSI Subclass	How much of weekly earnings	Employee	Employer	Employee & Employer
			%	%	%
Private and some public sector employments					
Up to €37.99	JO*	All	0	0.50	0.50
€38–€352	AO	All	0	8.50	8.50
€352.01–€356	AX	First €127	0	8.50	8.50
		Balance	4.00	8.50	12.50
€356.01–€500	AL	First €127	0	10.75	10.75
		Balance	4.00	10.75	14.75
More than €500	A1	First €127	0	10.75	10.75
		Balance	4.00	10.75	14.75

Worked Example 5.3

Chloe earns €650 per week. She is in Class A1 for PRSI, which has the following rates:

	First €127	Balance
Employee %	0	4
Employer %	10.75	10.75

Calculate:

(i) Her PRSI payment this week

(ii) Her employer's PRSI payment this week

(iii) The total amount of PRSI that will be paid this week

Solution

(i) **Step 1**

Calculate the amount she must pay PRSI on.

€650 – €127 = €523

Step 2

Calculate the PRSI.

€523 × 4% = €20.92

∴ Chloe's PRSI payment is €20.92.

(ii) **Step 1**

Calculate the amount of PRSI paid on the first €127.

€127 × 0.1075 = €13.6525

Step 2

Calculate the PRSI paid on the balance of her earnings.

€650 – €127 = €523

€523 × 0.1075 = €56.2225

Step 3

Calculate the total PRSI paid by the employer.

€13.6525 + €56.2225 = €69.875

∴ The PRSI payment by Chloe's employer is approximately €69.88.

(iii) Total PRSI payment = €20.92 + €69.88

= €90.80

∴ Total PRSI payment is €90.80.

Worked Example 5.4

Derek has a gross annual income of €50,000. His standard rate cut-off point is €32,000. The standard rate of tax is 20%. The higher rate is 40%. His tax credit is €3,500. Derek is in Class A1 for PRSI. Assuming a 52-week year, calculate Derek's:

(i) Gross tax

(ii) Tax payable

(iii) Net income (ignoring PRSI)

(iv) PRSI payment

(v) Net income after PRSI has been paid

Solution

(i) Gross tax = standard tax + higher tax

Standard tax = standard rate cut-off point × standard rate

$$= €32,000 × 0.20 = €6,400$$

Higher tax = income above standard cut-off point × higher rate

Income above standard rate cut-off point = €50,000 − €32,000 = €18,000

Higher tax = €18,000 × 0.40 = €7,200

Gross tax = standard tax + higher tax

$$= €6,400 + €7,200 = €13,600$$

∴ The gross tax is €13,600.

(ii) Tax payable = gross tax − tax credit

$$= €13,600 − €3,500 = €10,100$$

∴ The tax payable is €10,100.

(iii) Net income = gross income − tax payable

$$= €50,000 − €10,100 = €39,900$$

∴ Derek's net income is €39,900.

(iv) PRSI payment

The rate for the first €127 per week is 0% for the employee.

∴ Amount at 0% for one year = €127 × 52 = €6,604

PRSI is calculated based on €50,000 − €6,604 = €43,396.

€43,396 has a rate of 4%.

€43,396 × 0.04 = €1,735.84

∴ The PRSI payment is €1,735.84.

(v) Net income − PRSI

€39,900 − €1,735.84 = €38,164.16

∴ The net income after **all** deductions is €38,164.16.

ACTIVITIES 5.2, 5.3

Exercise 5.1

Ignore USC and PRSI unless asked to calculate.

1. Robert earns €25,000 per annum. He pays tax at a standard rate of 20%. Calculate his tax payable (assume no tax credits).

2. Angela earns €46,000 per annum and pays tax at a rate of 22.5%. She has a tax credit of €2,600. Calculate her tax payable.

3. Shane earns €41,500 per annum. He pays tax at a rate of 22%. He has a tax credit of €2,340. Calculate his net income.

4. Jolene recently moved jobs. She is now earning €46,000 per annum. She has a standard rate cut-off point of €36,000. She pays standard tax at a rate of 20%. She pays 41% on the remainder of her earnings. She has no tax credits due to an underpayment of tax last year. Calculate her net income.

5. Sally earns €94,500 per annum. She has a standard rate cut-off point of €34,000. She pays tax at a standard rate of 21% and a higher rate of 42%. Her tax credit is €2,450. Calculate:

   (i) Her tax payable   (ii) Her net pay

6. Ian earns €37,000 a year. His standard rate cut-off point is €37,400. The standard rate of tax is 21%. His tax credit is €2,100. His union fees are €450 and his annual health insurance is €350. What is Ian's annual take-home pay?

7. Abdul earns €33,000 a year. His tax bill for the year is €6,930. What percentage of his income is paid in tax?

8. Neasa's tax bill for last year was €6,300. Her tax credit was €1,300. Her gross income was €38,000. She paid tax at the standard rate only.

   (i) How much was her gross tax?

   (ii) What rate did she pay tax at?

9. A married couple earn €74,000 a year. They have a tax credit of €4,600. Last year they paid tax of €10,940. They pay tax at the standard rate. What is the standard rate in this case?

10. Lorraine and Ger had a net income of €60,400 last year. They paid tax at the standard rate which amounted to €14,700. They had a combined tax credit of €3,600. Their non-statutory deductions were €2,000. How much was their combined gross pay?

11. Bryan has a gross income of €50,000. He pays tax at 20% on the first €32,000 he earns and 42% on the remainder. His tax credit is €3,500. What is his tax payable?

12. Nicky earns €35,000 a year. What is her USC charge?

13. Conor has a gross income of €72,000. His standard rate cut-off point is €34,600. The standard rate of tax is 20% and the higher rate is 41%. He has a tax credit of €3,000. He is in the class A1 for PRSI. (Assume a 52-week year.)

   (i) What is his PRSI contribution per week (2 d.p.)?

   (ii) What is his employer's PRSI contribution per week?

   (iii) Calculate his USC payment for the year.

   (iv) What is his weekly net income after all deductions?

14. Larry has a gross income of €60,000 a year. His standard rate cut-off point is €36,400. The standard rate of tax is 20% and the higher rate is 41%. He has a tax credit of €2,400. He is in class A1 for PRSI. (Assume a 52-week year.)

   (i) What is his PRSI contribution per week?

   (ii) What is his employer's PRSI contribution per week?

   (iii) Calculate his USC payment for the year.

   (iv) What is his weekly net income after all deductions?

15. Peter and Siobhán have a combined income of €150,000. They pay tax at 20% on the first €65,300 they earn and 41% on the remainder. They both pay PRSI at class A1 rates.

   (i) What is their total PRSI payment for the year? (Assume a 52-week year.)

   (ii) What is their combined net pay for the year? (Ignore USC and tax credits.)

16. Carol has a standard rate cut-off point of €36,400. The standard rate of tax is 20% and the higher rate is 41%. If Carol's gross tax is €10,396, what is her gross income?

17. (i) Sorcha has tax credits of €2,800 for the year and her standard rate cut-off point is €32,000. Her gross income is €45,000. The standard rate of income tax is 20% and the higher rate is 41%. Calculate her total tax payable.

    (ii) Eoin pays tax at the same rate as Sorcha. Eoin's tax credits are €2,900, and he has the same standard cut-off point as Sorcha. His total tax payable amounts to €13,680. Calculate Eoin's gross income.

    (iii) What is Eoin's and Sorcha's universal social charge, respectively?

5.2 VAT: VALUE-ADDED TAX

> **VAT** is a tax charged by the government on consumer spending.

For example, if you buy a computer game, you pay **VAT** on the game.

VAT is collected by the Revenue Commissioner. It is collected in stages, starting with the manufacturing stage and ending with the sale of the finished product to the consumer. VAT is collected at the following stages from the following people:

A tax is placed on the value added to the product or service at each stage, and this is where the name 'value-added tax' comes from.

■	Manufacturer
	Wholesaler
■	Distributor
	Retailer
■	Consumer

VAT Rates

There are several different rates of VAT (standard for 2011):

Standard rate	Applies to most goods and services	21%
Reduced rate	Applies to labour-intensive services, e.g. hairdressing	13.5%
Zero rate	Applies to many foods and medicines and to children's clothes	0%
Special rate	Applies to the sale of livestock	4.8%

VAT is a tax on consumer spending. It is collected by VAT-registered traders on their supplies of goods and services effected within the State for consideration to their customers. Each such trader in the chain of supply from manufacturer through to retailer charges VAT on his or her sales and is entitled to deduct from this amount the VAT paid on his or her purchases. The effect of offsetting VAT on purchases against VAT on sales is to impose the tax on the added value at each stage of production - hence Value-Added Tax. The final consumer, who is not registered for VAT, absorbs VAT as part of the purchase price. The following example illustrates how this works:

	Purchase Transactions					Sale Transactions			
	Price Paid (Ex. VAT)	VAT	Total Purchase Price	Value Added	Price Charged (Ex. VAT)	VAT @ 21%	Total Sale Price	Credit for VAT Paid	Net to Collector General
	€	€	€	€	€	€	€	€	€
Manufacturer	-	-	-	100	100	21	121	0	21
Wholesaler	100	21	121	100	200	42	242	21	21
Distributor	200	42	242	100	300	63	363	42	21
Retailer	300	63	363	200	500	105	605	63	42
Consumer	500	105	605						
					500				105

As may be seen from the above example, the consumer pays a total of €605 for the finished product, of which €105 is VAT.

Source: VAT Guide 2008, www.revenue.ie

> Remember that these rates can change from year to year and country to country.

You can find which rate of VAT applies to different goods and services by checking the list available on the Revenue website at www.revenue.ie.

Rates of VAT vary depending on the product or service being purchased. For example, chocolate spread has a zero rate but chocolate biscuits have a 21% rate.

Worked Example 5.5

Claire sees a handbag in a shop window. The sign says '€250 + VAT @ 21%'.

How much will she pay for the bag?

€250 + VAT @ 21%

Solution

Step 1 Find 21% of €250.

$$VAT = €250 \times 0.21$$

$$\therefore VAT = €52.50$$

Step 2 Find the total price.

$$Total\ price = €250 + VAT$$

$$= €250 + €52.50$$

$$\therefore Price\ paid = €302.50$$

 Worked Example 5.6

Craig buys his boyfriend a birthday present that costs €215.65 including VAT @ 13.5%.

What was the original bill before VAT was added?

Solution

Original bill = 100%

Original bill + VAT = 113.5%

$$113.5\% = €215.65$$

$$\therefore 1\% = \frac{€215.65}{113.5}$$

$$1\% = €1.90$$

$$100\% = €1.90 \times 100$$

$$= €190$$

$$\therefore Original\ bill = €190$$

 Worked Example 5.7

Una bought a new TV for €484. When she looked at the receipt, she noticed the amount of VAT charged was €84. What rate of VAT was charged?

Solution

Step 1 Find the cost before VAT.

$$Cost\ before\ VAT = Final\ cost - VAT$$

$$= €484 - €84$$

$$\therefore Cost\ before\ VAT = €400$$

Step 2 Express the VAT as a percentage of the original cost.

$$Rate\ of\ VAT = \frac{VAT}{Cost\ before\ VAT} \times \frac{100}{1}$$

Note that VAT is charged on the **original** cost figure.

$$= \frac{84}{400} \times \frac{100}{1}$$

$$\therefore Rate\ of\ VAT = 21\%$$

 **ACTIVITY 5.4**

ARITHMETIC I

Exercise 5.2

Give all answers correct to the nearest cent where necessary.

1. If VAT charged on hairdressing is 13.5%, find the VAT to be charged on each of the following haircuts if the cost before VAT is:

   (i) €20   (iii) €16

   (ii) €14   (iv) €12.50

2. The VAT charged on TVs is 21%. Find the **total price** of the following TVs if the price before VAT is:

   (i) €450   (iii) €800

   (ii) €190   (iv) €899

3. Find the total price of ordering a pizza if the price of the pizza is €15 + VAT @ 21%.

4. The school canteen bought 600 bottles of fruit juice from a wholesaler at €0.50 each + VAT @ 21%. Find the total cost of the fruit juice.

5. Conor buys two DVDs. The DVDs cost €18 and €12 excluding VAT. VAT is charged at 20%.

   What is the total cost of the DVDs?

6. Mohamed was shopping in a cash and carry. He didn't realise that all the prices stated were before VAT. When he got to the cash desk his bill came to €283.75.

   If VAT was charged at 13.5%, what was the cost of his bill before VAT?

7. The government of a particular country have decided to charge one standard rate of VAT @ 25%. If the price of a car (including VAT) is €9,000, how much of this price is VAT?

8. A laptop costs €990.99 and this includes VAT at 21%.
   How much of the selling price should be given to the Revenue Commissioner?

9. An auctioneer charges VAT at a rate of 21%. If the auctioneer is successful in selling a house, she charges a fee of 1.25% of the selling price.

   If she sells a house for €270,000, how much will her fee to the client be:

   (i) Before VAT   (ii) After VAT

10. In a particular year's budget, the VAT rate falls from 13% to 12.5%. The price of a laptop drops by €3.50.

    (i) What was the price of the laptop before the change in VAT rate?

    (ii) What is the new VAT amount on the laptop?

    (iii) What is the total price of the laptop now?

    (iv) If the VAT rate had increased to 17%, how much would the laptop cost?

5.3 PERCENTAGE PROFIT AND LOSS; DISCOUNTS (ALLOWED AND RECEIVED)

Percentage Profit and Loss

> If a product or service is sold for more than it cost to buy or produce, then the seller has made a **profit**.

> If a product or service is sold for less than it cost to buy or produce, then the seller has made a **loss**.

> The **percentage profit mark-up** is the profit expressed as a percentage of the cost price: $\dfrac{\text{Profit}}{\text{Cost price}} \times 100$.

> The **selling price** is the cost price plus profit/loss.

> The **percentage profit margin** is the profit expressed as a percentage of the selling price: $\dfrac{\text{Profit}}{\text{Selling price}} \times 100$.

> Note: In practice, the profit margin and mark-up can also be given in euro, not just as a percentage.

Discounts (Allowed and Received)

Discounts are offered for several reasons, e.g. to encourage customers to buy a product or to encourage a customer to pay for goods quickly or with cash.

> A **discount** is a reduction in the price of a bill or charge.

Some manufacturers offer trade discounts. This is done to encourage wholesalers and retailers to sell their product. For example, the selling price of a product is €100, and the manufacturer offers a trade discount of 10%. The wholesaler now has to pay €100 – 10% of €100 = €90.

10% discount

The wholesaler can now sell the goods for €100, making a profit of €10.

Discounts are also offered to encourage customers to buy the goods or pay for goods bought on credit quickly. On an invoice (the bill sent by a seller to the customer for goods purchased), you may often see the word 'Terms'. This describes the discount that is offered for prompt payment.

Worked Example 5.8

Nick buys a DVD box set for €75 from an online retailer; he then sells it for €100.

What is:

   (i)   The cost price

   (ii)   The selling price

   (iii)   The profit or loss made

   (iv)   The percentage mark-up

   (v)   The percentage margin

Solution

   (i)   Cost price = €75 (the price Nick paid)

   (ii)   Selling price = €100 (the price Nick sells for)

   (iii)   Profit = Selling price – Cost price

                 = €100 – €75

      ∴ Profit = €25

(iv) Percentage mark-up $= \dfrac{\text{Profit}}{\text{Cost price}} \times \dfrac{100}{1}$

$$= \dfrac{25}{75} \times \dfrac{100}{1}$$

$$= 33\tfrac{1}{3}\%$$

(v) Percentage margin $= \dfrac{\text{Profit}}{\text{Selling price}} \times \dfrac{100}{1}$

$$= \dfrac{25}{100} \times \dfrac{100}{1}$$

$$= 25\%$$

Worked Example 5.9

A company can manufacture a product for €120 and sell it, making a profit of 30%.
What is the selling price?

Solution

Profit = 120 × 0.30

∴ Profit = €36

Selling price = Cost + Profit

$$= €120 + €36$$

$$= €156$$

The selling price is €156.

Worked Example 5.10

Paula has a business selling farm supplies.
The company's policy is sell all goods at cost plus 20% mark-up.

(i) If she sells fertiliser for €15, including a 20% mark-up, calculate the cost price of the fertiliser.

(ii) It is then decided to sell the goods at a 20% margin. Find the new selling price (to the nearest cent).

Solution

(i) Selling price = Cost + Profit

$$= 100\% + 20\%$$

∴ Selling price = 120% of cost price

Selling price = €15

∴ 120% = €15

$$1\% = \dfrac{€15}{120}$$

$$= €0.125$$

∴ 100% = €0.125 × 100

$$= €12.5$$

The cost price is €12.50.

(ii) Selling at a profit margin of 20% means that the profit is 20% of the selling price.

Therefore, the cost price must be 80% of the selling price.

Cost price = €12.50

$$80\% = €12.50$$

$$∴ 1\% = \dfrac{€12.50}{80}$$

$$= €0.15625$$

∴100% = €0.15625 × 100

$$= €15.625$$

The selling price is €15.63.

ARITHMETIC I

5

Worked Example 5.11

Matilda owns a clothes shop. She decides to sell off last season's stock at a loss of 10%. She sells a jacket for €18. How much did it cost her originally?

Solution

Selling price = Cost price – Loss

$$= 100\% - 10\%$$

∴ Selling price = 90% of cost price

$$90\% = €18$$

$$∴ 1\% = \frac{€18}{90}$$

$$= €0.20$$

$$∴ 100\% = 0.20 × 100$$

$$= €20$$

The cost price is €20.

 Worked Example 5.12

Asad receives an invoice for goods purchased. The total amount on the invoice is €500. If he pays within 21 days, he will receive a discount of 5%.

Calculate the amount that Asad must pay if he pays within 21days.

Solution

From the invoice, Asad owes €500.
As he is paying within 21 days, he will receive a 5% discount.

Discount = €500 × 0.05

$$= €25$$

Price to pay = €500 – €25

$$= €475$$

 Exercise 5.3

1. Fill in the missing figures in the table below.

	Cost price (€)	Selling price (€)	Profit (€)	% Mark-up (2 d.p.)	% Margin (2 d.p.)
(i)	25.00	30.00	5.00		
(ii)	31.00	36.00			
(iii)	15.00	20.00			
(iv)	14.00		14.00		
(v)	12.00	18.00	6.00		
(vi)	18.00	18.90			
(vii)		4.00	3.00		
(viii)		2.80	0.70		
(ix)	10.00		2.00		
(x)	11.00		4.50		

2. Find the selling price of each of the following:

	Cost price (€)	% Mark-up
(i)	150.00	5.00
(ii)	1,020.00	6.00
(iii)	2,240.00	12.50
(iv)	6,450.00	21.50
(v)	23,250.00	16.00

3. Find the cost price of each of the following:

	Selling price (€)	% Margin
(i)	40	2
(ii)	85	5
(iii)	135	10
(iv)	100	0.5
(v)	1,565	3

4. Find the selling price of each of the following:

	Cost price (€)	% Loss
(i)	50	5.00
(ii)	1,250	15.00
(iii)	34,000	25.00
(iv)	12,800	37.50
(v)	14,400	12.00

5. A product costs a company €13,250 to produce. Find the percentage mark-up and percentage margin (2 d.p.) if the company sells the product for €15,900.

6. Jack imports jerseys for €10 and sells them at cost plus 12.5%. What is the selling price?

7. A retailer buys goods from a cash and carry outlet for €120. The recommended selling price is cost plus 15%.

  (i) How much should she sell the goods for?

  (ii) What is her percentage margin (to the nearest percent)?

8. In each of the following, calculate:

  (a) The discount

  (b) The price after the discount

	Selling price (€)	% Discount
(i)	1,200	5
(ii)	200	15
(iii)	1,600	15
(iv)	4,400	2
(v)	1,400	25
(vi)	1,500	12
(vii)	1,460	37.50
(viii)	28,400	12

9. In each of the following, calculate the percentage discount (2 d.p.):

	Selling price (€)	Discount (€)
(i)	150.00	25.00
(ii)	144.00	12.00
(iii)	270.00	30.00
(iv)	165	13
(v)	2,610.00	313.20

10. For the invoice below, calculate:

  (i) The discount received if paid within 1 month

  (ii) The price to be paid if paid within 1 month

Invoice no. 234			
Terms: Discount 4% if paid within 1 month			
Quantity	**Description**	**Unit price (€)**	**Total ex. VAT (€)**
200	Pencils	0.20	40.00
120	Erasers	0.25	30.00
			70.00
		VAT 0%	0.00
		Total due	70.00

11. For the invoice below, calculate:

  (i) The discount received if paid within 1 month

  (ii) The price to be paid if paid within 1 month

Invoice no. 3546			
Terms: Discount 12% if paid within 1 month			
Quantity	**Description**	**Unit price (€)**	**Total ex. VAT (€)**
200	Decks of cards	2.00	400.00
120	Spinning tops	1.25	150.00
			550.00
		VAT 21%	115.50
		Total due	665.50

12. Henry owns an electrical store. He purchases 10 cameras at €25 each. The wholesaler offers him a trade discount of 15%.
How much does Henry pay in total for the cameras?

13. Elaine has an apartment in the city centre. She charges €550 rent per month. She tells her tenants that she will offer them a 2.5% discount if they pay the rent in cash before the last day of every month. How much rent will she receive if they pay before the last day of the month?

14. Leona and Barbara were shopping in Mahon Point. Leona saw a sign on a shop window: '20% off'.

  (i) Leona bought a camera for €120. What was the original price?

  (ii) Barbara bought make-up for €25. What was the original price?

5.4 COMPOUND INTEREST: FUTURE VALUES

Individuals and businesses don't always have enough cash to buy what they want or to pay their bills. It is sometimes necessary for them to borrow money. Equally there are individuals and businesses that have large amounts of cash, and so they decide to invest some of it.

If you borrow money from a bank or financial institution, they will expect you to pay back the money you borrowed, but they will also charge you for the use of the money they loaned you. This is called **interest payable**.

When you invest money in an investment account or a financial institution, you are giving the people who run the account or institution the use of your money. So they have to pay you a charge for the use of this money. This is called **investment interest**.

When a loan or an investment is paid back in full, the total amount is the sum borrowed plus the interest that was paid.

When dealing with interest, we use the following symbols:

- F = final value (amount borrowed or invested + interest)
- P = Principal (amount borrowed or invested)
- i = Rate of interest per annum (year) (always use decimal form)
- t = Time (length of time, usually in years, you had the loan or investment)

FORMULA

$$F = P(1 + i)^t$$

This formula appears on page 30 of *Formulae and Tables*.

The rate of interest (i) that is used in the formula shown here is the Annual Equivalent Rate (AER) or Annual Percentage Rate (APR), as the formula $F = P(1 + i)^t$ assumes that compounding takes place once every year. The Annual Percentage Rate (APR) is used when dealing with loan and credit agreement calculations. The Annual Equivalent Rate (AER) is used when dealing with investments and savings; it can also be called the Annual Effective Rate or Effective Rate.

 Worked Example 5.13

Niall borrows €100 for six years at an APR of 2% compounded annually. How much interest will he pay on the loan?

Solution

$F = P(1 + i)^t$

$P = 100$

$i = 2\% = 0.02$

$t = 6$

$F = 100 (1 + 0.02)^6$

$\approx €112.62$

Interest $= F - P$

$= €112.62 - €100$

$= €12.62$

Worked Example 5.14

€10,000 is invested at 3% per annum. At the beginning of the second year, €1,450 is withdrawn from this amount. The interest rate for the second year rises to 3.5%.

Calculate:

    (i)   The value of the investment at the end of Year 1

    (ii) The value of the investment at the end of Year 2

Solution

(i) Value of investment at end of Year 1:

$$P_1 = €10,000 \quad t = 1 \text{ year} \quad i = 0.03$$

$$F = P(1 + i)^t$$

$$F = 10,000(1 + 0.03)^1$$

$$\therefore F = 10,000(1.03)^1$$

$$= 10,000(1.03)$$

$$\therefore F = 10,300$$

The value of the investment at the end of Year 1 is €10,300.

(ii) Value of investment at end of Year 2:

At the beginning of Year 2, €1,450 is withdrawn.

$$P_2 = €10,300 - €1,450 = €8,850$$

$$t = 1 \text{ year} \quad i = 0.035$$

$$F = P(1 + i)^t$$

$$F = 8,850(1 + 0.035)^1$$

$$= 8,850(1.035)^1$$

$$= 8,850(1.035)$$

$$\therefore F = 9,159.75$$

The value of the investment at the end of Year 2 is €9,159.75.

 Worked Example 5.15

A sum of €100 is invested in a three-year savings bond with an annual equivalent rate (AER) of 3.23%. Find the value of the investment when it matures in three years' time (to the nearest euro).

Solution

$$F = P(1 + i)^t$$

Method 1

	Principal	Rate of interest (i)	Interest	Amount at year end
Year 1	100	0.0323	$100(1.0323)^1$	103.23
Year 2	103.23	0.0323	$103.23(1.0323)^1$	106.5643
Year 3	106.5643	0.0323	$106.5643(1.0323)^1$	110.0064

The value of the investment at the end of three years is approximately €110.

Method 2

$$P = €100 \quad t = 3 \text{ years} \quad i = 0.0323$$

$$F = 100(1 + 0.0323)^3$$

$$= 110.0064$$

$$\therefore F \approx €110$$

 ACTIVITY 5.5

Worked Example 5.16

Aidan invested money in a 5.5-year bond when he started First Year. In the middle of Sixth Year, the bond matures and he has earned 21% interest in total. Calculate the AER for this bond.

Solution

Step 1 Write down the formula.

$$F = P(1+i)^t$$

Step 2 Identify the parts that we are given in the question.

Final value (F) = Original amount + interest

$$= 100\% + 21\%$$

$$= 121\%$$

$$= 1.21$$

Principal (P) = original amount

$$= 100\%$$

$$= 1.00$$

Time in years (t) = 5.5

Step 3 Solve for the unknown value i.

$$1.21 = 1.00(1 + i)^{5.5}$$

$$1.21 = (1 + i)^{5.5}$$

$$\sqrt[5.5]{1.21} = 1 + i$$

$$1.0353 = 1 + i$$

$$1.0353 - 1 = i$$

$$i = 0.0353$$

$$i = 3.53\%$$

∴ The AER for this bond is 3.53%.

Exercise 5.4

1. €22,500 was invested at 5% for three years. Calculate the final value.

2. €1,600 was invested at 3% for six years. Calculate the interest.

3. €10,200 was invested at 4% for eight years. Calculate the final value.

4. €102,000 was borrowed at 8% for four years. Calculate the final value.

5. €105,000 was borrowed at 6% for five years. Calculate the interest.

6. €25,400 was borrowed at 3% for ten years. Calculate the interest.

7. €20,500 was invested at 4% for eight years. Calculate the interest.

8. €100,500 was borrowed at 5% for six years. Calculate the final value.

9. €1,000,000 was invested at 10.5% for three and a half years. Calculate the final value.

10. €9,600 was borrowed at 2% for four years. Calculate the interest.

11. Find the amount, to the nearest cent, that needs to be invested at a rate of 5% to give €2,500 in five years' time.

12. Find the amount, to the nearest cent, that needs to be invested at a rate of 3.2% to give €12,500 in six years' time.

13. How much would Louise need to invest, at a rate of 3.5%, to have €1,500 two years from now?

14. Haidir borrows €160,000 at 3%. At the end of Year 1, he repays €20,000. The rate of interest is then lowered to 2%.

    How much will he owe at the end of the second year?

15. A football club borrowed €15,000,000 to revamp their stadium. The rate for the first year was 3.5% and the rate for the second year was 4.2%.

    Calculate the amount owing at the end of the second year.

16. A business secures a three-year loan for €45,000 with the following conditions attached:

    ■ The loan must be repaid in full by the end of the third year.

    ■ The rate of interest is 3% for the first two years. Then it decreases by 0.5%. = 0.005

    Calculate the total interest that will be paid on this loan (to the nearest euro).

17. A 10-year loan is drawn down for €350,000. The rate of interest is 5.2% per annum compound interest.

    (i) How much interest is charged in the first year?

    (ii) How much interest will have been charged after 10 years if no repayment is made in the 10 years (to the nearest cent)?

    (iii) If €60,000 is paid off at the end of Year 1, what will the interest charge be for Year 2?

18. A business is given a loan from a private bank of €50,000 for five years at a rate of 6% per annum. If the loan is repaid with interest in one lump sum at the end of five years, the lender will give a 15% discount.

    Alternatively, the business can repay €10,000 at the end of each of Years 1–4 and the balance at the end of Year 5.

    Which option will cost the business less?

19. A sum of €6,000 is invested in an eight-year government bond with an annual equivalent rate (AER) of 6%.

    Find the value of the investment when it matures in eight years' time.

20. A sum of €5,000 is invested in an eight-year government bond with an annual equivalent rate (AER) of 3%.

    Find the value of the investment when it matures in eight years' time.

21. A bond offers a return of 20% interest after six years. Calculate the AER for this bond.

22. The National Treasury Management Agency offers a three-year savings bond with a return of 10%. Calculate the AER for this bond.

23. There are two types of National Solidarity bonds on offer:

    (A) A four-year bond offering a gross return of 15%

    (B) A 10-year bond offering a gross return of 50%

    Using the AER, compare the two bonds and state which bond offers the best return.

24. Calculate the AER offered on this bond.

5.5 DEPRECIATION (REDUCING-BALANCE METHOD)

Depreciation is calculated in order to write off the value of an asset over its useful economic life.

Causes of Depreciation

Wear and tear	Assets that are used over a period of time eventually wear out.	Example: Vehicles
Obsolescence	An asset becomes out of date because of the development of a more efficient or less expensive alternative.	Example: Computers
Passage of time	Assets lose value as they near the end of their licence.	Example: Patents
Extraction	The value of an asset reduces as the asset is extracted.	Example: Mining

Types of Depreciation

There are two methods of calculating depreciation in practice:

- **Straight-line method:** The amount written off the asset is the same each year until the total value of the asset is written off or it is reduced to its residual value.

- **Reducing-balance method:** Rather than charging a fixed amount every year, a (fixed) percentage of the remaining value of the asset is charged every year. Compared to straight-line depreciation, this method is more heavily weighted towards the early years.

For our syllabus, we will study the reducing-balance method only.

FORMULA

$F = P(1 - i)^t$

This formula appears on page 30 of *Formulae and Tables*.

 Worked Example 5.17

U-Deliver Ltd bought a new delivery van for €25,000. It is company policy to depreciate delivery vans at a rate of 20% per annum using the reducing-balance method.

   (i) What will be the net book value (NBV) of the asset after three years?

  (ii) How much depreciation is written off the van in the first three years?

Solution

(i) $F = P(1 - i)^t$

      $= 25{,}000(1 - 0.20)^3$

      $= 25{,}000(0.8)^3$

      $= €12{,}800$

    The NBV of the asset after three years will be €12,800.

(ii) Depreciation written off = Cost − Net book value

                     $= €25{,}000 - €12{,}800$

                     $= €12{,}200$

    ∴ Depreciation = €12,200

 Worked Example 5.18

ABC Ltd purchased a delivery van costing €60,000. It is the policy of the company to depreciate all delivery vans at a rate of 20% using the reducing-balance method.
What will be the value of the asset after five years?

Solution

Method 1 (Year by year)

Step 1 Calculate the depreciation for the first year.

Step 2 Calculate the net book value (NBV) of the asset at the end of Year 1.

        NBV = Cost − Depreciation

Step 3 Repeat for Years 2 to 5.

	Cost	Rate of depreciation	Depreciation	NBV
Year 1	€60,000.00	0.2	€12,000.00	€48,000.00
Year 2	€48,000.00	0.2	€9,600.00	€38,400.00
Year 3	€38,400.00	0.2	€7,680.00	€30,720.00
Year 4	€30,720.00	0.2	€6,144.00	€24,576.00
Year 5	€24,576.00	0.2	€4,915.20	€19,660.80

The value of the asset at the end of five years will be €19,660.80.

Method 2 (Using formula)

$F = P(1 - i)^t$

$F = 60{,}000(1 - 0.20)^5$

$\quad = 60{,}000(0.80)^5$

$\quad = 60{,}000(0.32768)$

$\quad = 19{,}660.80$

 ACTIVITY 5.7

The value of the asset at the end of five years will be €19,660.80.

Worked Example 5.19

An accountant is auditing a set of books and sees that the net book value (NBV) of an asset four years after the date of purchase is €28,710.34. The policy of the company is to depreciate this asset at a rate of 15% using the reducing-balance method. What was the original cost of the asset to the nearest euro?

Solution

$$F = P(1 - i)^t$$

$$28{,}710.34 = P(1 - 0.15)^4$$

$$28{,}710.34 = P(0.85)^4$$

$$28{,}710.34 = P(0.52200625)$$

$$P = \frac{28{,}710.34}{0.52200625}$$

$$P = 54{,}999.9928$$

The original cost of the asset was approximately €55,000.

Exercise 5.5

1. Using the reducing-balance method of depreciation, calculate the value of the following assets after the given number of years (correct to the nearest euro):

	Asset cost (€)	Rate of depreciation	Number of years	NBV
(i)	200,000	10%	1	
(ii)	1,500,000	15%	4	
(iii)	60,600	3%	8	
(iv)	21,000	3.5%	2	
(v)	34,000	18%	4	
(vi)	16,000	2%	6	
(vii)	12,000	25%	4	

2. Using the reducing-balance method of depreciation, calculate the missing values in the table below, correct to two decimal places where necessary.

	Asset cost (€)	Rate of depreciation	Number of years	NBV
(i)	200,000	17%	1	
(ii)	400,000		4	€208,802.50
(iii)	140,000	3%	8	
(iv)	100,000		2	€93,122.50
(v)	34,000,000	18%	4	
(vi)	24,000	2%	6	.
(vii)	120,000		4	€37,968.75

3. How much will a €30,000 car be worth at the end of five years given a depreciation rate of 20% per annum (reducing balance)?

4. A coal mine is depleted at a rate of 15% per annum. If the initial volume of coal in the mine is 400,000 m^3, what volume of coal would there be in the mine after six years?

5. A car has an NBV of €19,660.80 at the end of five years, having been depreciated at a rate of 20% per annum (reducing balance).

   What was the initial cost of the car?

6. A building has an NBV of €800,000 at the end of 10 years, having been depreciated at a rate of 2% (reducing-balance method). What was the original cost of the building?

   Give your answer to the nearest €100.

7. A computer was purchased at the start of 2010 for €2,500. By the end of the year 2012, it is expected that the computer will be worth only €1,378.42.

   What is the rate of depreciation (reducing-balance method)? Give your answer to the nearest percentage.

8. A lorry was purchased for €150,000 at the end of 2006. At the start of 2011, the lorry was sold at its NBV of €49,152.

   What was the rate of depreciation charged (reducing-balance method) on the lorry?

9. A pharmaceutical company has just received a 10-year patent for its newest headache tablet. In keeping with company policy, the accountants for the firm decide to write off the patent using the reducing-balance method. The patent is currently estimated to be worth €15,000,000.

   What rate of depreciation should the firm's accountants apply to the patent in order to write it off (to 1 cent) over the 10-year period? Give your answer as a percentage, to two decimal places.

10. A company has a policy to depreciate all its computers at a reducing-balance rate of 20%. The computers owned by the firm are valued (net book value) at €150,000. An auditor recently pointed out that, due to increases in technology, computers were currently losing value at a much faster rate than in previous years. The auditor estimated that the value of the computers in two years' time would only be €95,000.

   Does the firm have an adequate depreciation policy? Explain your answer.

Note: For USC rates, see table on page 97; for PRSI rates, see table on page 99.

1. Shane has an annual gross income of €60,000. He pays tax at 20% on the first €32,000 he earns and 42% on the remainder. His tax credit is €3,100.
   What is his tax payable?

2. Harry earns €35,600 per annum. What is his USC charge?

3. Laura has a gross income of €45,000 a year. Her standard rate cut-off point is €33,000. The standard rate of tax is 20% and the higher rate is 41%. She has a tax credit of €2,400. She is in Class A1 for PRSI. (Assume a 52-week year.)

   (i) What is her PRSI contribution per week?

   (ii) What is her employer's PRSI contribution per week?

   (iii) Calculate her USC payment.

   (iv) What is her weekly net income after all deductions?

4. Calculate the VAT to be paid to the Revenue Commissioner on the following invoice:

20 Chairs @ €25 each
12 Tables @ €235 each
16 Stools @ €12 each
VAT is charged @ 13.5% on all items.

5. A retailer buys in a product at €300 and sells the product on to customers at €1,000.

   (i) Calculate the profit made on the sale of this product.

   (ii) Calculate the mark-up in monetary terms.

   (iii) Calculate the percentage mark-up.

   (iv) Calculate the percentage margin.

   (v) Explain why the percentage mark-up exceeds the percentage margin.

6. In a particular year's budget, the VAT rate falls from 13.5% to 12.5%. The price of a phone drops by €4.50.

   (i) What was the price of the phone before the change in VAT rate?

   (ii) What is the new VAT amount?

   (iii) What is the price of the phone now?

   (iv) If the VAT rate had increased to 15%, how much would the phone have cost?

7. €25,000 was invested at 4.5% for eight years. Calculate the interest.

8. €90,000 was borrowed at 5% for 15 years. Calculate the final value.

9. A 15-year loan is drawn down for €250,000. The rate of interest is 5.3% per annum compound interest.

   (i) How much interest is charged in Year 1?

   (ii) How much interest will have been charged after 10 years if no repayment is made in the 10 years (to the nearest cent)?

   (iii) If €55,000 is paid off at the end of Year 1, what will be the interest charge for Year 2?

10. A finance company offers a car loan package, the details of which are as follows:

Option 1	10-year loan	Total interest = 15%
Option 2	7-year loan	Total interest = 10%
Option 3	5-year loan	Total interest = 9%
Option 4	3-year loan	Total interest = 6%

    (i) Calculate the annual percentage rate (APR) for each option.

    (ii) Which option would you choose? Give a reason for your answer.

11. A sum of €15,000 is invested in an eight-year government bond with an annual equivalent rate (AER) of 3.5%. Find the value of the investment when it matures in eight years' time.

12. A bond offers a return of 18% after six years. Calculate the AER for this bond.

13. Molly hopes to take a year off before college to travel. She estimates that she will need €5,000 for expenses in case she cannot find work abroad. Her local bank are offering a savings account with the following conditions:

■ Invest for three years at a rate of 7% per annum compounded annually.

■ The initial sum must be invested as a lump sum.

   (i) How much would she need to invest to make the €5,000 she will need in three years' time?

Her friend tells her about another offer:

■ Invest €4,000 now and earn 22.5% interest over three years.

   (ii) Calculate the annual equivalent rate (AER) for the second investment.

   (iii) Which investment will give Molly the best return?

14. (i) A sum of €5,000 is invested in an eight-year government bond with an annual equivalent rate (AER) of 6%. Find the value of the investment when it matures in eight years' time.

   (ii) A different investment bond gives 20% interest after eight years. Calculate the AER for this bond.

SEC Project Maths Paper I Sample paper, Leaving Certificate Ordinary Level, 2011

15. Calculate the net book value (NBV) of each of the following:

Cost (€)	Rate of depreciation	Number of years of depreciation
25,000	10%	5
105,000	12.5%	6
1,600,000	2%	8
364,800	16%	4
2,460,000	22.5%	12

16. A building has an NBV of €160,000 at the end of five years, having been depreciated at a rate of 2% per annum (reducing-balance method). What was the original cost of the building?

17. A computer was purchased at the start of 2010 for €25,000. By the end of 2011, it is expected that it will only be worth €16,000.

What is the rate of depreciation (reducing-balance method)?

18. A company has the following depreciation policy: all its equipment is to be depreciated at a rate of 25% (reducing-balance method).

A motor vehicle is purchased for €10,000 with an estimated useful economic life of 12 years. The company's accountant estimates a scrap value of €500 at the end of the 12 years.

Is this a reasonable estimate to give? Explain your answer.

19. What rate of depreciation should be applied to an asset with a cost price of €6,000, an estimated life of five years and a scrap value of €300?

20. At a recent board meeting, it was decided that all 100 Fifth Year students should have a laptop for their maths class. The board proposed that the laptops will be sold after three years and new laptops purchased.

The cost of a laptop is €400 and the expected selling price in three years is €100.

   (i) What rate of depreciation should the school apply given the value placed on the laptops at the end of their useful life?

   (ii) What will be the depreciation charge in Year 1, Year 2 and Year 3?

6

Algebra II

Learning Outcomes

In this chapter you will learn to:

- ⊃ Solve linear equations using trial and error
- ⊃ Solve linear equations in the form $ax + b = cx + d$, where $a, b, c, d \in Q$
- ⊃ Solve simultaneous linear equations
- ⊃ Solve problems using:
    - ⊃ Linear equations
    - ⊃ Simultaneous equations
- ⊃ Solve linear inequalities
- ⊃ Manipulate formulae

6.1 SOLVING LINEAR EQUATIONS BY TRIAL AND ERROR

When solving an equation, we are being asked to find the value(s) of the unknown(s). In many cases this unknown is represented by the letter x.

For example, consider the equation:

$$3x + 6 = 9$$

Here, $x = 1$, as $3(1) + 6 = 9$.

One way to figure out the value of an unknown is by guessing your answer. This is called trial and error – we make an educated guess as to what the answer is.

From Activity 6.1, we can see that trial and error involves the following steps:

- Make a guess as to what x may be.
- Check to see if your guess is correct by substituting your value into the equation.
- Keep guessing until you arrive at the correct solution.

x^2 Worked Example 6.1

Using trial and error, solve the following linear equation:

$4(x - 4) = 12$

Solution

x	$4(x - 4)$	$= 12$	
0	$4(0 - 4)$	$= -16$	The answer is too small. We will pick a number much bigger than 0.
10	$4(10 - 4)$	$= 24$	The answer is too big. We will pick a number smaller than 10.
8	$4(8 - 4)$	$= 16$	The answer is still too big, but not by much.
7	$4(7 - 4)$	$= 12$	✓

Answer: $x = 7$

Simultaneous Equations

Simultaneous equations are sets of equations that have common variables.

For example:

$4x + 2y = 16 \quad \rightarrow 4(3) + 2(2) = 12 + 4 = 16$

$3x - 2y = 5 \quad \rightarrow 3(3) - 2(2) = 9 - 4 = 5$

∴ In both equations, $x = 3$ and $y = 2$.

x^2 Worked Example 6.2

Is $x = 4$ and $y = -1$ the correct solution for the following simultaneous equations?

$2x + y = 7$

$x + 2y = 5$

Solution

We let $x = 4$ and $y = -1$ for both equations.

$2x + y = 7$	$x + 2y = 5$
$2(4) + (-1) = 7$	$4 + 2(-1) = 5$
$8 - 1 = 7$	$4 - 2 = 5$
$7 = 7$	$2 = 5$
True	False

$\therefore x = 4$ and $y = -1$ is **not** the correct solution.

Exercise 6.1

1. Using trial and error, find the value of the unknown variable.

   (i) $4x - 12 = 4$ (vi) $5x + 35 = -10$

   (ii) $6x + 10 = 52$ (vii) $-2x + 6 = -12$

   (iii) $-2x - 4 = 20$ (viii) $18 = 7x - 3$

   (iv) $4y - 8 = 12$ (ix) $10x + 4 = 9$

   (v) $4x - 5 = 7$ (x) $5y + 2 = 12$

2. Check to see if the correct solution is given for the following simultaneous equations:

   (i) $2x + y = 11$

   $x - 2y = 3$

   Solution: $x = 3$

   $y = -3$

   (ii) $x + y = 4$

   $2x + 4y = 14$

   Solution: $x = 1$

   $y = 3$

   (iii) $-x - 2y = 4$

   $x - y = -4$

   Solution: $x = -4$

   $y = 1$

   (iv) $x + 3y = 10$

   $5x - y = 18$

   Solution: $x = 4$

   $y = 2$

   (v) $x + 2y = 3$

   $2x - 5y = 6$

   Solution: $x = 1$

   $y = 5$

3. Using trial and error, find the value of the unknown variables in the following simultaneous equations:

   $x - y = 1$

   $2x + 3y = 12$

   Explain the drawbacks of using trial and error to solve this question.

6.2 SOLVING LINEAR EQUATIONS

Trial and error may only give an estimate of the solution and can be time-consuming.

A much more practical approach to solving an equation is to use algebra. Using algebra means that we can find an exact answer for the unknown value.

x^2 Worked Example 6.3

Solve for x in each of the following equations:

(i) $5x - 4 = 3x$ (ii) $3(x + 1) + 4 = 4(x + 3) - 3$

Solution

(i) $5x - 4 = 3x$

> To remove $3x$ from the right-hand side, we have to subtract $3x$ from both sides.

$$5x - 3x - 4 = 3x - 3x$$
$$2x - 4 = 0$$

> To remove -4 from the left-hand side, we have to add 4 to both sides.

$$2x - 4 + 4 = 0 + 4$$
$$\therefore 2x = 4$$

Divide both sides of the equation by 2.
$$\frac{2x}{2} = \frac{4}{2}$$
$$\therefore x = 2$$

(ii) $3(x + 1) + 4 = 4(x + 3) - 3$

Multiply out the brackets.
$$3x + 3 + 4 = 4x + 12 - 3$$

Tidy up both sides of the equation.
$$3x + 7 = 4x + 9$$
$$3x + 7 - 7 = 4x + 9 - 7$$
$$3x = 4x + 2$$
$$3x - 4x = 4x + 2 - 4x$$
$$-x = 2$$

Divide both sides by -1.
$$\therefore x = -2$$

 **ACTIVITY 6.2**

With practice we can speed up the process.

x^2 Worked Example 6.4

Solve the following equation and verify your answer:

$3(2x - 3) + 4(x - 3) = 5x - 25$

Solution

(i) Solve for x.

$$3(2x - 3) + 4(x - 3) = 5x - 25$$
$$6x - 9 + 4x - 12 = 5x - 25$$
$$10x - 21 = 5x - 25$$
$$10x = 5x - 4$$
$$5x = -4$$
$$\frac{5x}{5} = \frac{-4}{5}$$
$$x = -\frac{4}{5} \quad \text{(or } -0.8)$$

(ii) Verify the answer.

This means checking to see if our answer is correct.

We substitute the value that we got for x back into the original equation.

LHS (left-hand side): $3(2x - 3) + 4(x - 3)$

$\qquad\qquad\qquad = 3(2(-0.8) - 3) + 4(-0.8 - 3)$

$\qquad\qquad\qquad = -13.8 - 15.2$

$\qquad\qquad\qquad = -29$

RHS (right-hand side): $5x - 25$

$\qquad\qquad\qquad = 5(-0.8) - 25$

$\qquad\qquad\qquad = -4 - 25$

$\qquad\qquad\qquad = -29$

LHS = RHS

$\therefore x = -0.8$ is correct.

Exercise 6.2

Solve the following equations:

1. $5x = 15$	**11.** $2x + 4 = 12$	**21.** $5(7x + 3) = 2(3 - x) - 3 + x$
2. $3y = 6$	**12.** $4t - 2 = 5t - 5$	**22.** $2(2x - 4) = 12 - 3(2x - 1)$
3. $2x + 4 = 12$	**13.** $x = -5x + 5$	**23.** $3(x - 6) + 15 = 4(x - 1) + 4$
4. $3a + 7 = 34$	**14.** $4x + 7 = -1$	**24.** $-3(4x - 2) = 2(3x - 1) + 18$
5. $3x - 6 = -9$	**15.** $x + 5 = -x$	**25.** $11(a + 7) = 4 - 10(a - 1)$
6. $-4x - 5 = 15$	**16.** $2(x - 1) = 4x$	**26.** $5(2x - 1) = 2(2x - 3) + 4x - 23$
7. $7x + 8 = -13$	**17.** $4(x + 3) = 3(x + 2)$	**27.** $3(x - 2) = 7(x + 5) - 13$
8. $5y - 3 = 17$	**18.** $5(2y - 1) = 2(y - 1)$	**28.** $3(4x - 6) + 25(x + 2) = x - 4$
9. $4x + 10 = -14$	**19.** $3(x + 1) = 2(x - 3) + 7$	**29.** $11 = 7(x + 1) - 2(3 - 8x) - 3x$
10. $3x - 10 = 2x - 3$	**20.** $2(2x + 1) - 3(x - 1) = 9$	

30. Find the value of y that satisfies the equation $3(y - 1) = 1 + 4y$, and verify your solution.

31. Find the value of a that satisfies the equation $11a - 2 = 5(a - 2) - 2a$, and verify your solution.

32. Find the value of b that satisfies the equation $2(b + 3) - 4 = -(b + 2) - 3$, and verify your solution.

6.3 SOLVING LINEAR EQUATIONS WITH FRACTIONS

When solving equations that contain fractions, we multiply every term by the lowest common denominator (LCD).

x^2 Worked Example 6.5

Solve $\dfrac{8x-3}{3} - \dfrac{4x-2}{5} = 5$.

> Note: 5 can be written as $\dfrac{5}{1}$.

Solution

The LCD of 3, 5 and 1 is 15.

Multiply every term in the equation by 15.

$$\frac{15(8x-3)}{3} - \frac{15(4x-2)}{5} = 15(5)$$

$$\frac{^{5}\,\cancel{15}(8x-3)}{\cancel{3}_{1}} - \frac{^{3}\,\cancel{15}(4x-2)}{\cancel{5}_{1}} = 15(5)$$

> No term should still have a fraction part.

$$5(8x-3) - 3(4x-2) = 75$$
$$40x - 15 - 12x + 6 = 75$$
$$28x - 9 = 75$$
$$28x = 75 + 9$$
$$28x = 84$$
$$x = 3$$

x^2 Worked Example 6.6

Solve $\dfrac{2}{3}(x-11) + \dfrac{1}{4}(2x+2) = x$.

> Note: x can be written as $\dfrac{x}{1}$.

Solution

The LCD of 3, 4 and 1 is 12.

Multiply every term in the equation by 12.

$$12\left(\frac{2}{3}\right)(x-11) + 12\left(\frac{1}{4}\right)(2x+2) = 12(x)$$

$$^{4}\cancel{12}\left(\frac{2}{\cancel{3}_{1}}\right)(x-11) + {}^{3}\cancel{12}\left(\frac{1}{\cancel{4}_{1}}\right)(2x+2) = 12(x)$$

$$4(2)(x-11) + 3(1)(2x+2) = 12x$$
$$8(x-11) + 3(2x+2) = 12x$$
$$8x - 88 + 6x + 6 = 12x$$
$$14x - 82 = 12x$$
$$14x - 12x = 82$$
$$2x = 82$$
$$x = 41$$

ACTIVITY 6.3

Exercise 6.3

Solve the following equations:

1. $\dfrac{x+3}{5} = 1$

2. $\dfrac{5x-4}{3} = 2$

3. $\dfrac{x+4}{8} = 2$

4. $\dfrac{a+3}{4} = \dfrac{1}{2}$

5. $\dfrac{x+1}{3} = \dfrac{x}{2}$

6. $\dfrac{9x-4}{2} = 4$

7. $\dfrac{x}{6} - \dfrac{x}{2} = 5$

8. $\dfrac{2x}{7} - \dfrac{4x}{2} = \dfrac{2}{7}$

9. $\dfrac{x+1}{4} = \dfrac{x-1}{3}$

10. $\dfrac{2x-1}{3} = x - 4$

11. $\dfrac{3x+1}{5} - \dfrac{x-1}{2} = 1$

12. $\dfrac{5y-1}{8} + \dfrac{2y-4}{3} = 5$

13. $\dfrac{3x-2}{8} - \dfrac{x-1}{2} = 0$

14. $\dfrac{2x+2}{7} - \dfrac{4x-1}{3} = -3$

15. $\dfrac{5x-1}{7} = \dfrac{x+2}{2} + 1$

16. $\dfrac{t-3}{2} + \dfrac{2t+3}{4} = 3$

17. $\dfrac{x+2}{3} + \dfrac{x+1}{4} = \dfrac{1}{3}$

18. $\dfrac{x-2}{5} + \dfrac{x-3}{4} = \dfrac{11}{10}$

19. $\dfrac{x+1}{3} + \dfrac{2x-9}{4} = \dfrac{17}{12}$

20. $\dfrac{4x+5}{5} - \dfrac{2x-3}{7} = \dfrac{32}{35}$

21. $\dfrac{-x+2}{3} + \dfrac{5x+2}{6} = 1$

22. $\dfrac{11x+1}{10} + 3 = x + \dfrac{x-1}{2}$

23. $\dfrac{x+2}{4} + \dfrac{3x-2}{3} = \dfrac{4x+9}{12}$

24. $\dfrac{1}{2}x + \dfrac{1}{3}x = 5$

25. $\dfrac{1}{2}(x-4) - \dfrac{1}{3}(x-3) = 5$

26. $\dfrac{1}{6}x - \dfrac{2}{5}(x+1) = \dfrac{5}{2}(x-10)$

6.4 SOLVING SIMULTANEOUS LINEAR EQUATIONS BY ELIMINATION

x^2 Worked Example 6.7

Solve for x and y:

$2x + y = 7$

$x - 2y = 1$

Solution

Make all x coefficients or all y coefficients the same in each equation.

$2x + y = 7 \qquad \times 1 \qquad \rightarrow 2x + y = 7$

$x - 2y = 1 \qquad \times 2 \qquad \rightarrow 2x - 4y = 2$

As the x's are the same sign, we will subtract.

$\quad 2x + y = 7$

$-(2x - 4y = 2)$

$2x + y = 7$

$\underline{-2x + 4y = -2}$

$5y = 5$

$\therefore y = 1$

$$2x - 2x = 0$$
$$y + 4y = 5y$$
$$7 - 2 = 5$$

Pick one of the equations and substitute in $y = 1$.

$\quad 2x + y = 7$

$2x + (1) = 7$

$\quad 2x = 6$

$\quad \therefore x = 3$

So our answer is: $x = 3$, $y = 1$.

When solving simultaneous equations, they should always be in the form shown in this example: two variables on one side and a constant on the other side of the equal sign.

x^2 Worked Example 6.8

Solve for x and y.

$10x + 3y = 1$

$x = 7 + 2y$

Solution

First ensure that both equations are in the correct format.

$10x + 3y = 1$

$x - 2y = 7$

$10x + 3y = 1 \quad \times 2 \quad \rightarrow 20x + 6y = 2$

$x - 2y = 7 \quad \times 3 \quad \rightarrow \quad 3x - 6y = 21$

The y's are different signs, so we will add.

$20x + 6y = 2$

$\underline{+3x - 6y = 21}$

$\qquad 23x = 23$

$\qquad \therefore x = 1$

$20x + 3x = 23x$
$6y - 6y = 0$
$2 + 21 = 23$

If $x = 1$, we can now find the value of y.

$10x + 3y = 1$

$10(1) + 3y = 1$

$10 + 3y = 1$

$\quad 3y = -9$

$\quad \therefore y = -3$

So our answer is: $x = 1$, $y = -3$.

 ACTIVITY 6.4

We may also encounter simultaneous equations that involve fractions or decimals or whose x-values and y-values are fractions or decimals.

---

x^2 Worked Example 6.9

Solve the following simultaneous equations:

$\dfrac{x}{2} + \dfrac{y}{5} = 4 \qquad \dfrac{x}{4} + \dfrac{y}{2} = 6$

Solution

$\dfrac{x}{2} + \dfrac{y}{5} = 4$ LCD = 10	$\dfrac{x}{4} + \dfrac{y}{2} = 6$ LCD = 4
$10\left(\dfrac{x}{2}\right) + 10\left(\dfrac{y}{5}\right) = 10(4)$ $5(x) + 2(y) = 10(4)$	$4\left(\dfrac{x}{4}\right) + 4\left(\dfrac{y}{2}\right) = 4(6)$ $1(x) + 2(y) = 4(6)$
$5x + 2y = 40$	$x + 2y = 24$

We now proceed as normal.

$5x + 2y = 40$

$x + 2y = 24$

The y's are the same signs so we will subtract.

$5x + 2y = 40$

$-(x + 2y = 24)$

$5x + 2y = 40$

$\underline{-x - 2y = -24}$

$\qquad 4x = 16$

$\qquad \therefore x = 4$

$x + 2y = 24$

$4 + 2y = 24$

$\quad 2y = 20$

$\quad \therefore y = 10$

So our answer is: $x = 4$, $y = 10$.

x^2 Worked Example 6.10

Solve for x and y:

$5x + 3y = 0$

$10x + 15y = -3$

Solution

We will make the x's have the same coefficient.

$5x + 3y = 0$ $\times 2$ $\rightarrow 10x + 6y = 0$

$10x + 15y = -3$ $\times 1$ $\rightarrow 10x + 15y = -3$

As the x's have the same sign, we will subtract.

$$10x + 6y = 0$$
$$-(10x + 15y = -3)$$

$$10x + 6y = 0$$
$$\underline{-10x - 15y = +3}$$
$$-9y = 3$$

$$\frac{-9y}{-9} = \frac{3}{-9}$$

$$\therefore y = -\frac{1}{3}$$

If $y = -\frac{1}{3}$, we can now find the value of x.

$$5x + 3y = 0$$

$$5x + 3\left(-\frac{1}{3}\right) = 0$$

$$5x - 1 = 0$$

$$5x = 1$$

$$x = \frac{1}{5}$$

So our answer is: $x = \frac{1}{5}, y = -\frac{1}{3}$.

Exercise 6.4

Solve each of the following pairs of simultaneous equations:

1. $x + y = 7$
   $x - y = 1$

2. $x + y = 13$
   $x - y = 3$

3. $x + y = 4$
   $x - y = 10$

4. $4x + 3y = 10$
   $x + y = 3$

5. $x + 2y = 11$
   $2x + y = 10$

6. $2x + y = 9$
   $3x + y = 11$

7. $2x + y = 17$
   $x + y = 10$

8. $3x + 4y = 19$
   $x + 3y = 8$

9. $x + 2y = 6$
   $4x - y = 6$

10. $2x + 5y = -15$
    $4x + 3y = -9$

11. $3x + 5y = 17$
    $2x - 5y = -22$

12. $2x + 7y = 27$
    $3x + 5y = 13$

13. $4x + 3y = -21$
    $2x + 9y = -33$

14. $2x - 5y = 0$
    $x + 4y = 13$

15. $3x + 2y = 21$
    $4x - 5y = 28$

16. $6x + 5y = 19$
    $3x - 7y = 19$

17. $x - 3y - 5 = 0$
    $5x - y + 17 = 0$

18. $x - y + 1 = 0$
    $4x + 5y + 13 = 0$

19. $5x = 61 - 6y$
    $2x + 3y = 25$

20. $4x = 11 - 3y$
    $6y = 14 - 4x$

21. $x + 11 = -3y$
    $y + 12 = -2x$

22. $2x - 3y = -8$

$2x + 4y = 13$

23. $x - 9y = -1$

$2x + 3y = 5$

24. $4x + 5y = 2$

$4x - 5y = 0$

25. $14x - 12y = -3$

$10x + 5y - 6 = 0$

26. $3x + 9y = 36$

$8x = 6y - 9$

27. $x + 3(y - 1) = 5$

$5x + 13 - y = 5$

28. $\frac{5}{4}x - \frac{3}{4}y = 3$

$3x + 2y = 11$

29. $\frac{x}{2} + y = 13$

$\frac{x}{7} - \frac{y}{3} = 0$

30. $\frac{x + y}{5} + \frac{y - x}{2} = 5$

$\frac{x + 2y}{9} = 2$

6.5 SOLVING SIMULTANEOUS LINEAR EQUATIONS GRAPHICALLY

Linear equations can also be solved using graphs. The equation of a line can be written in the form $y = mx + c$, where c is the y-intercept. By graphing lines, we can also discover where the line intercepts the x-axis (x-intercept).

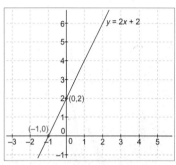

x^2 Worked Example 6.11

(i) Graph the line $y = 3x + 6$.

(ii) Find the x-intercept.

(iii) Use algebra to solve $3x + 6 = 0$.

(iv) Explain the significance of the x-intercept.

Solution

(i) $y = 3x + 6$.

As the line is in the form $y = mx + c$, the line has a slope of 3.

∴ The line has a rise of 3 and a run of 1. The y-intercept is 6.

We now graph this line.

(ii) The line hits the x-axis at the point $(-2,0)$.

∴ The x-intercept = -2.

(iii) Using algebra solve $3x + 6 = 0$.

$3x + 6 = 0$

$3x = -6$

$x = -2$

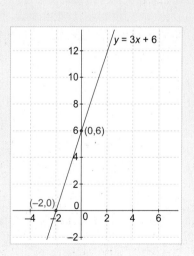

(iv) Explain the significance of the x-intercept.

The x-intercept point is the solution or root of the equation $3x + 6 = 0$.

We can solve linear equations by graphing and finding the x-intercept.

Remember that solving a linear equation by graphing may only give an estimate and not the exact answer that is required.

Sometimes it is required that we find the point of intersection of two lines.

x^2 Worked Example 6.12

(i) Graph the lines $y = 4x - 2$ and $y = 2$.

(ii) From your graph, find the point of intersection of these two lines.

(iii) Explain the significance of this point of intersection.

Solution

(i) We graph the line $y = 4x - 2$.

This line has a slope of 4 and the y-intercept is -2.

We also graph the line $y = 2$.

(ii) The point of intersection of these two lines is $(1,2)$.

(iii) $(1,2)$, the point of intersection, is the only point that is common to both graphs. It satisfies both equations → $y = 4x - 2$ **and** $y = 2$.

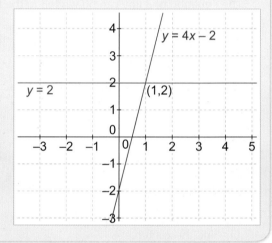

x^2 Worked Example 6.13

Solve graphically the equation $4x + 4 = 2x + 10$.

Solution

We let both sides of the equation equal y.

$4x + 4 = y$

$y = 2x + 10$

We now have two lines that we can plot.

4x + 4 = y		y = 2x + 10	
Let $x = 0$.	Let $y = 0$.	Let $x = 0$.	Let $y = 0$.
$4(0) + 4 = y$	$4x + 4 = 0$	$y = 2(0) + 10$	$0 = 2x + 10$
$4 = y$	$4x = -4$	$y = 10$	$-2x = 10$
	$x = -1$		$x = -5$
If $x = 0$, then $y = 4$.	If $y = 0$, then $x = -1$.	If $x = 0$, then $y = 10$.	If $y = 0$, then $x = -5$.
Point $(0,4)$	Point $(-1,0)$	Point $(0,10)$	Point $(-5,0)$

We now draw both lines on the same graph.

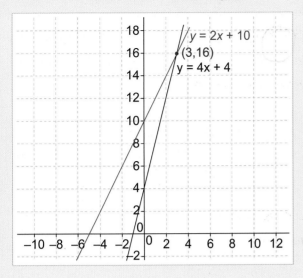

On our graph the point of intersection of these two lines is (3,16). The x co-ordinate is 3.

$$\therefore x = 3$$

Check:

$$4x + 4 = 2x + 10$$

$$\therefore 4(3) + 4 = 2(3) + 10$$

$$12 + 4 = 6 + 10$$

$$16 = 16 \qquad \text{True}$$

x^2 Worked Example 6.14

Solve the following simultaneous equations by graphing:

$$x - y = 2$$

$$2x + 3y = 24$$

Solution

We plot both lines.

x − y = 2		2x + 3y = 24	
Let x = 0.	Let y = 0.	Let x = 0.	Let y = 0.
$(0) - y = 2$	$x - (0) = 2$	$2(0) + 3y = 24$	$2x + 3(0) = 24$
$-y = 2$	$x = 2$	$3y = 24$	$2x = 24$
$y = -2$		$y = 8$	$x = 12$
If x = 0, then y = −2.	If y = 0, then x = 2.	If x = 0, then y = 8.	If y = 0, then x = 12.
Point (0,−2)	Point (2,0)	Point (0,8)	Point (12,0)

We draw these two lines and mark the point of intersection.

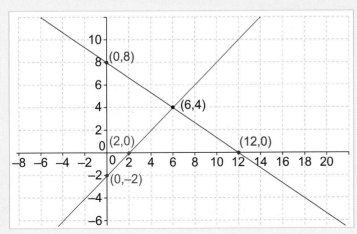

Reading from your graph, find where theses two lines intersect. From our graph, the point of intersection is (6,4).

$$\therefore x = 6 \text{ and } y = 4$$

ACTIVITY 6.5

Exercise 6.5

1. Solve the following linear equations by graphing:

   (i) $3x + 2 = 0$

   (ii) $4x - 12 = 0$

   (iii) $4x - 5 = 3$

   (iv) $3x + 10 = -5$

   (v) $2x + 1 = x + 3$

   (vi) $x - 3 = 2x - 7$

   (vii) $3x + 4 = 2x + 1$

   (viii) $4(x - 3) = 20$

   (ix) $-(x - 3) = 10$

   (x) $5(3x + 4) = 4(x - 6)$

2. Solve the following simultaneous equations by graphing each line:

   (i) $2x + y = 4$ (iv) $x + y = 7$
       $4x - 5y = 20$ $x - 2y = 2$

   (ii) $2x + y = 6$ (v) $x - y = 4$
       $2x - y = 2$ $x + 5y = -2$

   (iii) $x + 2y = 5$ (vi) $2x + y = 0$
       $3x - y = -6$ $x + 2y = -3$

3. For each of the following:

   (a) Solve the following simultaneous equations by graphing each line.

   (b) Check your answer using algebra.

   (i) $2x - y = 2$ (ii) $x + 2y = 2$
       $2x - 5y = -6$ $6x - 2y = 5$

6.6 INEQUALITIES

Sometimes, when we solve for an unknown, we cannot find an exact value of x. Instead we have to give a range of values. We are dealing with an **inequality**.

> In maths, one side of an equation = the other side of the equation.
>
> In an **inequality**, one side of the inequality is:
> - greater than,
> - greater than or equal to,
> - less than, or
> - less than or equal to
>
> the other side.

Inequality Signs

When trying to solve an inequality, we must be able to distinguish between different inequality signs.

> Greater than	$x > 4$	The value of x is greater than 4.
≥ Greater than or equal to	$x \geqslant 4$	The value of x is greater than or equal to 4.
< Less than	$x < 2$	The value of x is less than 2.
≤ Less than or equal to	$x \leqslant 2$	The value of x is less than or equal to 2.

When dealing with inequalities, we may be asked to show our answer (solution set) on a numberline. To do this, we must first understand the three different types of numbers we may meet when solving inequalities.

Natural Numbers – N

A **natural number** is any positive whole number (i.e. any whole number greater than 0).

$N = \{1, 2, 3, 4, ...\}$

These numbers are denoted by the letter N.

> We are usually told when we are dealing with natural numbers – the question will say $x \in N$. This means that x is an element of N, i.e. from the set of natural numbers.

As natural numbers are whole numbers, in order to graph them on the numberline we use dots.

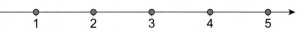

Integers – Z

An **integer** is any whole number.

$Z = \{..., -3, -2, -1, 0, 1, 2, 3, ...\}$

These numbers are denoted by the letter Z. > This is written as $x \in Z$.

As integers are also whole numbers, in order to graph them on the numberline we use dots.

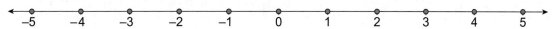

Real Numbers – R

Real numbers are all the numbers on the numberline. They can be positive, negative or neutral (zero) whole numbers, decimals or fractions. They also include irrational numbers, e.g. $\sqrt{2}$.

These numbers are denoted by the letter R. > This is written as $x \in R$.

As real numbers can be any number, in order to show them on the numberline we use a solid line.

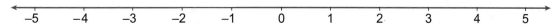

x^2 **Worked Example 6.15**

Draw separate numberlines to show the following inequalities:

(i) $x \geqslant 5, x \in Z$ (ii) $x < 4, x \in N$

Solution

(i) $x \geqslant 5, x \in Z$

As $x \in Z$, we use dots on the numberline.

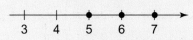

The next integer greater than 5 is 6, then 7.
The arrow shows that the inequality continues on past 7.

(ii) $x < 4, x \in N$

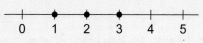

As natural numbers stop at 1, we do not put an arrow in.

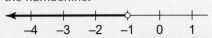
Worked Example 6.16

Draw separate numberlines to show the following inequalities:

    (i) $x < -1, x \in R$ (ii) $x \geqslant -3, x \in R$

Solution

In both questions we are dealing with real numbers, so we use a heavy line to denote this on the numberline.

    (i) $x < -1, x \in R$ means that x represents **all** numbers less than but **not including** −1.

    An **empty circle** is used to show this on the numberline.

    (ii) $x \geqslant -3, x \in R$ means that x represents **all** numbers greater than **and including** −3.

    A **full circle** is used to show this on the numberline.

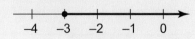

Exercise 6.6

1. Write down the first three values of the following inequalities:

    (i) $x > 7, x \in Z$

    (ii) $x > 5, x \in N$

    (iii) $x > -9, x \in Z$

    (iv) $x \leqslant 3, x \in N$

    (v) $x \geqslant -4, x \in Z$

2. Draw separate number lines to show the following inequalities.

    (i) $x \leqslant 3, x \in Z$ (vi) $x < 0, x \in R$

    (ii) $x < 5, x \in N$ (vii) $x \geqslant -3, x \in R$

    (iii) $x \geqslant -4, x \in R$ (viii) $x < -4, x \in R$

    (iv) $x > -1, x \in R$ (ix) $x < 5, x \in Z$

    (v) $x < 2, x \in Z$ (x) $x < 3, x \in N$

6.7 SOLVING INEQUALITIES

Solving an inequality is very similar to solving any linear equation.

When solving an inequality, we usually end up with a range of values for the unknown.

    $3x > 9$ $\therefore x > 3$

This means the x can only have a value greater than 3. This range or set of values can be called the **solution set**.

Provided $x > 3$, the left-hand side of our inequality ($3x$) will always be greater than (>) the right-hand side (9).

$3(4) = 12 > 9$ True

$3(5) = 15 > 9$ True

If x is equal to or less than 3, the inequality will not hold true, i.e. $3x$ will not be >9.

$3(2) = 6 > 9$ False

> When solving an inequality, we generally move the variable to the left-hand side of the inequality.

Worked Example 6.17

Solve the following inequality and show the solution set on the numberline.

$4(x - 1) < 2(x - 3), x \in Z$

Solution

$4(x - 1) < 2(x - 3)$

$4x - 4 < 2x - 6$

$4x - 2x < -6 + 4$

$2x < -2$

$\therefore x < -1, x \in Z$

We then draw this set on the numberline. Remember that $x \in Z$.

(numberline: points at $-4, -3, -2$; marks at $-1, 0$)

An Important Case

When solving an inequality, we may sometimes end up with a negative x term ($-x$). A very specific rule applies when multiplying or dividing an inequality by a negative number.

From Activity 6.7, we see that:

> When we multiply or divide both sides of an inequality by a negative number, we **flip** or **reverse** the inequality sign, as well as changing the signs of the terms.

Consider the inequality $-3x \geq 9$.

To correct this, we divide both sides by -3 and **flip** the sign of the inequality.

$-3x \geq 9$

$\dfrac{-3x}{-3} \leq \dfrac{9}{-3}$

$\therefore x \leq -3$

We only have to do this when we have a **negative x term.**

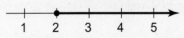

Worked Example 6.18

Solve the following inequality and show the solution on the numberline:

$2(x - 2) \leq 3(x - 2), x \in R$

Solution

$2x - 4 \leq 3x - 6$

$2x - 3x \leq -6 + 4$

$-x \leq -2$

Divide both sides by -1, so change signs and flip the inequality sign.

$x \geq 2, x \in R$

(numberline: full circle at 2, heavy line and arrow to right, marks 1,2,3,4,5)

As we are dealing with real numbers, we draw a full circle at 2, with a heavy line to the right and an arrow to the right.

Compound Inequalities

We may also be asked to solve compound inequalities, where two inequalities are linked.
This can be asked in two separate ways.

x^2 Worked Example 6.19

Solve the following inequality and show the solution on the numberline:

$-8 < 3x + 1 \leqslant 13, x \in R$

Solution

> First, we try to make the middle term of the inequality have an x term only.

$-8 < 3x + 1 \leqslant 13$

$-8 - 1 < 3x + 1 - 1 \leqslant 13 - 1$

> We now divide every term by the number in front of the x term.

$-9 < 3x \leqslant 12$

$\therefore -3 < x \leqslant 4$

x lies between -3 and 4.

$x \in R$, so we will represent these values using a heavy line.

As -3 is **not** included, we will have an empty circle at -3.

4 **is** included, so we will have a full circle at 4.

We then draw a heavy line between these two values.

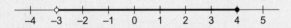

x^2 Worked Example 6.20

(i) Find the solution set of A: $-4 \leqslant x + 2, x \in Z$

(ii) Find the solution set of B: $4x + 1 < -7, x \in Z$

(iii) List the elements of $A \cap B$.

Solution

(i) $-4 \leqslant x + 2$

$-x \leqslant 2 + 4$

$-x \leqslant 6$

$\therefore x \geqslant -6$

(ii) $4x + 1 < -7$

$4x < -7 - 1$

$4x < -8$

$\therefore x < -2$

(iii) $x \geqslant -6$, so x must be greater than or equal to -6.

$x < -2$, so x must be less than -2.

$\therefore A \cap B = \{-6, -5, -4, -3\}$

Exercise 6.7

Solve each of the following inequalities and show the solution on the numberline:

1. $3x > 6, x \in N$

2. $4x - 4 \geqslant 8, x \in N$

3. $3x + 3 < 9, x \in N$

4. $5x + 3 \leqslant -2, x \in Z$

5. $7x + 8 \leqslant 1, x \in R$

6. $3x - 8 > 4, x \in R$

7. $\dfrac{x-5}{7} > -3, x \in Z$

8. $10x \leqslant 10 + 5x, x \in R$

9. $x + 3 > -4, x \in Z$

10. $2x + 1 \leqslant 3x + 2, x \in R$

11. $\dfrac{x+1}{2} < 5, x \in R$

12. $4x + 3 \geqslant 6x - 4, x \in N$

13. $\dfrac{5x-2}{2} > \dfrac{8x+10}{4}, x \in R$

14. $2(x + 2) \leqslant 5x - 2, x \in R$

15. $3(2x + 1) > 3(x - 3), x \in R$

16. $\dfrac{-3(2x+3)}{2} \leqslant \dfrac{-4(x+4)}{3}, x \in Z$

17. $4(x - 3) \geqslant -2(x + 1) + 2, x \in R$

18. $4(3x + 1) + 2(x - 3) + 9 \geqslant 0, x \in Z$

19. Graph the following inequalities on a numberline.

    (i) $-1 < x < 3, x \in Z$

    (ii) $1 < x < 5, x \in N$

    (iii) $-5 \leqslant x \leqslant 3, x \in R$

    (iv) $-10 \leqslant 2x < 2, x \in R$

    (v) $-2 < -x \leqslant 4, x \in R$

20. Solve the following inequalities and show the solution on the numberline:

    (i) $-1 < x + 3 < 9, x \in Z$

    (ii) $-2 \leqslant x - 5 < 4, x \in N$

    (iii) $3 \leqslant 2x + 9 \leqslant 11, x \in R$

    (iv) $0 \leqslant 9 - 3x < 9, x \in R$

    (v) $2 \leqslant \dfrac{-x+5}{2} < 4, x \in R$

21. List the elements of N that satisfy the inequality $5x - 3 \leqslant 28$.

22. (i) Find the solution set E of:
       $2x - 1 \leqslant 13, x \in Z$

    (ii) Find the solution set F of:
       $1 - 2x \leqslant 3, x \in Z$

    (iii) Find the solution set of E ∩ F.

23. Show on three separate numberlines the following sets:

    (i) A = $\{x \mid 6x + 2 < 20, x \in R\}$

    (ii) B = $\{x \mid 6 - 2x < 20, x \in R\}$

    (iii) A ∩ B

24. (i) Find the solution set P of: $5x - 1 \geqslant 4, x \in R$

    (ii) Find the solution set Q of: $3x - 10 < -1$, $x \in R$

    (iii) Show on a numberline the elements of P ∩ Q.

25. (i) Graph the solution set M of:
       $\dfrac{3x-1}{4} > \dfrac{7}{2}, x \in R$

    (ii) Graph the solution set N of:
       $3 \geqslant 4x - 25, x \in R$

    (iii) List the elements of M ∩ N.

26. Show on three separate numberlines the following sets:

    (i) Set D: $\dfrac{(7x-3)}{2} + \dfrac{(2x-1)}{5} > 10, x \in Z$

    (ii) Set E: $\dfrac{(4x+11)}{2} < 14, x \in Z$

    (iii) The solution set of D ∩ E

6

ALGEBRA II

6.8 MANIPULATION OF FORMULAE

Some countries measure temperature using the Fahrenheit scale (°F) instead of the Celsius scale (°C).

To convert degrees Fahrenheit (°F) into degrees Celsius (°C), we can use the following formula:

FORMULA

$$C = \frac{5(F - 32)}{9}$$

For example, if the temperature at a beach is 50°F, we can use this formula to convert 50°F into degrees Celsius (°C).

$$C = \frac{5(50 - 32)}{9} = 10°C$$

However, we may need to change degrees Celsius into degrees Fahrenheit.

The formula must be manipulated to do this.

FORMULA

$$F = \frac{9C}{5} + 32$$

To manipulate any formula, we follow a set of rules.

ACTIVITY 6.8

x^2 Worked Example 6.21

Make x the subject of the formula when $y = mx + c$.

Solution

Making x the subject of the formula means that the final formula must be in the form $x = ...$

> **Rule:** We move any variable (letters) we do **not** want to the **other side** of the equal sign. Make sure to follow correct mathematical procedure.

$$\therefore y = mx + c$$
$$\Rightarrow y - c = mx$$

mx is in fact $(m) \times (x)$. So in order to isolate x, we must divide both sides of the equation by m.

$$\therefore y - c = mx$$
$$\Rightarrow \frac{y - c}{m} = x$$

x^2 Worked Example 6.22

Make a the subject of the formula if $\dfrac{a+b}{3} = \dfrac{c}{2}$.

Solution

The LCD of 3 and 2 is 6.

$$\dfrac{^2 6(a+b)}{3_1} = \dfrac{^3 6c}{2_1}$$

$$2(a+b) = 3c$$

$$2a + 2b = 3c$$

$$2a = 3c - 2b$$

$$\dfrac{\not2 a}{\not2} = \dfrac{3c - 2b}{2}$$

$$\therefore a = \dfrac{3c - 2b}{2}$$

x^2 Worked Example 6.23

Express b in terms of a and c:

$$2ab = 2a - 3bc$$

Solution

$$2ab = 2a - 3bc$$

$$2ab + 3bc = 2a$$

> **Rule:** Bring the terms that contain the desired variable to the same side.

Factorise using b as the HCF.

$$\therefore b(2a + 3c) = 2a$$

$$\Rightarrow b = \dfrac{2a}{2a + 3c}$$

x^2 Worked Example 6.24

Express r in terms of p and q:

$$\dfrac{1}{p} + \dfrac{1}{q} = \dfrac{1}{r}$$

Solution

The LCD of $\dfrac{1}{p} + \dfrac{1}{q} = \dfrac{1}{r}$ is pqr.

Multiply all terms by pqr.

$$pqr\left(\dfrac{1}{p}\right) + pqr\left(\dfrac{1}{q}\right) = pqr\left(\dfrac{1}{r}\right)$$

$$\therefore qr + pr = pq$$

> Factorise $qr + pr$.

$$r(q + p) = pq$$

$$\therefore r = \dfrac{pq}{q + p}$$

Exercise 6.8

1. In each case, make the highlighted variable the subject of the formula.

(i) $3x = 9$	(vi) $3x + y = 9$	(xi) $3xy + y = 9$
(ii) $4y = 16$	(vii) $4y + x = 16$	(xii) $4xy + x = 16$
(iii) $4a + 3 = 7$	(viii) $4a + 3b = 7$	(xiii) $4a + 3ab = 7$
(iv) $2b - 9 = 5$	(ix) $2b - 3c = 5$	(xiv) $2b - 3bc = 5$
(v) $3r = r - 4$	(x) $3r = r - 4t$	(xv) $3p + t = r - 4t$

2. In each case, make the highlighted variable the subject of the formula.

(i) $\frac{x}{4} = 5$	(vi) $\frac{x}{4} + y = 5$	(xi) $\frac{4}{x} + \frac{2}{y} = 5$
(ii) $\frac{y}{6} = 2$	(vii) $\frac{y}{6} + x = 2$	(xii) $\frac{2}{y} + \frac{3}{x} = 2$
(iii) $\frac{a}{2} - 1 = 5$	(viii) $\frac{a}{2} - 2b = 5$	(xiii) $\frac{2}{a} - \frac{1}{b} = 5$
(iv) $\frac{3b}{5} - 2 = \frac{1}{3}$	(ix) $\frac{3b}{5} - \frac{c}{2} = \frac{1}{3}$	(xiv) $\frac{5}{3b} - \frac{2}{c} = \frac{1}{3}$
(v) $\frac{2r}{3} = r - \frac{1}{2}$	(x) $\frac{2r}{3} = r - \frac{1}{2}t$	(xv) $\frac{3}{2}p = \frac{1}{r} - \frac{1}{2}t$

In Questions 3–29, express the variable in the square brackets in terms of the other variables.

3. $t = 4n + 5$ [n]   **12.** $p = 2rs - q$ [q]   **21.** $A = \frac{1}{2}(x + y)z$ [z]

4. $A = lw$ [w]   **13.** $a = b - 2c$ [c]   **22.** $A = \frac{1}{2}(x + y)z$ [x]

5. $p = mv$ [v]   **14.** $a = \frac{b + c}{3}$ [c]   **23.** $ax = bx + c$ [x]

6. $v = u + at$ [u]   **15.** $s = \frac{a + b + c}{2}$ [b]   **24.** $pq = c + rq$ [q]

7. $v = u + at$ [a]   **16.** $ab + bc = c$ [b]   **25.** $a + b = bx + x$ [b]

8. $K = \frac{1}{2}mv^2$ [m]   **17.** $s = ut + \frac{1}{2}at^2$ [u]   **26.** $2\frac{(a - t)}{c} = a$ [a]

9. $E = mc^2$ [c]   **18.** $s = ut + \frac{1}{2}at^2$ [a]   **27.** $T = 2\pi\sqrt{\frac{l}{g}}$ [l]

10. $F = \frac{mv^2}{r}$ [m]   **19.** $x + \frac{y}{3} = 2z$ [y]   **28.** $a = \frac{bc}{b+c}$ [b]

11. $F = \frac{mv^2}{r}$ [r]   **20.** $\frac{1}{a} + \frac{1}{b} = \frac{1}{c}$ [b]   **29.** $v = \sqrt{2gh}$ [g]

30. The density of a substance (g/cm³) is given by the formula $D = \frac{M}{V}$, where M is mass (in grams) and V is volume (in cm³).

  (i) Express V in terms of the other variables.

  (ii) Find the volume of a substance which has a mass of 50 g and a density of 1.2 g per cm³.

31. Given the formula $\frac{3x - y}{a + b} = k$:

  (i) Write y in terms of the other variables.

  (ii) Write x in terms of the other variables.

32. The formula for the volume of a cylinder is $V = \pi r^2 h$.

  (i) What is the volume of a cylinder with $h = 20$ cm, $r = 5$ cm and $\pi = 3.14$?

  (ii) Write h in terms of the other variables and hence find the height of a cylinder of $r = 10$ cm, $\pi = 3.14$ and $V = 3{,}768$ cm³.

  (iii) Write r in terms of the other variables and hence find the radius of a cylinder of $h = 2$ cm, $\pi = \frac{22}{7}$ and $V = 3{,}773$ cm³.

33. The time taken (T) for a simple pendulum to swing back and forth (period), is given by the formula $T = 2\pi\sqrt{\frac{L}{g}}$. L = length of pendulum in metres and g = acceleration due to gravity, 9.81 m/s².

  (i) What would be the period of a pendulum of length 2 m? (Take $\pi = 3.14$)

  Give your answer correct to two decimal places.

  (ii) How long would the pendulum have to be in order to have a period of 3 seconds?

  Give your answer correct to three significant figures.

6

ALGEBRA II

ACTIVE MATHS

6.9 WRITING EXPRESSIONS

We can use algebra to help us solve various mathematical problems. To use algebra in this way, we must be able to write down the information using letters to represent the unknowns.

For example, 'Five coffees cost €7.50' could be written as $5x = 7.50$, where x represents the price of a single coffee.

We must first practise how we change words into algebraic expressions.

what?

ACTIVITY 6.9

x^2 Worked Example 6.25

Seán is x years old. Gavin is five years older. Abby is five times Sean's age.
Write down in terms of x an expression for (i) Gavin's age and (ii) Abby's age.

Solution

(i) Seán is x years old.

Gavin is five years older than Seán.

$\therefore$ Gavin's age $= x + 5$

(ii) Abby is five times as old as Seán.

$\therefore$ Abby's age $= 5x$

x^2 Worked Example 6.26

Susan buys nine shirts. If y shirts are blue, how many shirts are in other colours?

Solution

y = blue shirts

$\therefore$ Other shirt colours $= 9 - y$

x^2 Worked Example 6.27

How many months are there in:

(i) Four years and five months?

(ii) n years and m months?

Solution

(i) Four years and five months

$4(12) + 5 = 53$ months

(ii) n years and m months

$n(12) + m = (12n + m)$ months

ALGEBRA II

Exercise 6.9

1. (i) How many days are there in five weeks?
   (ii) How many days are there in seven weeks?
   (iii) How many days are there in n weeks?

2. (i) How many seconds are there in one minute?
   (ii) How many seconds are there in four minutes?
   (iii) How many seconds are there in t minutes?

3. (i) How many points does a hurling team get for 3 goals and 10 points?
      [1 goal = 3 points]
   (ii) How many points does a hurling team get for x goals and y points?

4. (i) Barry is 22 years old. How old will he be in 4 years' time?
   (ii) Carol is x years old. How old will she be in 4 years' time?

5. A car uses l litres of petrol per minute.
   (i) Write an expression for the total number of litres used during a 45-minute drive.

   Another car uses m litres of petrol per hour.
   (ii) Write an expression for how many litres this car would use on a 45-minute drive.

6. Bertie is x years old. Edna is n years older than Bertie.
   Write down an expression for Edna's age.

7. (i) 4 is a natural number. Write down the next five consecutive natural numbers.
   (ii) n is a natural number. Write down the next five consecutive natural numbers.

8. (i) 10 is an even number. Write down the next four consecutive even numbers.
   (ii) p is an even number. Write down the next four consecutive even numbers.

9. (i) Harry is 80 years old. His son is half as old. How old was his son three years ago?
   (ii) Ivan is x years old. His son is half as old. How old was his son three years ago?

10. There is €100 in your wallet.
    (i) If you take out €50, how much is left in your wallet?
    (ii) If you take out €70, how much is left in your wallet?
    (iii) If you take out €x, how much is left in your wallet?

11. (i) There are 29 students in a class. If 17 of them are girls, how many are boys?
    (ii) There are 29 students in a class. If x of them are girls, how many are boys?

12. A garden has a length of 10x m and a width of $(4x - 1)$ m. Write down an expression for the perimeter of the garden.

13. A woman leaves €1,000 to her four children. €x is for the eldest. The rest is to be divided equally amongst the other three children. How much does each child get (in terms of x)?

14. A rectangular field has length x metres and width y metres. Write down an expression for:
    (i) The area of the field
    (ii) The perimeter of the field

15. (i) 31 is an odd number. Write down the next three consecutive odd numbers.
    (ii) q is also an odd number. Write down the next three consecutive odd numbers.

16. A rectangle is x cm long by y cm wide. A 2 cm square is cut from each corner of the rectangle as shown. The sides are then folded along the dotted line to make an open-topped box.

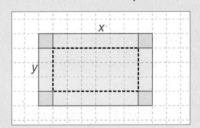

    (i) Write an expression for the surface area of this box.
    (ii) Write an expression for the volume of this box.

6.10 SOLVING PROBLEMS INVOLVING LINEAR EQUATIONS

Using the techniques we learned in the previous section, we can now find the actual value of the unknown variable.

x^2 Worked Example 6.28

A is two years older than B. C is five years younger than A. The sum of their ages is 113.
Find the ages of all three.

Solution

> When using algebra to solve a problem, we generally follow these steps:
>
> - Let x = the unknown value.
> - Form a maths equation from the word equation.
> - Solve for x.
> - Remember to **answer** the question asked.

It is usually better to start with the unknown that requires the fewest changes to be made.

B's age = x

A is two years older than B.

$\therefore$ A's age = $x + 2$

C is five years younger than A.

$\therefore$ C's age = $(x + 2) - 5$

$\qquad\qquad = x + 2 - 5$

$\therefore$ C's age = $x - 3$

Word equation: The sum of their ages is 113.

A's + B's + C's ages added together equals 113.

Maths equation: $x + (x + 2) + (x - 3) = 113$

$\qquad\qquad x + x + 2 + x - 3 = 113$

$\qquad\qquad\qquad\qquad 3x - 1 = 113$

$\qquad\qquad\qquad\qquad 3x = 113 + 1$

$\qquad\qquad\qquad\qquad 3x = 114$

$\qquad\qquad\qquad\qquad x = 38$

We now must write down the ages of all three.

- B's age = x = 38 years
- A's age = $x + 2$ = 38 + 2 = 40 years
- C's age = $x - 3$ = 38 - 3 = 35 years

We can check our answer: 38 + 40 + 35 = 113.

x^2 Worked Example 6.29

A pet shop has hamsters and gerbils for sale. They have 30 in total for sale. They sell four hamsters. Two gerbils are also sold. The shop now has twice as many gerbils as hamsters.
How many of each type did the shop start with?

Solution

Start: Number of hamsters = x

$\qquad\therefore$ Number of gerbils = $30 - x$

Present: The shop sells four hamsters: $x - 4$

$\qquad$ Two gerbils are also sold: $30 - x - 2 = 28 - x$

Word equation

The shop **now** has twice as many gerbils as hamsters.

> Use 'Present' expressions to form the equation.

Twice the number of hamsters is equal to the number of gerbils.

Maths equation

$2(x - 4) = 28 - x$

$2x - 8 = 28 - x$

$2x + x = 28 + 8$

$\qquad 3x = 36$

$\qquad x = 12$

- Number of hamsters = x = 12
- Number of gerbils = $30 - x$ = 30 - 12 = 18

1. If you double a number and add 17, the result is 35. Find the number.

2. When you multiply a number by 4 and subtract 5, you get 79. What is that number?

3. When a number is trebled and 7 is taken away, the result is 26. Find the number.

4. When I multiply a number by 12 and add 37, the result is 325. Find the number.

5. When a number is trebled, the result is the same as when 14 is added to the number. What is the number?

6. Find two consecutive natural numbers whose sum is 83.
   [Hint: Let the numbers be n and $(n + 1)$]

7. Find two consecutive natural numbers such that eight times the first is 1 less than seven times the second.

8. Find three consecutive natural numbers such that five times the first is 24 more than the sum of the other two.

9. Annie is y years old. Her sister is twice as old as her. Their mother is 25 years older than Annie's sister. The total of all their ages is 80. How old is Annie?

10. There are 100 seats in a cinema. Some are luxury seats, costing €2 each; the rest are ordinary seats, costing €1 each. When the cinema is full, the takings come to a total of €170. How many of the seats are 'luxury'?

11. Find two consecutive even numbers such that six times the first is equal to five times the second.
    [Hint: Let the numbers be n and $(n + 2)$]

12. Find two consecutive odd numbers such that seven times the smaller is 12 more than five times the bigger.

13. Emily's age is x. Frances is three years older. Their father's age is twice the sum of their ages. If their three ages add up to 93, find their ages.

14. Two rectangles of equal area are shown. Write an equation in terms of x and, using this equation, find all the dimensions of the rectangles.

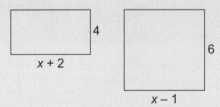

15. The diagram shows the angles of two triangles. In each case, find the value of x, and hence, find the value of the three angles.

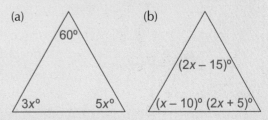

(a)   (b)

16. The sum of four consecutive natural numbers is 54.
    Find all four numbers.

17. A small bag of cement weighs x kg. A large bag of cement is four times as heavy as the small bag. A medium bag of cement is 5 kg lighter than the large bag. Two small bags plus a heavy bag of cement weigh the same as two medium bags.

    How much does each type of bag of cement weigh?

18. A bag contains y amount of yellow marbles. There are five more blue marbles than yellow in the bag and three fewer green marbles than yellow.

    If the bag contains 32 marbles in total, how many marbles of each colour are in the bag?

19. Five consecutive even numbers add up to 130. Find the smallest number of the sequence.

20. Amy gets €x as a prize. Brendan gets three times as much as Amy and Chloe gets half as much as Brendan. If the total money received is €550, how much does each person get?

21. Arthur owns 30% of a company. Each percentage owned of the company usually pays the owner a salary of €x per month.

■ During January, the company pays as normal.

■ During February, the company pays out €500 less than normal.

~~wurt dur furk!!~~

■ Arthur then buys another 5% of the company.

■ During March, the company pays as normal.

■ On average, Arthur receives €2,050 per month for these three months.

How much does the company pay out for each percentage owned?

6.11 SOLVING PROBLEMS USING SIMULTANEOUS EQUATIONS

Sometimes we encounter algebra problems with two unconnected unknowns, x and y. These problems may be solved using simultaneous equations.

ACTIVITY 6.11

x^2 **Worked Example 6.30**

A set meal for five adults and three children costs €210 in a restaurant.
The next day it costs two adults and five children €160 to get the same set meals.

Find the cost of the meal per adult and per child.

Solution

Cost of adult meal = €x   Cost of child meal = €y

Word equation (1): A set meal for five adults and three children costs €210.

Word equation (2): A set meal for two adults and five children costs €160.

Maths equation (1): $5x + 3y = 210$

Maths equation (2): $2x + 5y = 160$

> Both equations **must** be equal to the same units, in this case euros.

We now solve for x and y:

$5x + 3y = 210 \quad \times 2 \rightarrow 10x + 6y = 420$

$2x + 5y = 160 \quad \times 5 \rightarrow 10x + 25y = 800$

First we find the value of y:

$$10x + 6y = 420$$
$$\underline{-10x - 25y = -800}$$
$$-19y = -380$$
$$\frac{-19y}{-19} = \frac{-380}{-19}$$
$$\therefore y = 20$$

If $y = 20$, we can now find the value of x:

$$2x + 5y = 160$$
$$2x + 5(20) = 160$$
$$2x + 100 = 160$$
$$2x = 160 - 100$$
$$2x = 60$$
$$\therefore x = 30$$

Cost of adult meal = x = €30

Cost of child meal = y = €20

> Remember to answer the question asked.

x^2 Worked Example 6.31

A customer in a clothes shop buys three navy suits and two black suits for a total price of €600. The clothes shop sells a navy suit and a black suit for a total of €250.

Find the price per suit.

Solution

Cost of navy suit = x   Cost of black suit = y

Word equation (1): A customer in a clothes shop buys three navy suits and two black suits for a total price of €600.

Maths equation (1): $3x + 2y = 600$

$3x + 2y = 600 \quad \times 1 \rightarrow 3x + 2y = 600$

$x + y = 250 \quad \times 3 \rightarrow 3x + 3y = 750$

First we find the value of y:

$\begin{aligned} 3x + 2y &= 600 \\ \underline{-3x - 3y} &= \underline{-750} \\ -y &= -150 \\ y &= 150 \end{aligned}$

Word equation (2): The clothes shop sells a navy suit and a black suit for a total of €250.

Maths equation (2): $x + y = 250$

If y = 150, we can now find the value of x:

$\begin{aligned} x + y &= 250 \\ x + 150 &= 250 \\ x &= 250 - 150 \\ x &= 100 \end{aligned}$

Cost of navy suit = x = €100   Cost of black suit = y = €150

Exercise 6.11

1. The sum of two numbers is 25. Twice the first number plus the second number is equal to 35. Find the two numbers.

2. The sum of two numbers is 20. The difference between the two numbers is 5. Find the two numbers.

3. The sum of two numbers is 45. The first is 11 greater than the second. Find the two numbers.

4. Three soft drinks and six bars cost €9. Five soft drinks and two bars cost €11. Write down two equations and hence find the cost of each item.

5. A pen and a pencil cost €1. Four pens and two pencil cost €3.40. Write down two equations and hence find the cost of each item.

6. A bar and a drink cost €1.90. Five bars and two drinks cost €7.40. Write down the two equations and hence find the cost of each item.

7. Find the value of x and y in the following rectangle.

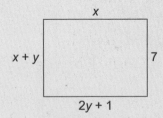

8. In an election Alan receives 105 more votes than Carol. The total number of votes cast was 735. How many votes did each candidate receive?

9. Chris has €99 to spend. He can buy either two computer games and five music CDs or one computer game and 10 music CDs. How much does each item cost?

10. A shop sells 50 sofas in a week. A leather sofa sells for €1,000 and a fabric sofa sells for €750. The shop sells €42,500 worth of these types of sofas.

How many of each type does the shop sell?

11. Sheena spends €100 on a coat and bag. During a sale, the same coat and bag are sold at $\frac{3}{5}$ and $\frac{1}{4}$ the price that Sheena paid for them. She would have saved herself €54 if she had bought these items in the sale.

How much did the coat and bag cost originally?

12. Barbara gets €1.50 for her pocket money each week. One week she spends all of her pocket money on nine toffees and three ice-pops. The next week she spends it all on five toffees and 10 ice-pops.

Find the cost of each item.

13. The first two sections of a race are x and y metres long. Henry runs the first part of the race at 3 m/s and the second part at 6 m/s. George runs the same sections at 5 m/s and 3 m/s. It takes Henry half a minute to run these two sections, whereas it takes George 46 seconds to do the same distance.

How long are these two sections of the race?

14. One-third of a number is four more than one-half of another number. The first number is one more than twice the second.

Find the two numbers.

15. Karl's and Eddie's ages added together are equal to 65. Ten years ago, Karl was twice as old as Eddie. How old are they now?

Revision Exercises

1. Solve these equations:

   (a) (i) $2x + 5 = 11$

   (ii) $7x + 1 = 43$

   (iii) $8x - 5 = 19$

   (iv) $11x - 7 = 81$

   (v) $5 = 2x - 11$

   (b) (i) $\dfrac{x + 4}{3} = \dfrac{x + 1}{2}$

   (ii) $\dfrac{x + 1}{5} = \dfrac{x}{3} - 1$

   (iii) $\dfrac{5x + 1}{3} = \dfrac{x + 1}{2} + 8$

   (c) (i) $x + 3y = 7$ (iii) $2x + 3y = 25$
   $\ 2x - y = 0$ $4x - y = 1$

   (ii) $x + y = 8$ (iv) $x + y = 10$
   $\ 2x - y = 7$ $x - y = 4$

2. (a) Solve these equations:

   (i) $9x + 8 = 6x + 20$

   (ii) $x + 1 = 7 - x$

   (iii) $2x + 1 = 8x - 53$

   (iv) $5x + 7 = 9x - 5$

   (v) $15x - 1 = 9x - 19$

   (b) List the elements of each of the following:

   (i) $2x < 8, x \in N$

   (ii) $x + 3 \leqslant 8, x \in N$

   (iii) $2x + 1 \leqslant 7, x \in N$

   (c) (i) There are 44 people in a room. If n of them are adults, how many are children?

   (ii) Marie is x years old. Her brother, Ned, is 5 years older. Oliver, their father, is three times as old as Ned. The sum total of their three ages is 95. How old is Marie?

3. (a) Solve these equations:

  (i) $x + 17 = 27 - 9x$

  (ii) $5(x + 7) = 25(x - 1)$

  (iii) $8(x + 3) = 5(x + 6)$

  (iv) $5(x + 1) + 1 = 12(x - 3)$

  (v) $4(x + 7) = 5(2 - x)$

(b) In each case below, write the variable in the square bracket in terms of the other variables.

  (i) $y = pq - t$ [q]

  (ii) $p = tv$ [t]

  (iii) $ax + by + c = 0$ [a]

  (iv) $z = 2(4x - y)$ [x]

  (v) $t = a + (n - 1)d$ [a]

  (vi) $t = a + (n - 1)d$ [d]

  (vii) $A = 2\pi rh$ [r]

(c) (i) There are 53 people in a room. x of them are children. The adults are divided equally into male and female. Write down an expression for the number of female adults in the room.

  (ii) The sum of two numbers is 21. Twice the first number added to three times the other is equal to 52. Find the numbers.

4. (a) Solve these equations:

  (i) $9(2x - 3) = 25(x - 1) + 5$

  (ii) $2(x + 7) - 5(x - 1) = 13$

  (iii) $3(x - 1) = x + 2$

  (iv) $5(x - 1) = 2(x + 2) - x$

  (v) $5x - 1 - 2(x + 2) = x$

(b) Solve these simultaneous equations:

  (i) $x + 3y = 2$ (iv) $5x - 3y = 1$

      $2x + y = 9$ $x - y = 0$

  (ii) $x + y = 1$ (v) $x = y + 7$

      $2x + y = -1$ $2x + 5y = 0$

  (iii) $x - 3y = 4$

       $5x - 2y = 7$

(c) (i) There are n people in a town. Two-fifths of them are female. Two hundred males leave the town. How many males remain?

  (ii) I have 20 coins. All of them are either 1 euro coins or 50 cent coins. They are worth €11. How many euro coins and how many 50 cent coins do I have?

5. (a) Solve these equations:

  (i) $\dfrac{4x + 1}{5} + 1 = x$

  (ii) $\dfrac{2x - 1}{5} = \dfrac{x + 2}{3}$

  (iii) $\dfrac{1}{3}x - \dfrac{1}{4}x = 2$

  (iv) $\dfrac{x + 1}{5} - \dfrac{x + 9}{4} = 1 - \dfrac{x + 19}{6}$

(b) Show on the numberline the solution set for each of the following:

  (i) $4x + 1 > 13, x \in Z$

  (ii) $2x - 1 \leqslant 13, x \in N$

  (iii) $5x + 7 \leqslant 27, x \in R$

  (iv) $3 - 2x > 7, x \in R$

  (v) $13 - 5x \geqslant -7, x \in R$

(c) (i) Write 34 as the sum of two numbers such that two-thirds of the larger number is equal to three-quarters of the smaller number.

  (ii) Find two numbers, such that seven times the first is 1 more than twice the second, and twice the first added to three times the second gives 36.

6. (a) Show on the numberline the solution set for each of the following:

  (i) $3 + 3x < x + 11, x \in R$

  (ii) $8 - 2x \leqslant x - 7, x \in R$

  (iii) $1 - 12x \geqslant 10x - 65, x \in R$

  (iv) $8(x - 3) > x + 4, x \in R$

  (v) $\dfrac{2}{5}x + \dfrac{1}{2} \leqslant \dfrac{9}{10}, x \in R$

(b) In each case, write the variable in the square bracket in terms of the other variables:

   (i) $2(s - 3t) = q$ [t]

   (ii) $v = \dfrac{1}{3}\pi r^2 h$ [h]

   (iii) $v^2 = u^2 + 2as$ [a]

   (iv) $v^2 = u^2 + 2as$ [u]

   (v) $v^2 = u^2 + 2as$ [s]

   (vi) $v(2 - 3a) = u(b - c)$ [c]

(c) (i) Two apples and an orange cost 32 cent. Three apples and five oranges cost 90 cent.
   Find the cost of an apple and the cost of an orange.

   (ii) Find three consecutive numbers such that the sum of one-half of the smallest, one-fifth of the middle one and one-quarter of the largest is equal to 14.

7. (a) Solve the following linear equations by graphing:

   (i) $5x - 10 = 20$ (iii) $-7x + 21 = 21$

   (ii) $-3 + 4x = 9$

(b) Solve the following simultaneous equations by graphing each line. Check your answer using algebra.

   (i) $4x - 5y = 12$ (ii) $5x + 7y = -6$
       $x + 2y = -10$ $-2x + y = 10$

   Explain which method gives a more accurate answer.

8. (a) (i) (1) Find the solution set E of:
       $4x - 1 \leqslant 13, x \in Z$

   (2) Find the solution set F of:
       $1 - 3x \leqslant 7, x \in Z$

   (3) List the elements of E ∩ F.

   (ii) (1) Find the solution set E of:
       $3x + 1 < 16, x \in R$

   (2) Find the solution set F of:
       $1 - 4x \leqslant 17, x \in R$

   (3) Show E ∩ F on a numberline.

   (iii) (1) Find the solution set E of:
       $9x + 1 \leqslant 46, x \in N$

   (2) Find the solution set F of:
       $21 - 8x \geqslant 5, x \in N$

   (3) List the elements of E \ F.

(b) Solve these equations:

   (i) $\dfrac{x - 1}{3} - \dfrac{x + 2}{6} - \dfrac{x - 6}{4} = 0$

   (ii) $\dfrac{1}{4}(5x + 1) - \dfrac{4x - 7}{3} = 1\dfrac{5}{12}$

   (iii) $\dfrac{1}{7}(6x - 1) + \dfrac{1}{6}(2x + 5) = 1 - \dfrac{3}{14}(x + 8)$

   (iv) $\dfrac{3}{4}(3x + 1) = \dfrac{2}{3}(5x - 1) - 4$

(c) (i) I have 12 coins in my pocket. All of them are either 10 cent coins or 50 cent coins. They are worth €2.40. How many 10 cent coins and how many 50 cent coins do I have?

   (ii) Graham is x years old. Hilda is three times as old. In four years' time, Hilda's age will be twice Graham's age. How old are they now?

9. (a) Solve these simultaneous equations:

   (i) $5x - 3y - 11 = 0$
       $3x + 10y + 17 = 0$

   (ii) $2x - 3y - 2 = 0$
        $3x + 8y - 3 = 0$

   (iii) $4(x - 3) + 3(y + 1) = 10$
         $6(x - 4) + 5y = 5$

   (iv) $5x - 12y - 17 = 0$
        $\dfrac{1}{9}(x + 2) - (y + 1) + \dfrac{3}{2} = 0$

   (v) $y = \dfrac{x + 3y}{5} + 5$
       $3x + 5y - 46 = 0$

(b) In each case, write the variable in the square bracket in terms of the other variables:

   (i) $ax = c - kx$ [x]

   (ii) $r = 1 = rs + c$ [r]

   (iii) $\dfrac{a - b}{k} = a$ [a]

   (iv) $\dfrac{a - b}{b + 1} = c$ [b]

   (v) $\dfrac{a - 5c}{c + 1} = d$ [c]

(c) (i) I mix x kg of Kenyan tea (which costs €3 per kg) with y kg of China tea (which costs €4 per kg). I get a total of 10 kg of a blend, which costs €3.70 per kg.
   Find the values of x and y.

(ii) A blender mixes 2 kg of Kenyan tea worth 30 cent per kg with x kg of Indian tea worth 24 cent per kg. The mixture is worth 26 cent per kg. Find x.

10. (a) (i) Show on three separate numberlines the following sets:

(1) $E = \{x \mid 3 - 2x \leqslant 1, x \in N\}$

(2) $F = \left\{x \mid \dfrac{1}{2}x - \dfrac{2}{3} \leqslant \dfrac{5}{6}, x \in N\right\}$

(3) $F \cap E$

(ii) Show on three separate numberlines the following sets:

(1) $E = \{x \mid 15 - 4x \geqslant -1, x \in N\}$

(2) $F = \left\{x \mid \dfrac{2x + 1}{2} - \dfrac{x + 2}{3} \leqslant x \in N\right\}$

(3) $E \cap F$

(iii) Show on a numberline the set $\{x \mid -3 \leqslant x \leqslant 2, x \in Z\}$.

(b) Given the formula $\dfrac{2a - b}{3x} = c$:

(i) Write a in terms of the other variables.

(ii) Find the value of a if $x = 3$, $b = 5$ and $c = 7$.

(c) Darren is five times as old as his little sister, Stacey. In five years' time, Darren will be three times as old as Stacey. How old is Stacey now?

11. (a) 150 children have to go on a school tour. They can use minibuses, which carry x pupils each, or cars, which carry y pupils each. The Mathematics teacher works out that they could just manage with 10 minibuses and 6 cars, or with 5 minibuses and 18 cars.

Write down two equations in x and y to represent this information and, hence, find the value of x and y.

(b) Given the formula $S = \dfrac{a}{1 - r}$:

(i) Write r in terms of the other variables.

(ii) Find the value of r if $a = 10$ and $S = 40$.

(c) When the two digits of a two-digit number are added together, the answer is 12. The two-digit number obtained by swapping the digits around is 18 less than the original number.

Find the two digits.

12. (a) $\dfrac{2}{3}$ of a number is 10 more than $\dfrac{3}{7}$ of the number. What is the number?

(b) A guesthouse has 10 rooms to let. Some of these sleep two people and some sleep three people. On a certain day all rooms are taken and full. There are 23 people in the guesthouse that day.

How many of each kind of room are there?

(c) One-half of a number is one more than double another. Two-thirds of the first is one less than three times the second. Find the two numbers.

chapter 7

Algebra III

Learning Outcomes

In this chapter you will learn to:

- Solve quadratic equations using:
  - Factors
  - Quadratic formula
  - Trial and error
  - Graphs
- Form quadratic equations
- Solve problems using quadratic equations

7.1 SOLVING QUADRATIC EQUATIONS BY FACTORISING

Many problems that can be solved using algebra come down to one question. Can you find the value of the unknown when it is written in an equation?

This unknown is usually referred to as x.

A quadratic equation is of the form $ax^2 + bx + c = 0$, $a \neq 0$.
Solving quadratic equations means that we are finding the values of x that satisfy the equation.

One of the most common methods of solving a quadratic equation is to:

■ Find the factors of the equation.

■ Use these factors to find the solutions for the unknown.

You have already encountered this approach at Junior Certificate level.

Quadratic equations come in a variety of forms. To solve any quadratic equation, we usually must ensure that:

■ All the terms of the equation are on the same side of the equal sign.

■ The coefficient of x^2 is positive.

> For convenience, when discussing quadratics, we generally use the x variable in examples. However, other letters may be used instead of x.

ACTIVITY 7.1

KEY WORDS

■ **Solve**

■ **Solution**

■ **Roots**

■ **Factors**

■ **Highest common factor (HCF)**

■ **Difference of two squares**

■ **Quadratic trinomials**

■ **Quadratic formula**

■ **Co-ordinate plane**

Highest Common Factor

One type of quadratic equation is where we have an x^2 term and an x term only.

For example: $x^2 + 5x = 0$.

To solve equations of this type, we find the highest common factor (HCF).

x^2 Worked Example 7.1

Solve for x in each of the following:

    (i) $3x^2 - 8x = 0$

    (ii) $2x^2 = 10x$

Solution

(i) $3x^2 - 8x = 0$

$x(3x - 8) = 0$

$x = 0$ **OR** $3x - 8 = 0$

$3x = 8$

$x = 0$ **OR** $x = \dfrac{8}{3}$

(ii) $2x^2 = 10x$

First, we move the 10x term to the left-hand side.

$\Rightarrow 2x^2 - 10x = 0$

Then we divide all the terms by 2.

$x^2 - 5x = 0$

$x(x - 5) = 0$

$\quad\quad x = 0 \quad \textbf{OR} \quad x - 5 = 0$

$\quad\quad x = 0 \quad \textbf{OR} \quad\quad x = 5$

> An equation can sometimes be simplified by dividing a whole number evenly into all the terms. This can make finding the factors of the equation easier.

Difference of Two Squares

Another quadratic equation that we may be asked to solve is one that has only an x^2 term and a constant.

For example: $x^2 - 100 = 0$.

To solve equations of this type, we factorise using the **difference of two squares** method.

x^2 Worked Example 7.2

Solve:

(i) $y^2 - 36 = 0$ (ii) $4x^2 - 81 = 0$

Solution

(i) $y^2 - 36 = 0$

Method 1	Method 2
$y^2 - 36 = 0$ $(y)^2 - (6)^2 = 0$ $(y - 6)(y + 6) = 0$	$y^2 - 36 = 0$ $y^2 = 36$
$y - 6 = 0 \quad$ OR $\quad y + 6 = 0$ $\quad y = 6 \quad$ OR $\quad\quad y = -6$	$y = \pm\sqrt{36}$ $y = \pm 6$

(ii) $4x^2 - 81 = 0$

Method 1	Method 2
$4x^2 - 81 = 0$ $(2x)^2 - (9)^2 = 0$ $(2x - 9)(2x + 9) = 0$	$4x^2 - 81 = 0$ $4x^2 = 81$ $x^2 = \dfrac{81}{4}$
$2x - 9 = 0 \quad$ OR $\quad 2x + 9 = 0$ $\quad 2x = 9 \quad\quad\quad\quad 2x = -9$ $\quad x = \dfrac{9}{2} \quad$ OR $\quad\quad x = -\dfrac{9}{2}$	$x = \pm\sqrt{\dfrac{81}{4}}$ $x = \pm\dfrac{9}{2}$

Quadratic Trinomials

A quadratic trinomial in x has an x^2 term, an x term and a constant.

For example: $5x^2 + 22x + 8 = 0$.

x^2 Worked Example 7.3

Solve $3x^2 + 5x - 12 = 0$.

Solution

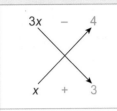

$$3x \times x = 3x^2 \checkmark$$
$$-4 \times 3 = -12 \checkmark$$

Using the arrows:

$$3x \times 3 = 9x$$
$$\underline{x \times -4 = -4x}$$
$$5x \checkmark$$

Let both factors equal 0 and solve:

$(3x - 4)(x + 3) = 0$

$3x - 4 = 0$	**OR**	$x + 3 = 0$
$3x = 4$	**OR**	$x = -3$
$x = \dfrac{4}{3}$	**OR**	$x = -3$

Alternatively, we can use the **Guide Number Method**.

Step 1: Multiply the coefficient of x^2 by the constant:

$$3x^2 + 5x - 12$$
$$3 \times -12 = -36$$

Step 2: Find two factors of -36 that will add up to give the middle term $5x$.

-4 and 9

Step 3: Use the answers from Step 2 to rewrite $3x^2 + 5x - 12$ as follows:

$3x^2 - 4x + 9x - 12$

$x(3x - 4) + 3(3x - 4)$ (Factorise by grouping)

$(x + 3)(3x - 4)$ (Distributive property)

$x + 3 = 0$	**OR**	$3x - 4 = 0$
$x = -3$	**OR**	$3x = 4$
$x = -3$	**OR**	$x = \dfrac{4}{3}$

x^2 Worked Example 7.4

Solve $10x^2 - 45x - 25 = 0$.

Solution

While we can factorise $10x^2 - 45x - 25$, it may be easier to factorise if we divide every term by 5 first.

$\Rightarrow 2x^2 - 9x - 5 = 0$

We will now factorise this equation.

$2x^2 - 9x - 5 = 0$

Let both factors equal 0 and solve:

$(2x + 1)(x - 5) = 0$

$2x + 1 = 0$	**OR**	$x - 5 = 0$
$2x = -1$	**OR**	$x = 5$
$x = -\dfrac{1}{2}$	**OR**	$x = 5$

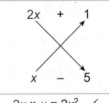

$$2x \times x = 2x^2 \checkmark$$
$$1 \times -5 = -5 \checkmark$$

Using the arrows:

$$2x \times -5 = -10x$$
$$\underline{x \times 1 = 1x}$$
$$-9x \checkmark$$

x^2 Worked Example 7.5

Solve $(x + 3)(2x - 3) = 11$.

Solution

To solve any quadratic it must be in the form $ax^2 + bx + c = 0$.

As this equation is not in the correct form, we first multiply out the brackets.

$$(x + 3)(2x - 3) = 11$$
$$x(2x - 3) + 3(2x - 3) = 11$$
$$2x^2 - 3x + 6x - 9 = 11$$
$$2x^2 + 3x - 9 = 11$$

We bring all the terms over to one side.

$$2x^2 + 3x - 9 - 11 = 0$$
$$2x^2 + 3x - 20 = 0$$

We will now factorise this equation.

$$2x^2 + 3x - 20 = 0$$
$$(2x - 5)(x + 4) = 0$$
$$2x - 5 = 0 \quad \textbf{OR} \quad x + 4 = 0$$
$$2x = 5 \quad \textbf{OR} \quad x = -4$$
$$x = \frac{5}{2} \quad \textbf{OR} \quad x = -4$$

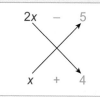

$2x \quad - \quad 5$

$x \quad + \quad 4$

$2x \times x = 2x^2$ ✔

$-5 \times 4 = -20$ ✔

Using the arrows:

$2x \times 4 = 8x$

$x \times -5 = -5x$

$3x$ ✔

Exercise 7.1

Solve the following equations:

1. $x^2 + 7x + 12 = 0$

2. $x^2 + 10x + 9 = 0$

3. $x^2 - 3x - 10 = 0$

4. $x^2 + 17x + 72 = 0$

5. $x^2 + 2x - 15 = 0$

6. $x^2 - x - 72 = 0$

7. $x^2 - \frac{5}{2}x + 1 = 0$

8. $2x^2 + 3x = 0$

9. $x^2 - 81 = 0$

10. $5x^2 + 19x + 12 = 0$

11. $5x^2 + 33x + 18 = 0$

12. $7x^2 - 24x + 9 = 0$

13. $12x^2 - 36x = 0$

14. $9x^2 - 9 = 0$

15. $2x^2 + 13x - 45 = 0$

16. $2x^2 - 8x - 10 = 0$

17. $5x^2 - 4x - 33 = 0$

18. $2x^2 - \frac{15}{2}x + \frac{9}{2} = 0$

19. $49y^2 - 225 = 0$

20. $7x^2 - 40x - 12 = 0$

21. $11x^2 - 121x = 0$

22. $3x^2 - \frac{4}{15}x - \frac{1}{15} = 0$

23. $5x^2 + 34x - 7 = 0$

24. $2x^2 - 4x + 2 = 0$

25. $3x^2 + \dfrac{1}{10}x = \dfrac{1}{25}$

26. $5x^2 - 14x - 24 = 0$

27. $2x^2 - 5x - 12 = 0$

28. $3x^2 + 5x - 8 = 0$

29. $144x^2 = 16$

30. $3x^2 - 21x - 24 = 0$

31. $7x^2 - 40x - 12 = 0$

32. $3x^2 - 51x + 126 = 0$

33. $6x^2 + 13x + 2 = 0$

34. $3x^2 = x$

35. $2x^2 - \dfrac{1}{32} = 0$

36. $10x^2 + 15x - 10 = 0$

37. $7x^2 + 41x + 30 = 0$

38. $6x^2 + 7x - 5 = 0$

39. $10x^2 - 7x = 0$

40. $-400 = -100x^2$

41. $10x^2 + 48x + 32 = 0$

42. $6x^2 + 8x - 14 = 0$

43. $14x^2 + 15x - 9 = 0$

44. $9x^2 + 42x + 24 = 0$

45. $2x^2 - \dfrac{27}{2}x + \dfrac{13}{4} = 0$

46. $(2x + 1)(x - 4) = 0$

47. $(2 + x)(8 - x) = 9$

48. $(x + 1)(x - 1) = 99$

49. $(x - 1)(x + 1) = 5x + 13$

50. $13x + 30 = 3x^2$

51. $6 - 31x = -5x^2$

52. $10x^2 = 3x + 4$

53. $\dfrac{x^2}{7} + \dfrac{x}{14} - \dfrac{3}{2} = 0$

54. $\dfrac{x^2}{4} + \dfrac{7}{20}x + \dfrac{1}{10} = 0$

7.2 SOLVING QUADRATIC EQUATIONS BY FORMULA 1

There are alternative methods of solving quadratic equations. One approach is to use the quadratic formula shown:

We can use this formula instead of factorising an equation and finding its roots.

Many quadratic equations cannot be solved by factorisation because they do not have simple factors. Using the quadratic formula will allow you to solve **any** quadratic equation (provided it can be solved).

When using the quadratic formula, it is important to note that in, for example, the equation $x^2 - 2x - 8$:

- $a = 1$; the coefficient of x^2
- $b = -2$; the coefficient of x
- $c = -8$; the constant

To use the quadratic formula, we should ensure that:

- All the terms of the equation are on the same side of the equal sign.
- The a value is positive (this is just to make calculations easier).

> The symbol $\pm$ requires two procedures:
>
> (i) Add $\sqrt{b^2 - 4ac}$ to $-b$ in the numerator.
>
> (ii) Subtract $\sqrt{b^2 - 4ac}$ from $-b$ in the numerator.

FORMULA

$$x = \dfrac{-b \pm \sqrt{b^2 - 4ac}}{2a}$$

a = coefficient of x^2
b = coefficient of x
c = constant term

This formula appears on page 20 of *Formulae and Tables*.

x^2 Worked Example 7.6

Solve $2x^2 + 5x - 12 = 0$.

Solution

Using the quadratic formula $x = \dfrac{-b \pm \sqrt{b^2 - 4ac}}{2a}$:

$a = 2 \qquad b = 5 \qquad c = -12$

$x = \dfrac{-(5) \pm \sqrt{(5)^2 - 4(2)(-12)}}{2(2)}$

> Use brackets as shown.

$x = \dfrac{-5 \pm \sqrt{25 + 96}}{4}$

$x = \dfrac{-5 \pm \sqrt{121}}{4}$

$x = \dfrac{-5 \pm 11}{4}$

We now use the $\pm$ sign:

$x = \dfrac{-5 + 11}{4}$ **OR** $x = \dfrac{-5 - 11}{4}$

$x = \dfrac{6}{4}$ $\qquad\qquad x = \dfrac{-16}{4}$

$x = \dfrac{3}{2}$ **OR** $x = -4$

x^2 Worked Example 7.7

Find the roots of the equation $6x^2 - 7x = 24$.

> Remember, if we are asked to find the roots, we are being asked to solve.

Solution

Before we try to solve the equation, we make sure that all terms are on the same side of the equal sign and that the x^2 term is positive.

$6x^2 - 7x = 24$

$\Rightarrow 6x^2 - 7x - 24 = 0$

Using the quadratic formula $x = \dfrac{-b \pm \sqrt{b^2 - 4ac}}{2a}$:

$a = 6 \qquad b = -7 \qquad c = -24$

$x = \dfrac{-(-7) \pm \sqrt{(-7)^2 - 4(6)(-24)}}{2(6)}$

$x = \dfrac{7 \pm \sqrt{49 + 576}}{12}$

$x = \dfrac{7 \pm \sqrt{625}}{12}$

$x = \dfrac{7 \pm 25}{12}$

$x = \dfrac{7 + 25}{12}$ **OR** $x = \dfrac{7 - 25}{12}$

$x = \dfrac{32}{12}$ $\qquad\qquad x = \dfrac{-18}{12}$

$x = \dfrac{8}{3}$ **OR** $x = -\dfrac{3}{2}$

ACTIVITY 7.2

Exercise 7.2

Solve the following equations using the quadratic formula.

1. $x^2 + 6x + 5 = 0$

2. $x^2 + 5x - 14 = 0$

3. $x^2 - 7x + 12 = 0$

4. $x^2 + x - 12 = 0$

5. $x^2 + 5x - 36 = 0$

6. $x^2 + \dfrac{5}{2}x - 6 = 0$

7. $2x^2 + 11x + 14 = 0$

8. $3x^2 + 2x - 5 = 0$

9. $4x^2 + 3x - 7 = 0$

10. $7x^2 - 5x - 2 = 0$

11. $3x^2 - 26x - 9 = 0$

12. $2x^2 + 15x - 27 = 0$

13. $13x^2 - 8x - 5 = 0$

14. $5x^2 + 28x - 12 = 0$

15. $2x^2 + \dfrac{8}{7}x + \dfrac{1}{14} = 0$

16. $3x^2 + 3x - 6 = 0$

17. $14x^2 - 51x + 7 = 0$

18. $3y^2 - 19y + 28 = 0$

19. $2x^2 - x - 10 = 0$

20. $5x^2 - 9x + 4 = 0$

21. $3x^2 - \dfrac{7}{4}x + \dfrac{1}{8} = 0$

22. $7a^2 + 21a + 14 = 0$

23. $12x^2 + 34x + 20 = 0$

24. $x^2 + x - 132 = 0$

25. $4x^2 - 30x + 14 = 0$

26. $2x^2 = -39x - 85$

27. $9x^2 - \dfrac{3}{4}x = 0$

28. $5x^2 - 17x = 12$

29. $x^2 - 64 = 0$

30. $10x^2 - 2\dfrac{1}{8}x - \dfrac{5}{16} = 0$

31. $2x^2 = 5x$

32. $-3x^2 + 21x = 0$

33. $\dfrac{x^2}{12} + \dfrac{x}{2} + \dfrac{3}{4} = 0$

34. $\dfrac{5}{2}x^2 + \dfrac{11}{12}x = \dfrac{1}{6}$

7.3 SOLVING QUADRATIC EQUATIONS BY FORMULA 2

One of the main reasons for using the quadratic formula instead of other methods is when the roots of the equation are decimals or surds.

x^2 Worked Example 7.8

Solve, to two decimal places, $8x^2 - x - 15 = 0$.

Solution

We know that we have to use the quadratic formula, as the question asks for the solution to be given to a decimal place.

Using the quadratic formula $x = \dfrac{-b \pm \sqrt{b^2 - 4ac}}{2a}$:

$a = 8 \qquad b = -1 \qquad c = -15$

$x = \dfrac{-(-1) \pm \sqrt{(-1)^2 - 4(8)(-15)}}{2(8)}$

$x = \dfrac{1 \pm \sqrt{1 + 480}}{16}$

$x = \dfrac{1 \pm \sqrt{481}}{16}$

$x = \dfrac{1 \pm 21.9317122}{16}$

As we are asked to give our answer to two decimal places, we can change 21.9317122 to four decimal places to help simplify our calculations.

$x = \dfrac{1 + 21.9317}{16}$ **OR** $x = \dfrac{1 - 21.9317}{16}$

$x = \dfrac{22.9317}{16}$ $\qquad x = \dfrac{-20.9317}{16}$

$x = 1.4332$ **OR** $x = -1.3082$

Answer, to two decimal places:

$x = 1.43$ **OR** $x = -1.31$

The quadratic formula can also be used when we are asked to express the roots of an equation in surd (square root) form.

x^2 Worked Example 7.9

Find the roots of the equation $2x^2 + 8x + 3 = 2$, leaving the answer in surd form.

> Remember, if we are asked to find the roots, we are being asked to solve.

Solution

Again, we make sure that all terms are on the same side of the equal sign and that the x^2 term is positive.

$$2x^2 + 8x + 3 - 2 = 0$$

$$2x^2 + 8x + 1 = 0$$

Using the quadratic formula:

$$a = 2 \quad b = 8 \quad c = 1$$

$$x = \frac{-(8) \pm \sqrt{(8)^2 - 4(2)(1)}}{2(2)}$$

$$x = \frac{-8 \pm \sqrt{64 - 8}}{4}$$

$$x = \frac{-8 \pm \sqrt{56}}{4}$$

Our answer must be in surd form, so we simplify $\sqrt{56}$:

$$x = \frac{-8 \pm \sqrt{4 \times 14}}{4}$$

Most calculators will give the following answer:

$$x = \frac{-8 \pm 2\sqrt{14}}{4}$$

This answer can then be simplified further by dividing all terms by their highest common factor, in this case 2:

$$\therefore x = \frac{-4 \pm \sqrt{14}}{2}$$

$$x = \frac{-4 + \sqrt{14}}{2} \quad \textbf{OR} \quad x = \frac{-4 - \sqrt{14}}{2}$$

 ACTIVITY 7.3

Exercise 7.3

Use the quadratic formula to solve each of the following equations.

> 1 d.p. = Answer to one decimal place.
>
> 2 d.p. = Answer to two decimal places.
>
> 3 d.p. = Answer to three decimal places.
>
> 4 d.p. = Answer to four decimal places.
>
> Surd = answer in surd form.

1. $x^2 + 4x + 2 = 0$ (1 d.p.)

2. $x^2 + 9x + 6 = 0$ (1 d.p.)

3. $2x^2 + 9x + 1 = 0$ (2 d.p.)

4. $x^2 - 5x - 28 = 0$ (2 d.p.)

5. $x^2 - \frac{4}{5}x - \frac{1}{2} = 0$ (2 d.p.)

6. $6x^2 + 9x + 2 = 0$ (1 d.p.)

7. $2x^2 - 3x - 23 = 0$ (2 d.p.)

8. $9x^2 + 6x + 1 = 0$ (3 d.p.)

9. $6x^2 - 2x - 9 = 0$ (1 d.p.)

10. $3x^2 - \frac{8}{3}x - \frac{7}{2} = 0$ (1 d.p.)

11. $3x^2 + 5x - 15 = 0$ (2 d.p.)

12. $7x^2 - 8x - 16 = 0$ (1 d.p.)

13. $x^2 + 6x + 4 = 0$ (surd)

14. $x^2 - 8x + 9 = 0$ (surd)

15. $5x^2 + 2x - 25 = 0$ (surd)

16. $3x^2 - x - 13 = 0$ (2 d.p.)

17. $6b^2 + 8b - 13 = 0$ (1 d.p.)

18. $5x^2 - \dfrac{10}{3}x + \dfrac{1}{9} = 0$ (surd)

19. $8x^2 + 8x - 3 = 0$ (surd)

20. $7x^2 + 4x - 4 = 0$ (surd)

21. $5x^2 - 2x - 11 = 0$ (2 d.p.)

22. $4x^2 + 2x - 21 = 0$ (1 d.p.)

23. $4x^2 + \dfrac{1}{2}x - \dfrac{3}{7} = 0$ (3 d.p.)

24. $5x^2 + 4x - 3 = 0$ (surd)

25. $5x^2 + 2x - 28 = 0$ (surd)

26. $7x^2 + 4x - 2 = 0$ (surd)

27. $4x^2 = -x + 6$ (3 d.p.)

28. $17 - 9x^2 = 9$ (4 d.p.)

29. $0 = 3x^2 + 6x - 10$ (surd)

30. $-\dfrac{4}{5}x^2 + \dfrac{3}{2}x = \dfrac{2}{3}$ (2 d.p.)

7.4 SOLVING EQUATIONS INVOLVING FRACTIONS

x^2 Worked Example 7.10

Solve: $\dfrac{1}{y + 1} + \dfrac{2}{2y - 1} = 1,\, y \neq \dfrac{1}{2}, -1$

Solution

$\dfrac{1}{y + 1} + \dfrac{2}{2y - 1} = \dfrac{1}{1}$

The LCD is $(1)(y + 1)(2y - 1)$.

Multiply all terms by the LCD.

$$\frac{1(1)(y + 1)(2y - 1)}{y + 1} + \frac{2(1)(y + 1)(2y - 1)}{2y - 1} = 1(1)(y + 1)(2y - 1)$$

$$(2y - 1) + 2(y + 1) = (y + 1)(2y - 1)$$

$$2y - 1 + 2y + 2 = 2y^2 - y + 2y - 1$$

$$4y + 1 = 2y^2 + y - 1$$

$$2y^2 - 3y - 2 = 0$$

$$(2y + 1)(y - 2) = 0$$

$$2y + 1 = 0 \quad \textbf{OR} \quad y - 2 = 0$$

$$2y = -1 \quad \textbf{OR} \quad y = 2$$

$$y = -\frac{1}{2} \quad \textbf{OR} \quad y = 2$$

x^2 Worked Example 7.11

Solve to two decimal places: $\dfrac{2}{3x-1} - \dfrac{5}{x-3} = \dfrac{2}{3}$, $x \neq \dfrac{1}{3}$, 3

Solution

$\dfrac{2}{3x-1} - \dfrac{5}{x-3} = \dfrac{2}{3}$

The LCD is $(3)(3x-1)(x-3)$.

$\therefore \dfrac{2(3)(3x-1)(x-3)}{3x-1} - \dfrac{5(3)(3x-1)(x-3)}{x-3} = \dfrac{2(3)(3x-1)(x-3)}{3}$

$2(3)(x-3) - 5(3)(3x-1) = 2(3x-1)(x-3)$

$6(x-3) - 15(3x-1) = 2(3x^2 - 9x - x + 3)$

$6x - 18 - 45x + 15 = 2(3x^2 - 10x + 3)$

$-39x - 3 = 6x^2 - 20x + 6$

$6x^2 + 19x + 9 = 0$

Using the quadratic formula: $x = \dfrac{-b \pm \sqrt{b^2 - 4ac}}{2a}$

$a = 6 \qquad b = 19 \qquad c = 9$

$x = \dfrac{-19 \pm \sqrt{(19)^2 - 4(6)(9)}}{2(6)}$

$x = \dfrac{-19 \pm \sqrt{361 - 216}}{12}$

$x = \dfrac{-19 \pm \sqrt{145}}{12}$

$x = \dfrac{-19 + \sqrt{145}}{12}$ **OR** $x = \dfrac{-19 - \sqrt{145}}{12}$

$x = -0.58$ **OR** $x = -2.59$ (correct to two decimal places)

Exercise 7.4

Solve the following equations:

1. $\dfrac{5}{x} + \dfrac{2}{x} = 7$, $x \neq 0$

2. $x + \dfrac{1}{x} = 2$, $x \neq 0$

3. $3x - 5 + \dfrac{2}{x} = 0$, $x \neq 0$

4. $\dfrac{1}{x} + \dfrac{9}{x+8} = 1$, $x \neq 0, -8$

5. $\dfrac{1}{x+3} + \dfrac{1}{x} = \dfrac{7}{10}$, $x \neq -3, 0$

6. $\dfrac{1}{x+4} + \dfrac{1}{x+1} = \dfrac{1}{2}$, $x \neq -4, -1$

7. $\dfrac{2}{x+1} + \dfrac{4}{2x-1} = 2$, $x \neq -1, \dfrac{1}{2}$

8. $\dfrac{5}{x+1} - \dfrac{3}{3x-1} = 1$, $x \neq -1, \dfrac{1}{3}$

9. $10 - \dfrac{5}{6x-1} = \dfrac{15}{2x+1}$, $x \neq \dfrac{1}{6}, -\dfrac{1}{2}$

10. $\dfrac{1}{x+1} + \dfrac{2}{x+3} = \dfrac{11}{15}$, $x \neq -1, -3$

11. $\dfrac{4}{2x-5} - \dfrac{3}{5x-1} = -3$, $x \neq \dfrac{5}{2}, \dfrac{1}{5}$

Using the quadratic formula, solve the following equations to two decimal places:

12. $\dfrac{1}{2x-3} = 5 - \dfrac{4}{3x}$, $x \neq 0, \dfrac{3}{2}$

13. $\dfrac{1}{x+3} + \dfrac{1}{x+4} = 2$, $x \neq -3, -4$

14. $\dfrac{2}{x-3} + \dfrac{4}{x+2} = 1$, $x \neq 3, -2$

15. $\dfrac{5}{2x-1} - \dfrac{3}{7x-2} = 5$, $x \neq \dfrac{1}{2}, \dfrac{2}{7}$

16. $\dfrac{4}{x-5} - \dfrac{1}{2x+4} = \dfrac{1}{3}$, $x \neq 5, -2$

7.5 FORMING QUADRATIC EQUATIONS

If we are given the roots of an equation, it is possible to work backwards to find a possible equation that was solved. This process involves first changing the roots into factors and then, using these factors, finding the equation.

Roots
$x = -2$ OR $x = -4$

↓

Factors
$(x + 2)(x + 4)$

↓

Equation
$(x + 2)(x + 4) = 0$
$\Rightarrow x^2 + 6x + 8 = 0$

x^2 Worked Example 7.12

Form a quadratic equation from each of the following pairs of roots:

    (i) 3, 7   (ii) −5, −1

Solution

(i) 3, 7

Let the two roots equal x.	$x = 3$	$x = 7$
Write as factors.	$x - 3 = 0$	$x - 7 = 0$
Multiply the factors and put equal to 0 to find the equation.	$(x - 3)(x - 7) = 0$	
	$x(x - 7) - 3(x - 7) = 0$	
	$x^2 - 7x - 3x + 21 = 0$	
	$x^2 - 10x + 21 = 0$	

(ii) −5, −1

$x = -5$	$x = -1$
$x + 5 = 0$	$x + 1 = 0$
$(x + 5)(x + 1) = 0$	
$x(x + 1) + 5(x + 1) = 0$	
$x^2 + x + 5x + 5 = 0$	
$x^2 + 6x + 5 = 0$	

Exercise 7.5

Form a quadratic equation with the following pairs of roots:

1. 3 and 4
2. 2 and 5
3. −1, 2
4. −3, −3
5. 11, −1
6. 7, 0

7. −8 and 8
8. 0, −4
9. ± 3
10. $p, 2p$
11. p, q
12. $p, -p$

13. The roots of a quadratic equation $x^2 + bx + c = 0$ are 5 and 3. Find the values of b and c.

14. The roots of a quadratic equation $x^2 + bx + c = 0$ are 0 and −6. Find the values of b and c.

15. The roots of a quadratic equation $x^2 + 8x + r = 0$ are the same. Find the value of r.

16. The roots of a quadratic equation $x^2 - 12x + c = 0$ are the same. Find the value of c.

7.6 SOLVING SIMULTANEOUS EQUATIONS: ONE LINEAR AND ONE NON-LINEAR

In the previous chapter, we learned how to solve simultaneous linear equations.

We may be asked to solve simultaneous equations where one of the equations is linear and the other is non-linear (but of order 2).

x^2 Worked Example 7.13

Solve the following simultaneous equations:

$x + 4y = 17$

$x^2 + y^2 = 34$

Solution

Step 1: **Linear**	We look first at the linear equation: $x + 4y = 17$ We pick the variable that has a coefficient of positive 1 and move the other terms to the other side of the equation. $x = 17 - 4y$

Step 2: **Substitution** Always substitute from the linear into the non-linear.	Next we consider the non-linear equation: $x^2 + y^2 = 34$ We now know that $x = 17 - 4y$ and so we substitute this expression into the non-linear equation. $(17 - 4y)^2 + y^2 = 34$ $(17 - 4y)(17 - 4y) + y^2 = 34$ $17(17 - 4y) - 4y(17 - 4y) + y^2 = 34$ $289 - 68y - 68y + 16y^2 + y^2 = 34$ $289 - 136y + 17y^2 = 34$ This now can be written as: $17y^2 - 136y + 289 = 34$ Bring every term over to one side. $17y^2 - 136y + 289 - 34 = 0$ $17y^2 - 136y + 255 = 0$
Step 3: **Solving**	To make solving easier, divide all the terms by 17. $y^2 - 8y + 15 = 0$ 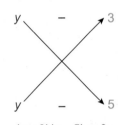 $(y - 3)(y - 5) = 0$ $y - 3 = 0$ OR $y - 5 = 0$ $y = 3$ OR $y = 5$
Step 4: **Solving other variable** Back to the **linear equation**	As we know the two values of y, we can now find the corresponding values of x. $x = 17 - 4y$ If $y = 3$: If $y = 5$: $x = 17 - 4(3)$ $x = 17 - 4(5)$ $x = 17 - 12$ $x = 17 - 20$ $x = 5$ $x = -3$
Step 5: **Write answer**	$x = 5, y = 3$ OR $x = -3, y = 5$ Answer: $(5,3)$ $(-3,5)$

x^2 **Worked Example 7.14**

Solve the simultaneous equations:

$y = 2x$

$x^2 - 2y^2 = -7$

Solution

Step 1: Linear	The linear equation is already in the correct form. $$y = 2x$$
Step 2: Substitution	$x^2 - 2y^2 = -7$ $x^2 - 2(2x)^2 = -7$ $x^2 - 2[(2x)(2x)] = -7$ $x^2 - 2(4x^2) = -7$ $x^2 - 8x^2 = -7$ $-7x^2 = -7$ The x^2 term is negative, so we can multiply across by -1. $$\therefore 7x^2 = 7$$
Step 3: Solving	$x^2 = 1$ Divide by 7 $x = \pm 1$
Step 4: Solving other variable	$y = 2x$ If $x = +1$: If $x = -1$: $\quad y = 2(1)$ $\quad y = 2(-1)$ $\quad y = 2$ $\quad y = -2$
Step 5: Write answer	$x = 1, y = 2$ **OR** $x = -1, y = -2$ Answer: $(1,2)$ $(-1,-2)$

ACTIVITY 7.4

Looking at the graph of $y = 2x$ and $x^2 - 2y^2 = -7$, we can see that the points of intersection of both graphs give us the solution of the simultaneous equation.

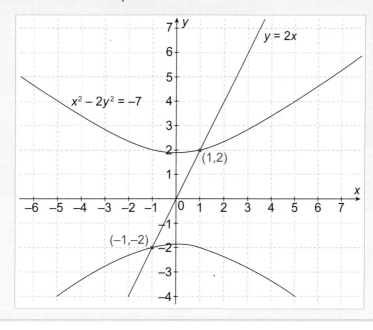

ALGEBRA III

Exercise 7.6

Solve the following simultaneous equations:

1. $x = 5 - y$
$x^2 + y^2 = 17$

2. $x = 1 + y$
$x^2 + y^2 = 25$

3. $x + y = 4$
$x^2 + y^2 = 16$

4. $x - y = 6$
$x^2 + y^2 = 26$

5. $y = -x - 2$
$x^2 - y^2 = 60$

6. $4x - y = -3$
$x^2 - y^2 = 0$

7. $x = y$
$x^2 + y^2 = 2$

8. $5x - y = -13$
$x^2 + y^2 = 13$

9. $x - 2y = -5$
$x^2 + y^2 = 10$

10. $x + 2y = 7$
$x^2 + 3y^2 = 28$

11. $x - 2y = -5$
$x^2 + y^2 = 85$

12. $x = y + 4$
$3x + y^2 = 16$

13. $x = y$
$x^2 + 2y = 35$

14. $x - y = 4$
$y^2 + 7x = 18$

15. $x - 2y = 1$
$x^2 - 3y^2 = 6$

16. $x + y = 7$
$xy = 12$

17. $x + 2y = 11$
$xy = 14$

18. $x - 2y + 1 = 0$
$x^2 - xy = 10$

19. $y = -2x$
$2x^2 - y^2 + xy = -16$

20. $2x = y + 3$
$x^2 + y^2 - 3xy = -45$

7.7 SOLVING QUADRATIC EQUATIONS BY TRIAL AND ERROR

When we are asked to solve an equation, we are being to ask to find the value of the unknown.

As with linear equations, one method is to:

- Make an educated guess as to what x may be.
- Check to see if your guess is correct by substituting your value into the equation.
- Keep repeating with another guess until you arrive at the correct solution.

 ACTIVITY 7.5

However, this method is complicated by the fact that, as shown in Activity 7.5, a quadratic equation usually has two solutions or two roots.

Unlike linear equations, quadratic equations do not follow a linear pattern and so it is more difficult to improve on our answer.

> Remember, trial and error may only give an estimate of the solution and not the exact answer that is required.

Another disadvantage of the trial-and-error method is that it can be time-consuming.

Worked Example 7.15

Using trial and error, find the two whole number solutions to the following quadratic equation:

$x^2 - 11x + 28 = 0$

Solution

A good place to start is to find the factors of the last term.

A pair of factors of 28 are 4 and 7, so we will substitute these two values for x into the equation.

x	$x^2 + 11x + 28$	= 0?	
4	$(4)^2 + 11(4) + 28$	= 88	✗
7	$(7)^2 + 11(7) + 28$	= 154	✗
−4	$(-4)^2 + 11(-4) + 28$	= 0	✓
−7	$(-7)^2 + 11(-7) + 28$	= 0	✓

Answer: $x = -4$ or -7

Worked Example 7.16

Using trial and error, find the one whole number root of $5x^2 - 7x - 6 = 0$.

Solution

x	$5x^2 - 7x - 6$	= 0?	
3	$5(3)^2 - 7(3) - 6$	= 18	✗
−3	$5(-3)^2 - 7(-3) - 6$	= 60	✗
2	$5(2)^2 - 7(2) - 6$	= 0	✓

Answer: $x = 2$

Exercise 7.7

1. Six possible roots are given for each equation. Use trial and error to determine the correct roots.

(i)

x	$x^2 + 5x + 4$	= 0?
1	$(\ )^2 + 5(\ ) + 4$	=
4	$(\ )^2 + 5(\ ) + 4$	=
−1	$(\ )^2 + 5(\ ) + 4$	=
2	$(\ )^2 + 5(\ ) + 4$	
−2	$(\ )^2 + 5(\ ) + 4$	
−4	$(\ )^2 + 5(\ ) + 4$	

(ii)

x	$x^2 - 12x + 32$	= 0?
4		
−4		
−2		
16		
8		
2		

(iii)

x	$x^2 - x - 12$	= 0?
0		
−1		
3		
−3		
4		
2		

2. Use trial and error to find one whole number root of each of the following equations.

   (i) $4x^2 + x - 3 = 0$

   (ii) $2x^2 - 3x - 27 = 0$

   (iii) $3x^2 + 24x + 45 = 0$

   (iv) $7x^2 + 32x - 15 = 0$

3. One root of the equation $4x^2 - 9x - 21 = 0$ lies between 3 and 4. Using trial and error, estimate this root.
   Give your answer to one decimal place.

7.8 SOLVING QUADRATIC EQUATIONS GRAPHICALLY

Another approach to solving a quadratic equation is to graph the equation.

From Activity 7.6, we can see that to find or estimate the roots of a quadratic equation, we read off the values of x where the graph intersects the x-axis.

ACTIVITY 7.6

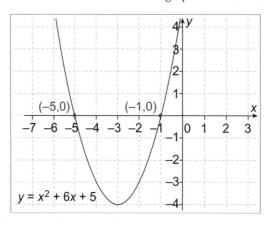

Roots: $x = -5$

OR

$x = -1$

As with trial and error, solving a quadratic equation by graphing may only give an estimate of the roots and not the exact answer.

x^2 Worked Example 7.17

(i) Match the equations graphed with the functions given.

(ii) Hence, find the roots to $x^2 + x - 2 = 0$ and $-x^2 + 2x + 3 = 0$.

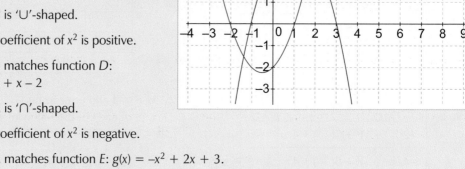

D: $f(x) = x^2 + x - 2$

E: $g(x) = -x^2 + 2x + 3$

Solution

(i) Graph B is '∪'-shaped.

∴ The coefficient of x^2 is positive.

Graph B matches function D:
$f(x) = x^2 + x - 2$

Graph A is '∩'-shaped.

∴ The coefficient of x^2 is negative.

Graph A matches function E: $g(x) = -x^2 + 2x + 3$.

(ii) Graph B crosses the x-axis at $x = -2$ and $x = 1$.
These are the roots of the equation $x^2 + x - 2 = 0$.

Graph A crosses the x-axis at $x = -1$ and $x = 3$.
These are the roots of the equation $-x^2 + 2x + 3 = 0$.

> **Remember:**
>
> - Coefficient of x^2 positive ⇒ ∪-shaped.
> - Coefficient of x^2 negative ⇒ ∩-shaped.

x^2 **Worked Example 7.18**

The graph of $y = 2x^2 - 6x + 4$ and $y = 4$ is shown.

(i) Explain the significance of the points A and B on this graph.

(ii) Check your answer by solving algebraically.

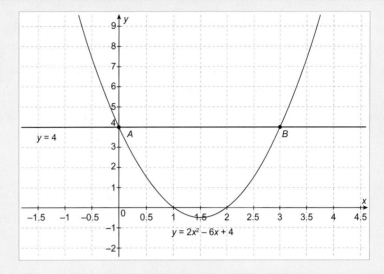

Solution

(i) At A, $x = 0$ and $y = 4$ for each function.

At B, $x = 3$ and $y = 4$ for each function.

(ii) Solve $2x^2 - 6x + 4 = 4$.

$$2x^2 - 6x + 4 - 4 = 0$$

$$2x^2 - 6x = 0$$

$$2x(x - 3) = 0$$

$$2x = 0 \quad \textbf{OR} \quad x - 3 = 0$$

$$x = 0 \quad \textbf{OR} \quad x = 3$$

$\therefore$ $A(0,4)$ and $B(3,4)$ are the points of intersection of the two functions.

x^2 **Worked Example 7.19**

Estimate the roots of $-x^2 + 7x - 8 = 0$ by graphing $f(x) = -x^2 + 7x - 8$ between $x = 0$ and $x = 7$.

Solution

We construct a table and substitute in our x-values to calculate our y-values.

x	$-x^2 + 7x - 8$	y	Point
0	$-(0)^2 + 7(0) - 8$	-8	$(0,-8)$
1	$-(1)^2 + 7(1) - 8$	-2	$(1,-2)$
2	$-(2)^2 + 7(2) - 8$	2	$(2,2)$
3	$-(3)^2 + 7(3) - 8$	4	$(3,4)$
4	$-(4)^2 + 7(4) - 8$	4	$(4,4)$
5	$-(5)^2 + 7(5) - 8$	2	$(5,2)$
6	$-(6)^2 + 7(6) - 8$	-2	$(6,-2)$
7	$-(7)^2 + 7(7) - 8$	-8	$(7,-8)$

We now plot our points on an x and y co-ordinate diagram and then draw a **curved** graph.

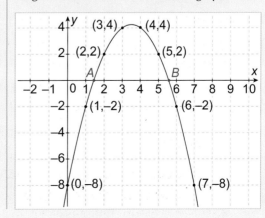

From our graph, we see that the points of intersection between the graph and the x-axis, points A and B, occur at approximately $x = 1.4$ and $x = 5.6$.

$\therefore x \approx 1.4$ or 5.6

When solving an equation graphically, we can usually solve up to one decimal place, depending on our graph.

$\approx$ is the symbol for 'approximately equal to'. We use this when we give a rough answer.

As with simultaneous linear equations, we can use graphs to solve simultaneous non-linear equations.

The solution, or roots, will be the point(s) of intersection between the linear and the quadratic graphs.

x^2 Worked Example 7.20

(i) Using the graph, find the points of intersection of the two equations shown.

(ii) Verify your answer.

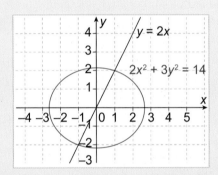

Solution

(i) We find the points of intersection between the two equations.

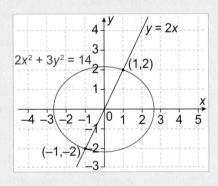

$\therefore x = 1, y = 2$ **OR** $x = -1, y = -2$

$(1,2)$ $\qquad\qquad$ $(-1,-2)$

(ii) Substitute back into the given equations.

	$y = 2x$	**$2x^2 + 3y^2 = 14$**
$(1, 2)$	$2 = 2(1)$	$2(1)^2 + 3(2)^2 = 14$
	$\therefore 2 = 2$ True	$2 + 12 = 14$ True

	$y = 2x$	**$2x^2 + 3y^2 = 14$**
$(-1,-2)$	$-2 = 2(-1)$	$2(-1)^2 + 3(-2)^2 = 14$
	$-2 = -2$ True	$2 + 12 = 14$ True

Exercise 7.8

1. In each graph, estimate the roots of the equation shown.

(i)
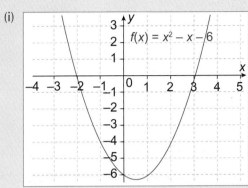
$f(x) = x^2 - x - 6$

(ii)
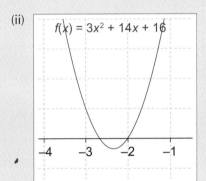
$f(x) = 3x^2 + 14x + 16$

(iii)
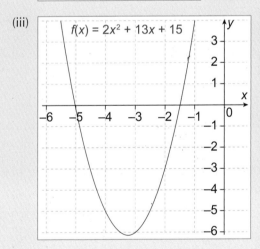
$f(x) = 2x^2 + 13x + 15$

(iv)
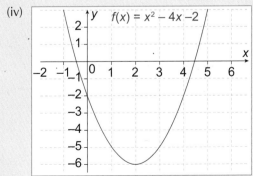
$f(x) = x^2 - 4x - 2$

(v)
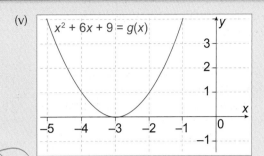
$x^2 + 6x + 9 = g(x)$

2. Estimate the point of intersection between the linear and non-linear graphs shown.
Interpret what these points of intersection represent in each case.

(i)
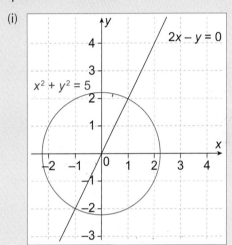
$2x - y = 0$
$x^2 + y^2 = 5$

(ii)
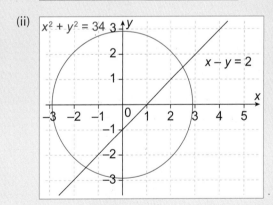
$x^2 + y^2 = 34$
$x - y = 2$

(iii)

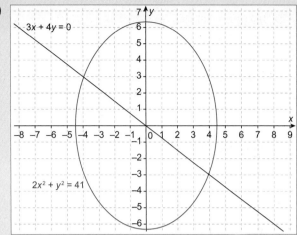

(iv)

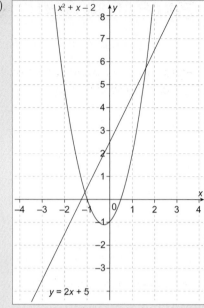

3. The graphs of three quadratic functions A, B and C are shown.

A: $x^2 - 9 = f(x)$

B: $x^2 + x - 6 = g(x)$

C: $-x^2 - 4x + 21 = h(x)$

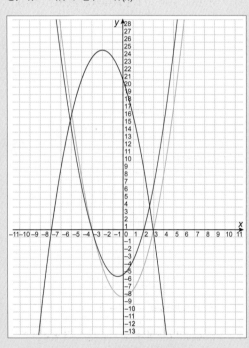

(i) Match each coloured graph to the correct function.

(ii) Hence, find the roots to each of the following:

$x^2 - 9 = 0$

$x^2 + x - 6 = 0$

$-x^2 - 4x + 21 = 0$

4. Graph the function $f(x) = 3x^2 - 11x + 8$ between $x = 0$ and $x = 4$.

Explain how you would use your graph to solve $f(x) = 0$.

5. Solve $x^2 - 3x - 4 = 0$ by graphing the function between $x = -2$ and $x = 5$.

6. Solve $x^2 - 6x + 6 = 0$ by graphing the function between $x = 0$ and $x = 6$.

7. Solve $-2x^2 - x + 6 = 0$ by graphing the function between $x = -3$ and $x = 2$.

8. Graph the function $y = 2x^2 - 7x + 8$ between $x = -1$ and $x = 4$.

   (i) Explain the problem you encounter when trying to solve $y = 0$.

   (ii) Use the quadratic formula to try to solve this equation. What do you notice?

9. (i) Graph $f(x) = x^2 - 3x - 4$ between $x = -2$ and $x = 5$.

   (ii) Use your graph to find the roots of the equation $x^2 - 3x - 4 = 0$.

   (iii) Graph the line $y = 2x - 4$.

   (iv) Use your graph to solve the equation $2x - 4 = 0$.

   (v) Mark the points of intersection between your two graphs.

Explain what these points of intersection signify.

7.9 SOLVING PROBLEMS INVOLVING QUADRATIC EQUATIONS

Algebra can be used to solve problems in many different parts of your course. This section shows how to approach these problems.

ACTIVITY 7.7

x^2 Worked Example 7.21

One number is four more than another number. The sum of their squares is 10.

Find the two numbers.

Solution

It is important to establish that there is a link between the two numbers. If so, both numbers can be expressed in the same variable.

First number = x Second number = $x + 4$

Word equation: One number is four more than the other number. The sum of their squares is 10.

Maths equation:

$$x^2 + (x + 4)^2 = 10$$
$$x^2 + (x + 4)(x + 4) = 10$$
$$x^2 + x^2 + 8x + 16 = 10$$
$$2x^2 + 8x + 16 - 10 = 0$$
$$2x^2 + 8x + 6 = 0$$

We can divide all the terms by 2 to make the equation easier to solve.

$$x^2 + 4x + 3 = 0$$
$$(x + 1)(x + 3) = 0$$
$$x + 1 = 0 \quad \textbf{OR} \quad x + 3 = 0$$
$$x = -1 \quad \textbf{OR} \quad x = -3$$

Check:

First number = x = –1	First number = x = – 3
Second number = x + 4 = –1 + 4 = 3	Second number = x + 4 = –3 + 4 = 1
$(-1)^2 + (3)^2 = 10$ True	$(-3)^2 + (1)^2 = 10$ True

Both solutions are correct.

Answer: –1, 3 **OR** –3, 1.

x^2 **Worked Example 7.22**

The linear path of a ship is given by the equation $2x + y = 6$.

A reef is represented by the equation $x^2 + y^2 = 17$.

At what two points will the ship cross the reef?

Solution

We have one linear and one non-linear equation.

<table>
<tr><td>Step 1:
Linear</td><td colspan="2">$2x + y = 6$
$y = 6 - 2x$</td></tr>
<tr><td>Step 2:
Substitution</td><td colspan="2">$x^2 + y^2 = 17$
$x^2 + (6 - 2x)^2 = 17$
$x^2 + (6 - 2x)(6 - 2x) = 17$
$x^2 + (36 - 24x + 4x^2) = 17$
$x^2 + 36 - 24x + 4x^2 = 17$
$5x^2 - 24x + 36 - 17 = 0$
$5x^2 - 24x + 19 = 0$</td></tr>
<tr><td>Step 3:
Solving</td><td colspan="2">$5x^2 - 24x + 19 = 0$

$5x \quad - \quad 19$
$x \quad - \quad 1$

$(5x - 19)(x - 1) = 0$
$5x - 19 = 0 \quad$ OR $\quad x - 1 = 0$
$5x = 19 \quad$ OR $\quad x = 1$
$x = 3.8 \quad$ OR $\quad x = 1$</td></tr>
<tr><td>Step 4:
Solving other variable</td><td>$y = 6 - 2x$
If $x = 3.8$
$y = 6 - 2(3.8)$
$y = -1.6$</td><td>If $x = 1$,
$y = 6 - 2(1)$
$y = 4$</td></tr>
<tr><td>Step 5:
Answer</td><td colspan="2">The ship crosses the reef at the co-ordinates $(3.8, -1.6)$ and $(1, 4)$.</td></tr>
</table>

> Double check your work in context questions, as you may need to reject an answer due to the nature of the question.

Exercise 7.9

1. A number is squared and added to three times the number to give a total of 18.

   Find all possible values for the number.

2. The sum of five times the square of a number and four times the number is 28.

   Find two possible values for the number.

$5x^2 + 4x = 28$

3. One number is three more than the other number. The sum of their squares is 65. Find two pairs of numbers for which this is true.

4. Find two consecutive natural numbers whose product is 56.

   (Let the numbers be x and $x + 1$.)

5. The length of a rectangle is 5 m more than its width. Its area is 234 m². Find the dimensions of the rectangle.

6. The square of a number is eight times more than seven times the number. Find the number.

7. Let x be equal to a number. Another number is five less than twice x. When the two numbers are multiplied, the answer is 7. Find two possible values for the number.

8. An empty warehouse has 3,332 m² of floor space. An extension increases the length by 12 m, the width by 6 m and the floor space by 1,068 m². Find the dimensions of the original warehouse (two possible sets of dimensions).

9. $2n$ and $(2n + 2)$ are two consecutive even natural numbers. Their product is 168. Write down an equation in n and, hence, find the smaller number.

10. $3n$ is an odd number. The product of this number and the next consecutive odd number is 483. Find the two consecutive odd natural numbers.

11. The dimensions of a garden are 10 m by 12 m. It is surrounded by a uniform path which is 48 m² in area. Find the width of this path.

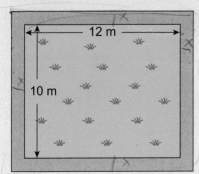

12. Find three consecutive numbers such that the second number squared is equal to the first and third added together.

13. The length of an office is 4 m less than the breadth. The area of the office is 221 m². Find the dimensions of the office.

14. Find three consecutive odd natural numbers such that the product of the first and the last is 11 greater than two times the middle one.

15. A sheet of metal is 30 cm by 40 cm. If a uniform strip of metal is cut from around the edge of this sheet, how wide must the strip be so as to leave half the area?

16. A child's age is x years. Her father's age is x^2 years. In 14 years' time, her father will be two and a half times her age. Find her age and her father's age now.

17. Amy is five years older than Bridget. Caroline is twice the age of Amy. When Amy's and Caroline's ages are multiplied, the answer is 722. Find all three ages.

18. The sides of a right-angled triangle are shown. Using the theorem of Pythagoras, find the length of all three sides.

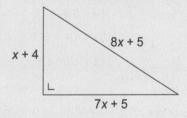

19. A net of an open rectangular box is shown.

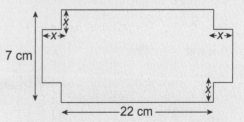

If the area of the base of the box is 110 cm², find the volume of the box.

20. A woman walks a distance of 10 km from A to B at a speed of x km/hr. She then walks 12 km from B to C at a speed of $(x - 1)$ km/hr. The total time for the journey is 5 hours.

(i) Copy and complete the table below.

Journey	A to B	B to C
Distance (km)	10	12
Speed (km/hr)	x	$x - 1$
Time		

(ii) Solve for x.

21. The members of a lottery syndicate win a prize of €400. If two more people had joined the syndicate, each member would have received €10 less.

(i) Copy and complete the table below.

Total prize	€400	
Number of members	x	
Prize share per member		

(ii) How many members are in the syndicate?

22. The sum of an integer (x) and its reciprocal $\left(\frac{1}{x}\right)$ is 2.5. Find the number.

23. A prize fund of €300 is divided equally among the n winners. If there had been two more winners, each prize-winners would have got €5 less. Find the value of n.

24. A rower rows for a distance of 10 km at a speed of x km/hr. He then rows the next 15 km at a speed 2 km/hr faster than the first part of his journey. He spends an equal time rowing for each part of his journey.

(i) Find the average speed for both parts of the journey.

(ii) Find the time taken for the first part of his journey.

25. On Monday, Ania runs a distance of 20 km at a speed of x km/hr. On Tuesday, she then runs the same distance but at an average speed 2 km/hr slower than Monday's. It takes her 50 minutes more to run this distance on Tuesday.

Find her average speed on both days.

26. Ann and Ben travel 45 km at steady speeds on their bikes. Ann travels 1 km/h faster than Ben. She finishes half an hour before Ben. Find their speeds on the journey.

27. The product of two natural numbers is 18. If one is added to four times the smaller number, this is equal to the larger number. Find both numbers.

28. The perimeter of a rectangular table is 2.4 m. The area of the table is 0.35 m².

Let x = width of table.

Let y = length of table.

Find the length and width of the table.

29. Find two consecutive natural numbers whose cubes differ by 61.

30. The perimeter of a rectangular garden is 32 m. The area is 60 m².

Find the dimensions of the garden.

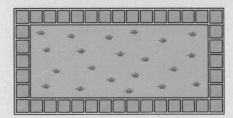

31. The length, width and height of a child's toy box are in the ratio 4 : 2 : 1.

It is decided to change the dimensions of the toy box, doubling the breadth, halving the height and keeping the length the same.

Calculate the percentage change of the new toy box's

(i) Volume   (ii) Surface area

when compared to the original box.

32. Paul has a set time that it takes for him to travel to work. On Monday he travels at an average speed of 40 km/hr and arrives 15 minutes later than normal. On Tuesday he travels at 60 km/hr and arrives 50 minutes earlier than normal. Find:

(i) The distance Paul travels to work

(ii) The time it normally takes him

33. The linear flight path of a plane is give by the equation $x + y = -3$. The airspace of a certain city is given by the equation $x^2 + y^2 = 29$.

(i) At what two points does the flight of this plane cross the boundary of the airspace of the city?

The airplane control tower is situated at the point $(0,0)$, and the point $(-2,4)$ is 2 km west and 4 km north of the tower.

(ii) Give the co-ordinates of each point of intersection as kilometres east/west and kilometres north/south.

(iii) How far are these two points from the tower?

Give your answer in surd form.

Revision Exercises

1. (a) Solve:

    (i) $x^2 - 2x - 8 = 0$

    (ii) $x^2 - 12x + 20 = 0$

    (iii) $x^2 + x - 6 = 0$

    (iv) $x^2 - 100 = 0$

    (v) $2x^2 + 5x - 12 = 0$

    (vi) $49x^2 = 100$

(b) Use trial and error to find one whole number root of each of the following equations:

    (i) $x^2 + 8x + 15 = 0$

    (ii) $x^2 + 7x + 10 = 0$

    (iii) $2x^2 - 3x - 14 = 0$

(c) (i) Find two consecutive natural numbers whose squares add up to 61.

    (ii) Two numbers differ by 3. Their product is 28. Find the numbers.

2. (a) Solve:

    (i) $x^2 = 5x + 6$

    (ii) $6x^2 + 23x + 20 = 0$

(iii) $2x^2 = 4 - 7x$

(iv) $5x^2 - 18x + 9 = 0$

(v) $10x^2 - x - 21 = 0$

(b) On separate graphs, solve $f(x) = 0$ by graphing each function between $x = -3$ and $x = 5$.

    (i) $f(x) = x^2 - 4$

    (ii) $f(x) = x^2 - 2x - 8$

    (iii) $f(x) = 3x^2 + 5x - 2$

Check your answers by using algebra to solve each equation.

Which method is more accurate? Why?

(c) Solve each of the following simultaneous equations:

    (i) $x = y + 1$ (iii) $x + y = 3$
        $x^2 + y^2 = 13$ $x^2 + y^2 = 5$

    (ii) $y = x + 2$ (iv) $x - y = 4$
        $x^2 + 2y = 12$ $y^2 + 7x = 18$

3. (a) Use the quadratic formula to solve these equations, giving your answer to two decimal places.

   (i) $x^2 + 2x - 5 = 0$

   (ii) $x^2 - 12x + 5 = 0$

   (iii) $x^2 + x - 10 = 0$

   (iv) $x^2 - 3x - 20 = 0$

   (v) $2x^2 + 2x - 1 = 0$

   (b) On separate graphs, solve $f(x) = 0$ by graphing each function between $x = -3$ and $x = 3$.

   (i) $f(x) = x^2 - x - 3$

   (ii) $f(x) = 3x^2 + 2x - 3$

   (iii) $f(x) = 2x^2 - 2x - 5$

   Check your answers by using the quadratic formula to solve each equation. Write your answers correct to one decimal place.

   (c) (i) The square of a number is 14 more than five times the number. Find the number (two possible values).

   (ii) The square of a number is 10 less than seven times the number. Find the number (two possible values).

4. (a) Form the quadratic equations with these pairs of roots:

   (i) 2 and 6

   (ii) 1 and 5

   (iii) 11 and –2

   (iv) –10 and 4

   (v) –5 and –7

   (b) Solve:

   (i) $(x + 1)(x - 1) = 24$

   (ii) $x(2x - 1) = 3x$

   (iii) $21x^2 = x^2 - 7x + 6$

   (iv) $(3x)^2 = 4(3x - 1)$

   (v) $(2 + x)(8 - x) = 0$

   (vi) $(5x - 6)(2x + 7) = 0$

   (c) Solve each of the following simultaneous equations:

   (i) $x - y = 3$
   $x^2 + y = 17$

   (ii) $x - 2y = 0$
   $x^2 + y^2 = 5$

   (iii) $x + y = 1$
   $x^2 + y^2 = 1$

5. (a) Use the quadratic formula to solve these equations, giving your answers in surd form:

   (i) $x^2 - 3x + 1 = 0$

   (ii) $2x^2 - 12x + 1 = 0$

   (iii) $3x^2 - 12x + 7 = 0$

   (iv) $5x^2 - 14x + 4 = 0$

   (v) $7x^2 + 4x - 2 = 0$

   (b) (i) There are two consecutive natural numbers, such that twice the square of the first is 34 more than the square of the second. Find the numbers.

   (ii) Find two consecutive **even** natural numbers, such that three times the square of the smaller one is 60 more than their product.

6. Solve:

   (a) (i) $x = 1 + \dfrac{56}{x}, x \neq 0$

   (ii) $7 = 5x + \dfrac{2}{x}, x \neq 0$

   (iii) $\dfrac{3}{x - 3} + \dfrac{2}{x - 1} = 2, x \neq 3, 1$

   (b) Solve: $\dfrac{18}{x} = x + 3, x \neq 0$

   (c) Solve: $\dfrac{3}{x + 1} + \dfrac{1}{x - 1} = 1\frac{1}{4}, x \neq \pm 1$

7. (a) Graph the function $f(x) = 2x^2 - 7x + 3$
between $x = -1$ and $x = 5$.

(i) Use your graph to find the roots of
the equation $2x^2 - 7x + 3 = 0$.

(ii) Graph the line $y = 3$.

(iii) Use your graph to solve the equation
$2x^2 - 7x + 3 = 3$.

(iv) Check your answers using algebra.

(v) Explain how you could use your
graph to solve $2x^2 - 7x + 3 = x^2 - 3$.

(b) (i) -4 is a repeated root of
$x^2 + px + q = 0$. Find the values
of p and q.

(ii) The roots of $x^2 + bx + c = 0$ are
both equal to 10. Find the values
of b and c.

(iii) The roots of $x^2 - 10x + k = 0$ are
equal. Find the value of k.

(c) The perimeter of a rectangular room is
22 m. The area is 30 m². If $x =$ the
width and $y =$ the length, write down
two equations and, hence, find the
dimensions of the room.

8. (a) In each graph, find the roots of the
function shown.

(i)

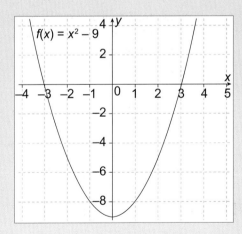

$f(x) = x^2 - 9$

(ii)

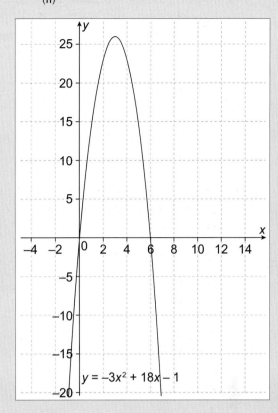

$y = -3x^2 + 18x - 1$

(iii)

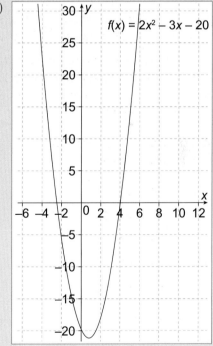

$f(x) = 2x^2 - 3x - 20$

(b) Match each function/equation to the correct graph.

Equation A: $f(x) = x^2 + 3x - 1$	**Graph P** 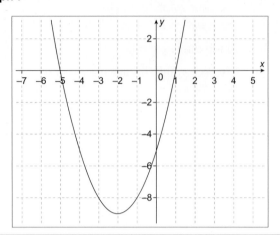
Equation B: $f(x) = x^2 + 4x - 5$	**Graph Q** 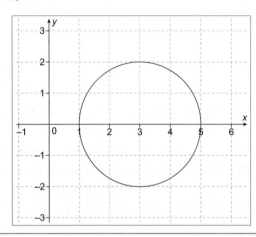
Equation C: $f(x) = -x^2 + 4x - 5$	**Graph R** 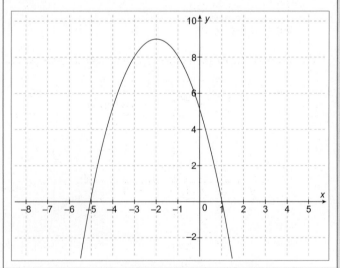

Equation D: $(x - 3)^2 + y^2 = 4$	Graph S
	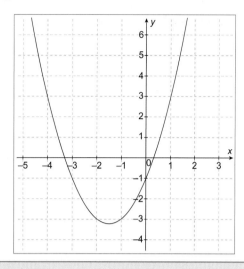

(c) Solve each of the following simultaneous equations:

(i) $2x - y = 7$
$xy = 15$

(ii) $x - 2y + 1 = 0$
$x^2 - xy = 10$

(iii) $x + 2y = 3$
$x^2 + y^2 = 2$

9. (a) The sum of a number (x) and its reciprocal $\left(\frac{1}{x}\right)$ is 2.9. Find two possible values for x.

(b) A boat travels a distance 30 km at a speed of x km/h. It then travels 20 km at a speed of $(x + 1)$ km/h. The total time for the two journeys is 15 hours. Solve for x.

(c) A migrating bird flies 400 km at a steady rate of x km/h. If the bird increased its speed by 4 km/h, the journey would take 5 hours less. Solve for x.

10. (a) Draw a sketch of a quadratic function that has:

(i) Two different roots

(ii) Two equal roots

(iii) No real roots

(b) Estimate from each graph the points of intersection of the linear and non-linear graphs.

(i)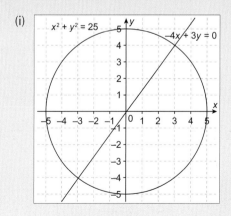

(ii)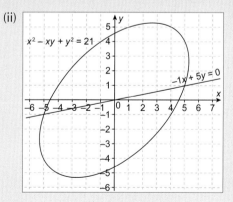

Check the answer to part (ii) by solving the simultaneous equations.

ALGEBRA III

(c) Using the same axes and scales, graph $f(x) = x^2 + 8x + 12$ and $g(x) = 2x^2 + 14x + 15$ between $x = -7$ and $x = 0$.

   (i) Mark the points of intersection of the two graphs.

  (ii) What do these points of intersection signify?

 (iii) Use another solving method to confirm your answer from part (ii).

11. (a) A ball is thrown straight up into the air. The height (h) of the ball after t seconds is given by the equation $h = 40t - 5t^2$.

     How long does it take the ball to reach its maximum height of 80 m?

  (b) A student scores x marks in one test and y marks in another test. The combined score for the two tests is 27. If the marks from both tests were squared and then subtracted, the score would be $\frac{1}{3}$ of the total of the added scores. Find the student's results in each test.

12. At a certain point during the flight of a space shuttle, the booster rockets separate from the shuttle and fall back to earth. The altitude of these booster rockets (their height above sea level) is given by the following formula:

$$h = 45 + \frac{7}{10}t - \frac{1}{200}t^2$$

where h is the altitude in kilometres, and t is the time in seconds after separation from the shuttle.

(a) Complete the table below, showing the altitude of the rockets at the indicated times.

Time in seconds, t	0	20	40	60	80	100
Altitude in km, h						

(b) Draw a graph of the altitude of the rockets for the first 100 seconds after separation from the shuttle.

(c) Use your graph to estimate the greatest altitude reached by the rockets.

(d) Use the graph to estimate **one** time at which the altitude is 60 km. Show your work clearly on the graph.

(e) Check your answer to part (d), using the formula for the altitude.

(f) By solving an equation, find the value of t at which the altitude of the rockets is 9 km.

(g) By finding the change in altitude in one second, or otherwise, find an estimate for the speed at which the rockets are falling when their altitude is 9 km.

SEC Project Maths Paper I, Leaving Certificate Ordinary Level, 2011

chapter 8

Functions

Learning Outcomes

In this chapter you will learn to:

- ⊃ Recognise that a function assigns a unique output to a given input
- ⊃ Form composite functions

8.1 INTRODUCTION

What Is a Function?

A **function** is a rule that maps an input to a unique output.

Functions are 'number machines' that transform one number into another. If we think of functions as machines, then something is put into the machine, something happens in the machine, and then something comes out.

Lowercase letters are used to name functions. *f* and *g* are often used, but remember any letter may be used to name/denote a function.

Functions in Everyday Life

You meet functions several times throughout your normal day.

Television remote controls are an example of functions at work. If you have programmed your television so that channel 103 is assigned to TV3 (for example), then when you key in 103 on your remote, TV3 appears on the television screen. Of course, you could also have TV3 pre-programmed for channel 104 (say), but you could not pre-programme two or more television stations for the same channel number. In other words, each input (channel number) is mapped to a unique output (television station).

Important Terms

- An **input** is an object that is put into the function.
- The **domain** is the set of actual inputs.
- An **output** is the object that comes out of the function.
- The **range** is the set of **actual** outputs.
- The **codomain** is the set of all **possible** outputs.

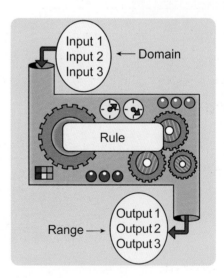

The following example illustrates the meanings of these terms.

Imagine a secondary school in which the Fifth Year classes are called 5.1, 5.2, 5.3 and 5.4. Each class is going on a class trip. They can choose from the following options:

cinema, ice-skating, go-karting, paint-balling or bowling.

5.1 choose ice-skating, 5.2 choose go-karting, 5.3 choose ice-skating and 5.4 choose paint-balling. These choices can be represented by a function illustrated in the mapping diagram below:

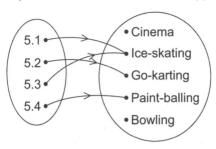

- 5.1 is an example of an input.
- Ice-skating is an example of an output.
- The **domain** is the set of all Fifth Year classes: {5.1, 5.2, 5.3, 5.4}.
- The **range** is the set of the three chosen activities: {ice-skating, go-karting, paint-balling}.
- The **codomain** is the set of all five options: {cinema, ice-skating, go-karting, paint-balling, bowling}.

Examples of Functions

Suppose you write $f(x) = x^2$. You have just defined a function f that transforms any number into its square.

Consider the following inputs to this function: {−1, 0, 1, 2}.

The resulting outputs can be computed using an input–output table:

Input	Application of function	Output
x	x^2	y
−1	$(-1)^2$	1
0	$(0)^2$	0
1	$(1)^2$	1
2	$(2)^2$	4

Here, y is the result of applying the rule (the function) to the input.

We can represent this function in a number of other ways.

Using function notation

$f(x) = x^2$

Pronounced 'f of x equals x-squared'.

So $f(-1) = (-1)^2$

$\qquad = 1$

$f(x) = x^2$ means that if you put x into the function, the output is x^2.

$f(0) = (0)^2$

$\qquad = 0$

$f(-1) = 1$ tells us that if −1 is the input, then 1 is the output.

$f(1) = (1)^2$

$\qquad = 1$

$f(2) = (2)^2$

$\qquad = 4$

OR

Using alternative function notation

$f: x \rightarrow x^2$

So $f: -1 \rightarrow 1$

$f: 0 \rightarrow 0$

$f: 1 \rightarrow 1$

$f: 2 \rightarrow 4$

Pronounced 'f maps x to x^2'.

$f: -1 \rightarrow 1$ tells us that if -1 is the input, then 1 is the output.

$f: x \rightarrow x^2$ can also be written as $f: x \mapsto x^2$.

OR

As a set of couples/ordered pairs

Set of couples = $\{(-1,1), (0,0), (1,1), (2,4)\}$

For example, (2,4) tells us that if 2 is the input, then 4 is the output.

OR

Using a mapping diagram

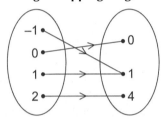

Points to Note: Inputs and Outputs

Look again at the function f defined as $f(x) = x^2$. You will note the following:

- An input can pass through the function and not change, i.e. the input 0 passes through the function and comes out as 0, giving the couple (0,0).
- Two inputs can result in the same output, i.e. the inputs -1 and 1 both result in the output 1.
- However, an input into a function will never result in two different outputs.

Worked Example 8.1

The function f is defined over the domain $\{0, 1, 2, 3, 4\}$, where $f(x) = 2x - 8$.

Calculate the range of this function.

Solution

x	$2x - 8$	y
0	$2(0) - 8$	-8
1	$2(1) - 8$	-6
2	$2(2) - 8$	-4
3	$2(3) - 8$	-2
4	$2(4) - 8$	0

Range = $\{-8, -6, -4, -2, 0\}$

Worked Example 8.2

The function j is defined such that $j(x) =$ the number of legs x has. The domain of j is $\{$a healthy cat, a parrot with all its legs, a sheep, a three-legged dog$\}$. Find the range of j.

Solution

Remember that the range is the list of all actual outcomes.

- j(a healthy cat) = 4
- j(a parrot with all its legs) = 2
- j(a sheep) = 4
- j(a three-legged dog) = 3

So the range is $\{2, 3, 4\}$.

Note: Even though 4 appears twice, we list it only once in the range.

Worked Example 8.3

The function h can be represented by the following set of ordered pairs:

$\{(-4,16), (-3,9), (0,0), (1,1), (3,9), (5,25)\}$

Draw a mapping diagram to illustrate the function h.

Solution

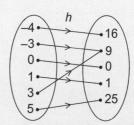

 Worked Example 8.4

$f: x \rightarrow 6x - n$ is a function.

(i) If $f(-2) = -23$, find the value of n.   (ii) Find the value of x for which $f(x + 3) = -29$.

Solution

(i) $f(-2) = 6(-2) - n$

$= -12 - n$

$\therefore -12 - n = -23$

$-n = -23 + 12$

$-n = -11$

$\therefore n = 11$

(ii) From part (i): $n = 11$

So $f: x \rightarrow 6x - 11$

$\therefore f(x + 3) = 6(x + 3) - 11$

$= 6x + 18 - 11$

$= 6x + 7$

$\therefore 6x + 7 = -29$

$6x = -36$

$\therefore x = -6$

 Worked Example 8.5

The diagram shows part of the graph of the function $y = ax^2 + bx - 2$.

Find the value of a and the value of b.

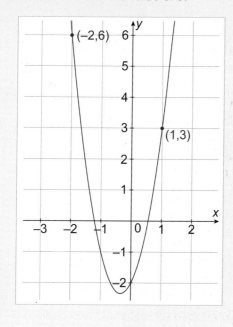

Solution

The couple $(1,3)$ is on the graph.

$\therefore a(1)^2 + b(1) - 2 = 3$

$a + b - 2 = 3$

$a + b = 5$ **Eq. 1**

The couple $(-2,6)$ is also on the graph.

$\therefore a(-2)^2 + b(-2) - 2 = 6$

$4a - 2b - 2 = 6$

$4a - 2b = 8$

$2a - b = 4$ **Eq. 2**

Now solve the simultaneous equations 1 and 2:

$a + b = 5$ **Eq. 1**

$\underline{2a - b = 4}$ **Eq. 2**

$3a = 9$

$\therefore a = 3$

Substitute $a = 3$ into Equation 1:

$3 + b = 5$

$\therefore b = 2$

Answer: $a = 3, b = 2$

FUNCTIONS

Exercise 8.1

1. Which of the following sets of ordered pairs represent functions?

Give a reason for your answer.

(a) $\{(1,4), (2,5), (3,6), (4,7)\}$

(b) $\{(1,2), (2,2), (3,4)\}$

(c) $\{(1,3), (3,5), (1,7), (4,9)\}$

(d) $\{(4,4), (3,4), (10,9)\}$

(e) $\{(1,-3), (-3,1), (2,0), (3,0), (4,0)\}$

2. Which of the following mappings are functions?

Give a reason for your answer.

(a)
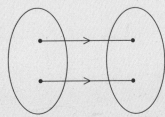

(b)
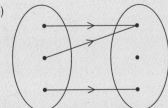

(c)
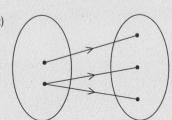

(d)
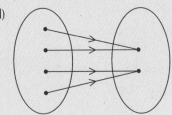

(e)
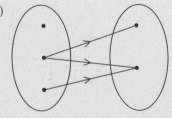

(f)
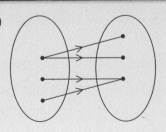

3. $f: x \rightarrow 2x + 6$ is a function.
Find:

(i) $f(2)$ (iv) $f(-3)$

(ii) $f(-2)$ (v) $f(4)$

(iii) $f(0)$ (vi) $f(3.5)$

4. $f(x) = 2x^2 - 6x + 1$ is a function.
Find:

(i) $f(0)$ (iv) $f(-3)$

(ii) $f(-2)$ (v) $f(4)$

(iii) $f(3)$ (vi) $f\left(\frac{1}{2}\right)$

5. A function g is defined as $g(t) = 6t - 4$.
For what values of t are the following true?

(i) $g(t) = 8$ (iv) $g(t) = 14$

(ii) $g(t) = -2$ (v) $g(t) = 1$

(iii) $g(t) = -8$ (vi) $g(t) = 0$

6. $f: x \mapsto 4x - 1$ defines a function.

Find:

(i) The value of $f(1)$

(ii) The value of $f\left(\frac{1}{2}\right)$

(iii) The value of k if $f(k) = 9$

(iv) The value of p if $f(p) = p$

7. $f(x) = 2x + g$ defines a function.
Find the value of g if $f(1) = 10$.

8. $g(x) = ax - 12$ defines a function.
Find the value of a if $g(3) = 0$.

9. Given that $f(x) = \dfrac{x - 1}{x^2 + 2}$, find:

(i) $f(0)$ (iv) $f(2x)$

(ii) $f(-2)$ (v) $f\left(\frac{1}{x}\right)$

(iii) $f(3)$ (vi) $f(x + h)$

10. A function is defined by the following rule:
'Multiply the input by 4 and subtract 1.'
The domain for this function is the set
A = {1, 2, 3, 4, 5, 6}.

List the elements of B, the range of this function.

11. A function is defined as 'square the input'.

List the range of this function if the domain is:

(i) {1, 2, 3, 5, 6}

(ii) The first five prime numbers

(iii) {−2, −1, 0, 1, 2, 3, 4}

12. Write down the domain, codomain and range of the following functions:

(i)
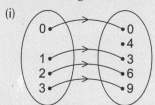

(ii)
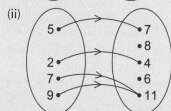

(iii)
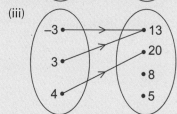

(iv)
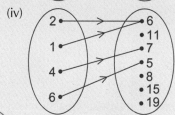

13. The following mapping is given:

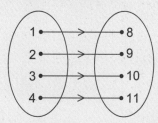

(i) Is this mapping a function?
Give a reason for your answer.

(ii) Write out the domain and range of this mapping.

(iii) Write an expression in terms of x for this mapping.

(iv) Use this expression to find the input which maps to 77.

14. A function g is defined as g(x) = the number of sides x has. Given the domain {triangle, hexagon, pentagon, rectangle, square, rhombus, octagon}, write out the range of this function.

15. A function p is defined as p(x) = the colour of an object.

Given a codomain {yellow, red, blue, white, black}, list a domain which would satisfy this function.

16. A function f is defined by the rule 'Divide the input by 2 and add 3.'

(i) Write an expression in x to represent this function.

(ii) Using this expression, find the value of f(4), f(18) and f(−6).

(iii) For what value of x is f(x) = 9?

17. If g(x) = 2x, show that g(x + 3) − g(x − 1) = 8.

18. f: x → 2x + 11 and g: x → x² − 4 are two functions.

(i) Evaluate f(4).

(ii) Evaluate g(4).

(iii) Verify that f(−3) = g(−3).

(iv) Find a value of k, other than −3, for which f(k) = g(k).

19. The diagram shows part of the graph of the function ax + by = 12.

Find the value of a and the value of b.

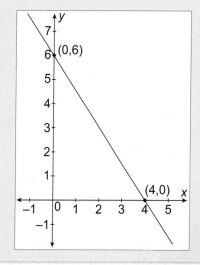

20. The diagram shows part of the graph of the function $y = ax + b$.

Find the value of a and the value of b.

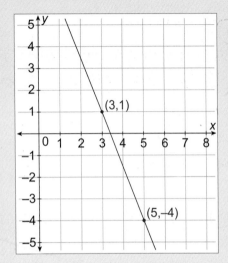

21. The diagram shows part of the graph of the function $f(x) = ax^2 + bx + 4$.

Find the value of a and the value of b.

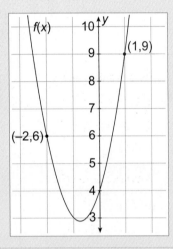

22. Addy is decorating his Christmas tree. For every red bauble he puts on the tree, he puts on four gold baubles.

(i) Taking x as the number of red baubles and y as the number of gold baubles, define a function h such that $y = h(x)$.

(ii) Draw a sketch of the function.

(iii) If Addy puts 20 red baubles on the tree, how many gold baubles will be on the tree? How many baubles will there be on the tree in total?

(iv) If there are 125 baubles on the tree, how many are red?

23. Water empties out of a leaking tank. The amount of water in the tank at any instant is given by the rule 'Two hundred minus the input squared', where the input is the number of minutes for which the tank has been leaking (volume measured in litres).

(i) Define the function f such that $y = f(x)$, where y is the number of litres of water in the tank and x is the number of minutes passed.

(ii) How long will it take the tank to empty?

(iii) At what time will the tank be half empty?

8.2 COMPOSITE FUNCTIONS

Let us say we have a function f given by $f(x) = x^2 + 1$, $x \in R$. You can replace x with any real number.

For example: $f(1) = (1)^2 + 1 = 2$ $f(-2) = (-2)^2 + 1 = 5$ $f(x + h) = (x + h)^2 + 1$

Now consider the function f given by $f(x) = 3x^2 + 5$.

If we take an input value of 4, let us describe what we do to find $f(4)$:

- Square the input, 4 in this case. $(4)^2 = 16$
- Multiply the input squared by 3. $3(16) = 48$
- Then add 5. $48 + 5 = 53$

ACTIVITIES 8.2, 8.3

We really have two separate functions here:

- Function 1 tells us to square the input.
- Function 2 tells us to multiply the output of Function 1 by 3 and then add 5.

We can understand this type of function more easily if we break f into two separate functions, g and h.

- The function g is defined as $g(x) = x^2$.
- The function h is defined as $h(x) = 3x + 5$.

We want to find $g(x)$ first, and then we use $g(x)$ as the input for our function h.

It means that we perform the function g first and then perform the function h.

> This is read as 'the composition of h and g'.
>
> It is also read as 'h after g'.

If we perform function g first and then function h, we express this as:

$h \circ g(x)$ **OR** $(h \circ g)(x)$ **OR** $h(g(x))$ **OR** $hg(x)$

Note that the order in which we compose two functions is usually important.

 Worked Example 8.6

Consider the functions g and h defined as:

$g(x) = x^2$ and $h(x) = 3x + 5$

(i) Evaluate $h(g(3))$.   (ii) Evaluate $g(h(3))$.   (iii) Is $h(g(3)) = g(h(3))$?

Solution

(i) $h(g(3))$

First evaluate $g(3)$:

$g(3) = (3)^2$

$\quad = 9$

Now evaluate $h(9)$:

$h(9) = 3(9) + 5$

$\quad = 27 + 5$

$\quad = 32$

$\therefore h(g(3)) = 32$

(ii) $g(h(3))$

First evaluate $h(3)$:

$h(3) = 3(3) + 5$

$\quad = 9 + 5$

$\quad = 14$

Now evaluate $g(14)$:

$g(14) = (14)^2$

$\quad = 196$

$\therefore g(h(3)) = 196$

(iii) $h(g(3)) \neq g(h(3))$, as $32 \neq 196$.

Therefore, the order of composition is important.

 Worked Example 8.7

$f(x) = 6x + 2$ and $g(x) = x^3$.

(i) Find the value of $f \circ g(2)$.

(ii) Find the value of $g \circ f(2)$.

(iii) Comment appropriately on your answers to parts (i) and (ii).

FUNCTIONS

Solution

(i) $f \circ g(2)$

First find $g(2)$.

$g(2) = (2)^3$

$= 8$

Now find $f(8)$.

$f(8) = 6(8) + 2$

$= 48 + 2$

$= 50$

$\therefore f \circ g(2) = 50$

(ii) $g \circ f(2)$

First find $f(2)$.

$f(2) = 6(2) + 2$

$= 12 + 2$

$f(2) = 14$

Now find $g(14)$.

$g(14) = (14)^3$

$= 2,744$

$\therefore g \circ f(2) = 2,744$

(iii) $\left.\begin{array}{l} f \circ g(2) = 50 \\ g \circ f(2) = 2,744 \end{array}\right\} \Rightarrow f \circ g(2) \neq g \circ f(2)$

 **ACTIVITY 8.4**

In general, composition of functions is not commutative, i.e. $f \circ g(x) \neq g \circ f(x)$.

Worked Example 8.8

Given the function f, where $f(t) = (6t + 4)^3$:

(i) Decompose f into two separate functions.

(ii) Decompose f into three separate functions.

Solution

(i) Define the function a such that $a(t) = 6t + 4$.

Define the function b such $b(t) = (t)^3$.

$\therefore f = b \circ a$

(ii) Define the function a such that $a(t) = 6t$.

Define the function b such that $b(t) = t + 4$.

Define the function c such $c(t) = (t)^3$.

$\therefore f = c \circ b \circ a$

Worked Example 8.9

Consider the functions a, b, c defined as:

$a(x) = \sin(x)^\circ$ $b(x) = 15x$ $c(x) = x^{\frac{1}{2}}$

If d is a function such that $d = a \circ b \circ c$, find the value of $d(4)$.

Solution

$d(4) = (a \circ b \circ c)(4)$

$c(4) = (4)^{\frac{1}{2}}$ $b(2) = 15(2)$ $a(30) = \sin 30^\circ$ $\therefore d(4) = 0.5$

$= 2$ $= 30$ $= 0.5$

Exercise 8.2

1. A function is defined by $h(x) = 2x$.
A second function is defined by $g(x) = x^2$.
The function f is defined as $f = h \circ g$.
Find:

(i) $f(0)$ (v) $f(-1)$

(ii) $f(3)$ (vi) $f(-2)$

(iii) $f(4)$ (vii) $f(-3)$

(iv) $f(6)$ (viii) $f(-6)$

2. A function is defined by $h(x) = 2x + 4$.
A second function is defined by $g(x) = x^2 + 1$.
The function f is defined as $f = h \circ g$.
Find:

(i) $f(0)$ (v) $f(-1)$

(ii) $f(3)$ (vi) $f(-2)$

(iii) $f(4)$ (vii) $f(-3)$

(iv) $f(6)$ (viii) $f(-6)$

3. A function is defined by $h(x) = x + 1$.
A second function is defined by $g(x) = x^2$
and a third function is defined by $j(x) = x - 2$.
The function f is defined as $f = h \circ g \circ j$.
Find:

(i) $f(0)$ (v) $f(-1)$

(ii) $f(2)$ (vi) $f(-2)$

(iii) $f(-4)$ (vii) $f\left(\frac{3}{4}\right)$

(iv) $f(1)$ (viii) $f\left(\frac{5}{2}\right)$

4. (a) Decompose the following functions into two simpler functions:

(i) $h(x) = x^2 + 1$ (ii) $f(x) = 2x^2$

(b) Decompose the following functions into three simpler functions:

(i) $g(x) = 3x^2 - 5$

(ii) $j(x) = (4x - 3)^2$

5. Write the following (a) as a single function and (b) as a composition of functions:

(i) Square the input and then add 6 to the answer (two functions).

(ii) Subtract 2 from the input, square the answer, and then multiply by 6 (three functions).

(iii) Find the square root of the input, then add 4 to this answer, and then cube it (three functions).

(iv) Find the sine of the input, square this answer, and then divide by 4 (three functions).

6. The function f is defined as $f = h \circ g \circ j$.
$j(x) = x + 2$, and $g(x) = x^2$.

Define a function h for each of the following:

(i) $f(1) = 12$ (iii) $f(2) = 32$

(ii) $f(1) = 3$ (iv) $f(-1) = -4$

7. Two functions are defined as $f(x) = 3x + 2$ and $g(x) = x^2 + 2$.

Evaluate:

(i) $f \circ g(x)$ (ii) $g \circ f(x)$

8. The function f is defined as
$f(x) = 6x^2 + 3x + 6$, and the function h is defined as $h(x) = 4x + 2$.

Evaluate:

(i) $f \circ h(1)$

(ii) $h \circ f(-1)$

9. The function g is defined as $g(x) = 4x + 3$.

(i) Write an expression for $g \circ g(x)$.

(ii) Evaluate $g \circ g(x)$ if $x = -2$.

10. Given that $f(x) = \frac{4}{x}$, $g(x) = 2^x$ and $h(x) = x + 1$:

(a) Find:

(i) $f(g(2))$ (iv) $g(h(-1))$

(ii) $g(f(2))$ (v) $f(h(4))$

(iii) $g(h(2))$

(b) Find in terms of x:

(i) $f \circ g(x)$ (iii) $h \circ g(x)$

(ii) $f \circ f(x)$ (iv) $g \circ h(x)$

(c) Find x if $f \circ g(x) = \frac{1}{2}$

(d) Find x if $h \circ g(x) = 9$

1. Which of the following are functions?

   Give a reason for your answer.

   (a) {(1,4), (3,5), (4,6), (5,7)}

   (b) {(11,22), (22,32), (32,44)}

   (c) {(1,3), (3,5), (1,8), (4,9)}

   (d) {(4,4), (3,4), (5,9)}

   (e) {(2,–3), (–3,1), (2,0), (3,6), (4,8)}

2. Which of the following are functions?

   Give a reason for your answer.

   (i)
   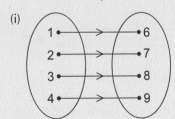

   (ii)
   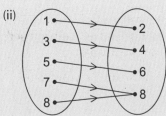

   (iii)
   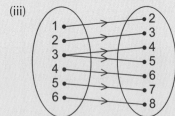

   (iv)
   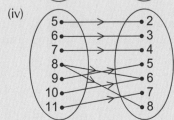

3. A function results in the following ordered pairs: (1,2), (2,4), (4,8), (8,16)

   List the following:

   (i)   The domain of the function

   (ii) The range

4. The local Vincent de Paul society is selling tickets for a raffle. Ciara has 15 tickets to sell, and she sells each ticket for €5. She knows that the amount raised by her is a function of the number of tickets sold.

   (i)   Define this function in terms of x and y, where x is the number of tickets sold and y is the amount of cash raised.

   (ii) What is the domain of this function?

   (iii) If Ciara sells 13 tickets, what amount does she raise?

5. $f(x) = 3x^2 - 5x + 4$ is a function.

   Find:

   (i) $f(1)$ (iv) $f(-3)$

   (ii) $f(-2)$ (v) $f(4)$

   (iii) $f(2)$

6. $f: x \rightarrow 4x^2 - 1$ is a function.

   Find:

   (i)   The value of $f(1)$

   (ii) The value of $f\left(\frac{1}{2}\right)$

   (iii) The value of k if $f(k) = 15$

   (iv) The value of p if $f(2) = p$

7. $f(x) = 3x + g$ defines a function.

   Find the value of g if $f(3) = 12$.

8. $g(x) = ax - 12$ defines a function.

   Find the value of a if $g(4) = 0$.

9. A function is defined as 'square the input and subtract 1'.

   List the range of this function if the domain is:

   (i)   {1, 2, 3, 5, 6}

   (ii) The first five prime numbers

   (iii) {–2, –1, 0, 1, 2, 3, 4}

10. A function is defined by:

$$f(x) = \frac{x^2 - 6}{x}, \; x \neq 0$$

  (i) Evaluate $f(6)$.

  (ii) Find the two values of x for which $f(x) = 1$.

  (iii) Show that there is no value of x for which $f(x) = x$.

11. A cookery book gives the following instruction for calculating the amount of time required to cook a turkey:

  'Allow 15 minutes per 450 g plus an extra 15 minutes.'

  (i) Write a function in terms of x (weight in grams) to represent the cooking time in minutes, y.

  (ii) For how many hours and minutes should a turkey weighing 9 kg be cooked?

12. Let $f(x) = x^3 + ax^2 + bx - 6$, where a and b are real numbers.

  Given that $f(1) = 0$ and $f(2) = 0$, find the value of a and the value of b.

13. The diagram shows part of the graph of the function $y = ax^2 + bx + 2$.

  Find the value of a and the value of b.

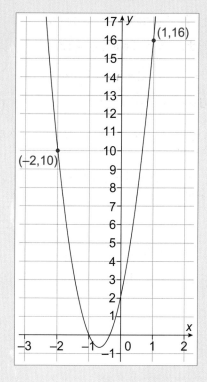

14. The diagram shows part of the graph of the function $y = ax^2 + bx - 3$.

  Find the value of a and the value of b.

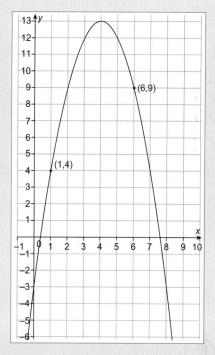

15. The diagram shows part of the graph of the function $y = ax^2 + bx + 16$.

  Find the value of a and the value of b.

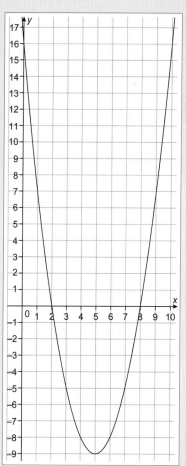

ACTIVE MATHS

16. Two fireworks were fired straight up in the air at $t = 0$ seconds.

The height, h metres, that each firework reached above the ground t seconds after it was fired is given by $h = 80t - 5t^2$.

The first firework exploded 5 seconds after it was fired.

(i) At what height was the first firework when it exploded?

(ii) What was the average speed of this firework?

The second firework failed to explode and it fell back to the ground.

(iii) At what two times was the firework at a height of 240 m?

17. A function is defined by $h(x) = 3x - 2$.
A second function is defined by $g(x) = x^2 + 2$.
The function f is defined as $f = h \circ g$.

Find:

(i) $f(0)$ (v) $f(-1)$

(ii) $f(3)$ (vi) $f(-2)$

(iii) $f(4)$ (vii) $f(-3)$

(iv) $f(6)$ (viii) $f(-6)$

> Write Questions 18–21 as single functions and also as compositions of functions.

18. Cube the input and then add 5 to the answer.

19. Subtract 4 from the input, square the answer, and then multiply by 0.5.

20. Find the square root of the input, add 3 to this answer, and then cube it.

21. Find the sine of the input, square this answer, and then divide by 3.

22. A store sells luxury products, all of which retail at prices above €75. The store decides to have a special offer on its 10th anniversary on 8 December, selling any item for €50 less than the marked price. Also, on any day in December the store will give a discount of 15% to any customer who can prove that he/she was a past customer.

Let x be the marked price of an item in the store in euros.

(i) Define the function f, the price paid for a product in the store on 8 December (in terms of x).

(ii) Define the function g, the price paid for a product in the store on any day in December by a past customer.

chapter 9

Graphing Functions

Learning Outcomes

In this chapter you will learn to:

- Graph functions of the form:
  - ax, where $a \in Q, x \in R$
  - $ax + b$, where $a, b \in Q, x \in R$
  - $ax^2 + bx + c$, where $a, b, c \in Z$, $x \in R$
  - $ax^3 + bx^2 + cx + d$, where $a, b,$ $c, d \in Z, x \in R$
  - ab^x, where $a \in N, b, x \in R$

- Interpret equations of the form $f(x) = g(x)$ as a comparison of the above functions

- Use graphical methods to find approximate solutions to
  - $f(x) = 0$
  - $f(x) = k$
  - $f(x) = g(x)$

  where $f(x)$ and $g(x)$ are of the stated form, or where graphs of $f(x)$ and $g(x)$ are provided

9.1 LINEAR FUNCTIONS

> A **linear function** is of the form $f(x) = ax + b$, where a and b are constants and x is a variable.

A constant is a value that does not vary.

A variable can change depending on the value we give it. Variables are represented by letters.

Example: $f(x) = 2x + 1$. Here, x is the variable; 1 is the constant.

A graph is a pictorial representation of information showing how one quantity varies with another related quantity. The graph of a linear function is a straight line. The graph of $f(x) = 2x + 1$ is shown below.

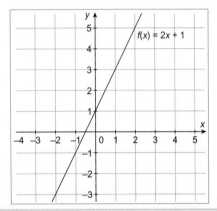

ACTIVITIES 9.1, 9.2

Worked Example 9.1

Draw the graph of the function $f(x) = 2x + 12$ for $0 \leqslant x \leqslant 10$, $x \in R$.

Solution

Step 1 Set up a table to show the input, the application of the rule (which performs the function) and the output.

Step 2 List the couples that will be graphed.

Step 3 Graph the couples and connect the plotted points with a straight line.

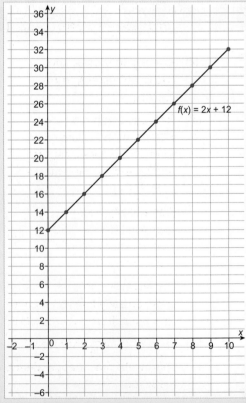

x (input)	2x + 12	y (output)	Couples to graph
0	2(0) + 12	12	(0,12)
1	2(1) + 12	14	(1,14)
2	2(2) + 12	16	(2,16)
3	2(3) + 12	18	(3,18)
4	2(4) + 12	20	(4,20)
5	2(5) + 12	22	(5,22)
6	2(6) + 12	24	(6,24)
7	2(7) + 12	26	(7,26)
8	2(8) + 12	28	(8,28)
9	2(9) + 12	30	(9,30)
10	2(10) + 12	32	(10,32)

Worked Example 9.2

The distances in metres that Rian and Eric are from school are given by the following functions:

Rian $r(t) = 250 - 1.3t$

Eric $e(t) = 325 - 2t$

where t is time in seconds.

   (i) Graph the functions using the same axes and scales.

   (ii) The bell for first class rings at $t = 0$. How far are Rian and Eric from school at this time?

   (iii) Use your graph to estimate the time to the nearest second that each boy will arrive at school.

   (iv) At what time will $r(t) = e(t)$ if the bell for first class rings at 8.40 a.m.? Explain what this means in the context of the question.

Solution

   (i) Decide what domain to use. In setting up this solution, you could make an estimate of the latest you expect the boys to be for school, e.g. 4 minutes or 240 seconds.

As both functions are linear functions, it is not necessary to plot all points in the domain, so pick three t-values for each function: $t = 0$, $t = 120$ and $t = 240$.

> Note: Always pick the first and end value of the domain (if given). Pick a third value as a checking method.

Rian					Eric			
t	$250 - 1.3t$	$r(t)$	Couples to plot		t	$325 - 2t$	$e(t)$	Couples to plot
0	$250 - 1.3(0)$	250	(0,250)		0	$325 - 2(0)$	325	(0,325)
120	$250 - 1.3(120)$	94	(120,94)		120	$325 - 2(120)$	85	(120,85)
240	$250 - 1.3(240)$	−62	(240,−62)		240	$325 - 2(240)$	−155	(240,−155)

   (ii) Rian is 250 metres, and Eric is 325 metres, from the school.

   (iii) From the graph, you are looking for the values of t where the graphs cross the x-axis, i.e. they are 0 metres from the school.

Rian will arrive at approximately $t = 192$ seconds after the bell rings for first class.

Eric will arrive at approximately $t = 163$ seconds after the bell rings for first class.

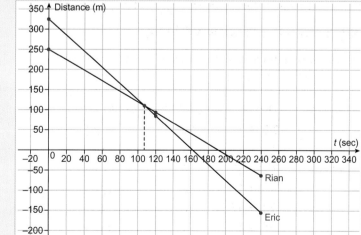

   (iv) $r(t) = e(t)$ at approximately $t = 107$ seconds.

This means that at approximately 8.41 and 47 seconds, Rian and Eric are the same distance from the school.

Exercise 9.1

1. Draw a graph of the following functions with the given domains:

	Function	Domain
(i)	$f(x) = 6x - 2$	$-2 \leqslant x \leqslant 2, x \in R$
(ii)	$g(x) = 2 - 4x$	$-3 \leqslant x \leqslant 1, x \in R$
(iii)	$h(x) = 2 - 3x$	$0 \leqslant x \leqslant 5, x \in R$
(iv)	$f: x \to x + 6$	$6 \leqslant x \leqslant 12, x \in R$
(v)	$g: x \to 2x + \frac{3}{4}$	$-8 \leqslant x \leqslant -2, x \in R$
(vi)	$h: x \to \frac{1}{5} - x$	$-2 \leqslant x \leqslant 2, x \in R$

2. Draw a graph of the following functions with the given domains:

	Function	Domain
(i)	$f(x) = \frac{2}{3}x - 2$	$-2 \leqslant x \leqslant 2, x \in R$
(ii)	$g(x) = -\frac{4}{3}x$	$-3 \leqslant x \leqslant 1, x \in R$
(iii)	$h(x) = \frac{x}{2} + \frac{3}{2}$	$0 \leqslant x \leqslant 5, x \in R$
(iv)	$i(x) = 3x + \frac{1}{2}$	$6 \leqslant x \leqslant 12, x \in R$
(v)	$f: x \to \frac{4}{5}x + \frac{1}{5}$	$-8 \leqslant x \leqslant -2, x \in R$
(vi)	$g: x \to -0.2x$	$-2 \leqslant x \leqslant 2, x \in R$

3. Draw the graph of the linear function $f: x \to 3x - 1$ in the domain $-3 \leqslant x \leqslant 4$, $x \in R$.

   Use your graph to estimate:

   (i) $f(1.3)$

   (ii) The value of x for which $f(x) = -6$

4. Draw the graph of the linear function $f: x \to 4x - 3$ in the domain $-3 \leqslant x \leqslant 4, x \in R$.

   Use your graph to estimate:

   (i) The value of $f(x)$, when $x = 2.5$

   (ii) The value of x for which $4x - 3 = 6$

   (iii) The value of x for which $4x - 3 = -7$

   (iv) The range of values of x for which $f(x) \geqslant 1$

5. Using the same axes and scales, draw the two graphs $y = 2x - 2$ and $y = 8 - 4x$ in the domain $-1 \leqslant x \leqslant 4, x \in R$. What is the point of intersection of the two graphs?

6. A car passes a point P, after which its speed v (in m/s) is given by the function $v = 15 - 3t$, where t is the time in seconds.

   Draw a graph of v for $0 \leqslant t \leqslant 5$.
   Use your graph to estimate:

   (i) The speed of the car at $t = 2.3$

   (ii) The time at which the speed is 10 m/s

   (iii) The speed as the car passes P

   (iv) The time taken by the car to stop after it passes the point P

7. The conversion formula for changing miles (M) into kilometres (K) is $K = 1.6M$.

   (i) Copy and complete the following table and, hence, graph the function, putting miles on the horizontal axis:

Miles	10	20	30	40	50	60	70	80	90	100
Kilometres					80					

   (ii) Estimate from your graph the distance in kilometres if 75 miles have been travelled.

   (iii) Estimate from your graph the distance in miles if 140 km have been travelled.

   (iv) What is the range of distances in kilometres if a trip is said to be between 65 and 75 miles long?

8. The variable cost per unit of a product is €5. Fixed costs are €45,000 (these costs are incurred regardless of the quantity produced). [Use the same axes and scales in parts (i)–(iv).]

(i) Graph the variable costs for this product for a range of production from 0 units to 50,000 units.

(ii) Graph the fixed costs for this product for the same range of production.

(iii) If total costs = fixed costs + variable costs, write a function in terms of x (quantity produced) to represent total costs.

(iv) Graph the function for total costs.

(v) If the selling price per unit is €6, write a function in terms of x to represent sales revenue for the same range of production (assuming all goods produced are sold).

(vi) Graph this function on the same axes as in part (iv).

(vii) The break-even point is the number of units at which sales revenue and total costs are equal – that is to say, neither a profit nor a loss is made. From your graph, estimate what this level of production is.

9.2 QUADRATIC FUNCTIONS

A quadratic function (in x) involves an x^2 term and is of the form $y = ax^2 + bx + c$, where a, b and c are constants and $a \neq 0$. The graph of a quadratic function takes the form of a curve, known as a parabola. The graph of a quadratic function can be drawn by making a table of values for x and finding the corresponding values for y. Then plot the resultant couples.

The graph can be ∩-shaped or ∪-shaped, depending on the coefficient of the squared variable.

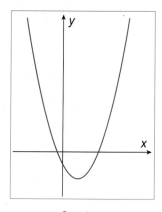

$y = ax^2 + bx + c$
Here, a is **positive**.

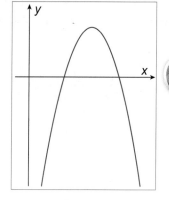

$y = ax^2 + bx + c$
Here, a is **negative**.

ACTIVITIES 9.3, 9.4, 9.5

Worked Example 9.3

Graph the function $f: x \rightarrow 3x^2 - 2x - 7$ in the domain $-2 \leqslant x \leqslant 3, x \in R$.

Estimate from your graph:

(i) The value of $f(2.5)$

(ii) The values of x for which $f(x) = 3$

(iii) The minimum value of $f(x)$ and the x-value at which it occurs

(iv) The values of x for which $3x^2 - 2x - 7 \geqslant 0$

Solution

x (input)	$3x^2 - 2x - 7$	y (output)	Couples to graph
–2	$3(-2)^2 - 2(-2) - 7$	9	(–2,9)
–1	$3(-1)^2 - 2(-1) - 7$	–2	(–1,–2)
0	$3(0)^2 - 2(0) - 7$	–7	(0,–7)
1	$3(1)^2 - 2(1) - 7$	–6	(1,–6)
2	$3(2)^2 - 2(2) - 7$	1	(2,1)
3	$3(3)^2 - 2(3) - 7$	14	(3,14)

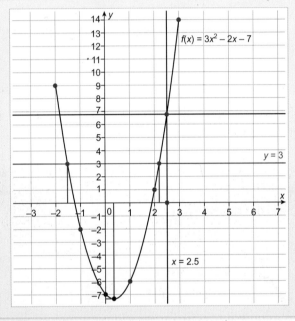

(i) Draw a line from $x = 2.5$ on the x-axis up to the graph. Then draw a line from here across to the y-axis. The reading is 6.75. Therefore, $f(2.5) = 6.75$.

(ii) Draw the line $y = 3$ (this is the horizontal red line on the diagram). Where this line cuts the graph of the function, drop perpendicular lines down to the x-axis. This gives the corresponding x-values: $x = -1.5$ and $x = 2.2$.

(iii) The minimum value of $f(x)$ is approximately –7.3 at $x = 0.3$.

(iv) The values of x for which $3x^2 - 2x - 7 \geqslant 0$

This means the values of x for which $f(x) \geqslant 0$, i.e. the values of x for which the graph is on or above the x-axis.

The graph is on the x-axis at $x = -1.2$ and $x = 1.9$.
$\therefore f(x) \geqslant 0$ for $-2 \leqslant x \leqslant -1.2$ or $1.9 \leqslant x \leqslant 3$.

Worked Example 9.4

Using the same scales and axes, graph the functions $g(x) = -x^2 + 6x$ and $h(x) = \frac{2}{3}x + 1$ in the domain $0 \leqslant x \leqslant 6, x \in R$.

Use your graph to estimate the values of x where:

(i) $g(x) = 5.5$ (ii) $h(x) = 3.5$ (iii) $g(x) = h(x)$ (iv) $\frac{2}{3}x - 1 = 0$

Solution

Set up a table for each function to find the couples that need to be graphed.

$h(x) = \frac{2}{3}x + 1$ is a linear function, so three points will be sufficient to graph it.

g(x)			
x	$-x^2 + 6x$	y	(x,y)
0	$-(0)^2 + 6(0)$	0	(0,0)
1	$-(1)^2 + 6(1)$	5	(1,5)
2	$-(2)^2 + 6(2)$	8	(2,8)
3	$-(3)^2 + 6(3)$	9	(3,9)
4	$-(4)^2 + 6(4)$	8	(4,8)
5	$-(5)^2 + 6(5)$	5	(5,5)
6	$-(6)^2 + 6(6)$	0	(6,0)

h(x)			
x	$\frac{2}{3}x + 1$	y	(x,y)
0	$\frac{2}{3}(0) + 1$	1	(0,1)
3	$\frac{2}{3}(3) + 1$	3	(3,3)
6	$\frac{2}{3}(6) + 1$	5	(6,5)

GRAPHING FUNCTIONS

ACTIVE MATHS

(i) Draw the line $y = 5.5$ (green line on graph)

Where this line cuts the graph of $g(x)$, drop perpendiculars to the x-axis and read off the x-values: $x = 1.2$ and $x = 4.8$.

(ii) Draw the line $y = 3.5$ (red line on graph)

Where this line cuts the graph of $h(x)$, drop a perpendicular to the x-axis and read off the x-value: $x = 3.7$.

(iii) These are the two x-values where the graphs of the functions intersect: $x = 0.2$ and $x = 5.2$.

(iv) $\frac{2}{3}x - 1 = 0$

$\Rightarrow \frac{2}{3}x + 1 - 2 = 0$

$\frac{2}{3}x + 1 = 2$

$\therefore h(x) = 2$

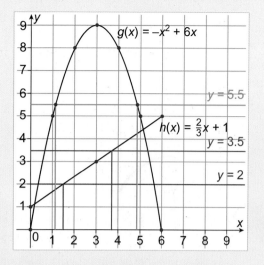

Draw the line $y = 2$ (blue line on graph). Where the line cuts the graph of $h(x)$, drop a perpendicular to the x-axis and read off the x-value: $x = 1.5$.

Exercise 9.2

1. By completing the following input–output table, graph the function $f(x) = x^2 + 2x + 3$ in the domain $-3 \leqslant x \leqslant 2, x \in R$.

x	$x^2 + 2x + 3$	y	(x,y)
-3	$(-3)^2 + 2(-3) + 3$	6	
-2			
-1			
0			
1			
2			

2. Graph the following functions in the domain $-3 \leqslant x \leqslant 1, x \in R$.

(i) $g(x) = x^2 + x + 2$

(ii) $h(x) = 2x^2 + x - 2$

(iii) $j(x) = 14 - 3x - 4x^2$

(iv) $h: x \rightarrow x^2 + 2x + 12$

(v) $f: x \rightarrow -x^2 - 3x + 7$

3. A tennis ball machine is malfunctioning and shoots out a tennis ball so that its height y (in metres) is given by the function $f(x) = 6x - x^2$, where x is the horizontal distance in metres travelled by the tennis ball.

(i) Complete a table of values relating x to y for the domain $0 \leqslant x \leqslant 6, x \in R$.

(ii) Draw the graph of y against x.

(iii) What is the maximum height reached by the tennis ball?

(iv) If the player hits the ball when it is at a height of 2 metres, estimate the two possible distances the ball has travelled.

4. Graph the function $f: x \rightarrow x^2 - 2x - 5$ in the domain $-2 \leqslant x \leqslant 4, x \in R$.

Find from your graph:

(i) The value of $f(2.2)$

(ii) The values of x for which $x^2 - 2x - 5 = 0$

(iii) The values of x for which $x^2 - 2x - 5 \leqslant 0$

(iv) The minimum value of $f(x)$

5. Graph the function $f: x \to x^2 + 6x - 3$ in the domain $-8 \leqslant x \leqslant 2, x \in R$.

Estimate from your graph:

  (i) The value of $f(x)$ if $x = -4.5$

  (ii) The values of x for which $x^2 + 6x - 3 = 0$

  (iii) The values of x for which $x^2 + 6x - 3 = 2$

  (iv) The values of x for which $x^2 + 6x - 8 = 0$

  (v) The minimum value of $f(x)$

6. A ball is thrown in the air so that t seconds after it is thrown, its height h (in metres) above the ground is given by $h = 25t - 5t^2$.

Another ball is fired from a machine, and its height above the ground is given by $g = 5 + 3t$, where g is height (in metres) and t is time (in seconds) after it is fired.

  (i) Using the same axes and scales, graph the two functions.

  (ii) Use your graph to estimate the time(s) at which the two balls will be at the same height.

  (iii) What is the maximum height reached by each ball in the first 5 seconds?

  (iv) At what time does each ball reach its maximum height?

  (v) For how long is the first ball above the second ball if they are both fired/thrown at the same time?

7. Draw the graph of the function $f: x \to 2x^2 + 3x - 3$ in the domain $-2 \leqslant x \leqslant 2, x \in R$.

Find from your graph:

  (i) The value of $f(1.5)$

  (ii) The value of x for which $2x^2 + 3x - 3 = 0$

  (iii) The values of x for which $2x^2 + 3x - 3 = 2$

8. The functions $f(x) = 8x - x^2$ and $g(x) = 0.5x + 4$ are graphed below.

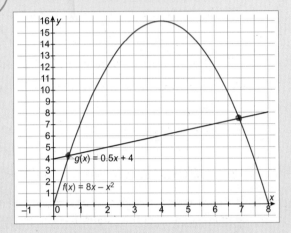

  (i) What is the maximum value of $f(x)$?

  (ii) Use the graph to estimate the values of x for which $f(x) = g(x)$.

  (iii) Use the graph to estimate the values of x for which $f(x) \geqslant g(x)$.

  (iv) Use the graph to estimate the values of x for which $f(x) \leqslant g(x)$.

9. Draw the graph of the function $g: x \to 2x^2 - 3x - 7$ in the domain $-2 \leqslant x \leqslant 3, x \in R$.

Find from your graph:

  (i) The value of $g(2.5)$

  (ii) The values of x for which $2x^2 - 3x - 7 = 0$

  (iii) The values of x for which $2x^2 - 3x - 3 = 0$

10. The perimeter of a rectangular garden is 16 m. If the width of the garden is x metres:

  (i) Show that the area of the garden is given by $8x - x^2$.

  (ii) Draw a graph to represent the area of the garden for $0 \leqslant x \leqslant 8$.

  (iii) From your graph, find the maximum area of the garden.

11. Draw the graph of the function $f: x \to 5 - 2x - x^2$ in the domain $-3 \leqslant x \leqslant 3, x \in R$.

Find from your graph:

  (i) The value of $f(-1.5)$

  (ii) The values of x for which $f(x) = 2$

  (iii) The maximum value of $f(x)$

  (iv) The range of values of k for which $5 - 2x - x^2 = k$ has two solutions, where $k \in R$.

12. Draw the graph of the function $f: x \rightarrow 6 - x - 2x^2$ in the domain $-3 \leqslant x \leqslant 3, x \in R$.

    Find from your graph the values of x for which:

    (i) $6 = x + 2x^2$ (ii) $2(6 - x^2) = x$ (iii) $6 \leqslant x(2x + 1)$

13. Use the same scales and axes to draw the graphs of the two functions $f(x) = 2 + 2x + x^2$ and $g(x) = 5 - 2x - x^2$ in the domain $-3 \leqslant x \leqslant 2, x \in R$.

    (i) Use your graph to estimate the values of x for which $f(x) = g(x)$.
    (ii) Use your graph to estimate the values of x for which $f(x) \geqslant g(x)$.

14. A missile is launched into the air following the trajectory mapped out by the quadratic function $h = 6t - t^2$, where h is the height in metres above the ground and t is the time in seconds.

    (i) Graph the trajectory of the missile for 0–6 seconds.
    (ii) At what times is the missile 8 metres above the ground?

    A counter-attack missile is launched at the same time from a height one metre above the ground. The trajectory of this missile is given by the function $j = 1.2t$, where t is time in seconds.

    (iii) Graph the trajectory of the counter-attack missile.
    (iv) At what time will the two missiles collide?
    (v) At what height will this collision take place?

15. The owner of a manufacturing company pays his workers on a piece rate basis. The owner uses a quadratic function to determine the pay each employee will receive each month. He has determined that above a certain level of production by each employee, he encounters a problem with wastage. To eliminate wastage, he has told his employees that above a given level of production, their pay will decline.

    The quadratic function he uses for calculating pay is defined as $P = 10Q - Q^2$, where P is monthly pay in €100s and Q is quantity produced in 100s.

    (i) Graph the function for pay, with quantity produced on the horizontal axis and monthly pay on the vertical axis. Use the domain $0 \leqslant Q \leqslant 10$.
    (ii) What is the optimal amount for an employee to produce?
    (iii) If the optimal amount is produced, what pay will the employee receive that month?
    (iv) If a worker receives monthly pay of €2,400, what are the two possible levels of production she has reached?
    (v) Is it more lucrative for an employee to produce 250 units or 725 units? Explain how you came to your decision.
    (vi) Pay of €2,100 can be achieved at two different levels of production. Explain how P can still be a function if this is the case.

9.3 CUBIC FUNCTIONS

Cubic functions (in x) are of the form:

$$f(x) = ax^3 + bx^2 + cx + d \qquad \text{where } a, b, c \text{ and } d \text{ are constants, } a \neq 0.$$

Examples of cubic functions:

$$f(x) = x^3 - 6x^2 + 11x - 6$$
$$g(x) = 4x^3 + 5$$
$$h: x \rightarrow x^3 + 9x$$

The graph of any function of this form is called a **cubic graph**. The shape of the graph depends on whether a, the coefficient of x^3, is negative or positive:

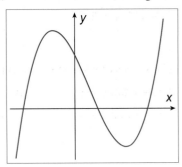

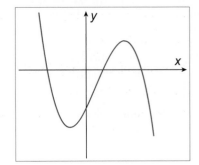

In this case, a, the coefficient of x^3, is positive.

If the coefficient of x^3 is **positive**, the graph will **start low and end high**.

In this case, a, the coefficient of x^3, is negative.

If the coefficient of x^3 is **negative**, the graph will **start high and end low**.

- A quadratic function may cross the x-axis at a maximum of two points. A cubic function may cross the x-axis at a maximum of three points.
- It is possible for the graph of a quadratic function not to cross the x-axis, i.e. if the function has no real roots. However, this is **not** the case for a cubic function. There will always be at least one point where the graph of the cubic function will cross the x-axis.
- Not all cubic functions have two turning points as shown above. These will be explored further in a later chapter.

Worked Example 9.5

Graph the function $g(x) = x^3 - 6x^2 + 11x - 6$ in the domain $0.5 \leqslant x \leqslant 3.5, x \in R$.

Solution

Set up the input–output table.

x	$x^3 - 6x^2 + 11x - 6$	y	(x,y)
0.5	$(0.5)^3 - 6(0.5)^2 + 11(0.5) - 6$	−1.875	(0.5,−1.875)
1	$(1)^3 - 6(1)^2 + 11(1) - 6$	0	(1,0)
1.5	$(1.5)^3 - 6(1.5)^2 + 11(1.5) - 6$	0.375	(1.5,0.375)
2	$(2)^3 - 6(2)^2 + 11(2) - 6$	0	(2,0)
2.5	$(2.5)^3 - 6(2.5)^2 + 11(2.5) - 6$	−0.375	(2.5,−0.375)
3	$(3)^3 - 6(3)^2 + 11(3) - 6$	0	(3,0)
3.5	$(3.5)^3 - 6(3.5)^2 + 11(3.5) - 6$	1.875	(3.5,1.875)

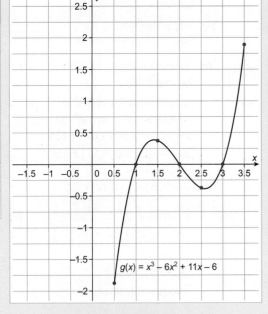

Graph the couples (x,y).

Points to note

- The graph starts low and finishes high.
  Reason: The coefficient of x^3 is positive ($=1$).
- The graph crosses the x-axis three times:
  At $x = 1$, $x = 2$ and $x = 3$.
  This indicates that the function has three real roots.

GRAPHING FUNCTIONS

Worked Example 9.6

Graph the function $f: x \rightarrow x^3 - 5x^2 + 3x + 9$ in the domain $-1.5 \leqslant x \leqslant 4, x \in R$.

Use your graph to estimate:

    (i) The values of x for which $f(x) = 0$ (iv) The values of x for which $f(x)$ is decreasing

    (ii) The value of $f(2.5)$ (v) The solutions of $x^3 - 5x^2 + 3x + 9 = 2$

    (iii) The minimum value of $f(x)$, where $x > 0$ (vi) The solutions of $x^3 - 5x^2 + 3x = -4$

Solution

Points to note

■ This function could be factorised to $f(x) = (x + 1)(x - 3)^2$.

■ In this case, we have three real roots. However, two are the same.

  (i) Using the graph, establish where the graph of the function crosses or touches the x-axis. This gives the values of x for which $f(x) = 0$.

      $f(x) = 0$ at $x = -1$ or $x = 3$

  (ii) Draw a perpendicular line through $x = 2.5$, reading off the y-value where it crosses the graph, i.e. $y = 0.9$.

      $\therefore f(2.5) = 0.9$

  (iii) The minimum value of $f(x)$ where $x > 0$ is 0.

  (iv) $f(x)$ is decreasing for $0.3 < x < 3$.

  (v) Draw the line $y = 2$, i.e. $x^3 - 5x^2 + 3x + 9 = 2$ (green line). Where the line cuts the graph of $f(x)$, drop perpendicular lines to the x-axis and read off the x-values.

      $x = -0.85, 2.2$ or 3.65

  (vi) $x^3 - 5x^2 + 3x = -4$

      $\Rightarrow x^3 - 5x^2 + 3x + 9 = -4 + 9$

      $\therefore f(x) = 5$

      Draw the line $y = 5$. This gives x-values of $x = -0.65, 1.65$ or 4.

x	$x^3 - 5x^2 + 3x + 9$	y	(x,y)
–1.5	$(-1.5)^3 - 5(-1.5)^2 + 3(-1.5) + 9$	–10.125	(–1.5,–10.125)
–1	$(-1)^3 - 5(-1)^2 + 3(-1) + 9$	0	(–1,0)
–0.5	$(-0.5)^3 - 5(-0.5)^2 + 3(-0.5) + 9$	6.125	(–0.5,6.125)
0	$(0)^3 - 5(0)^2 + 3(0) + 9$	9	(0,9)
0.5	$(0.5)^3 - 5(0.5)^2 + 3(0.5) + 9$	9.375	(0.5,9.375)
1	$(1)^3 - 5(1)^2 + 3(1) + 9$	8	(1,8)
1.5	$(1.5)^3 - 5(1.5)^2 + 3(1.5) + 9$	5.625	(1.5,5.625)
2	$(2)^3 - 5(2)^2 + 3(2) + 9$	3	(2,3)
2.5	$(2.5)^3 - 5(2.5)^2 + 3(2.5) + 9$	0.875	(2.5,0.875)
3	$(3)^3 - 5(3)^2 + 3(3) + 9$	0	(3,0)
3.5	$(3.5)^3 - 5(3.5)^2 + 3(3.5) + 9$	1.125	(3.5,1.125)
4	$(4)^3 - 5(4)^2 + 3(4) + 9$	5	(4,5)

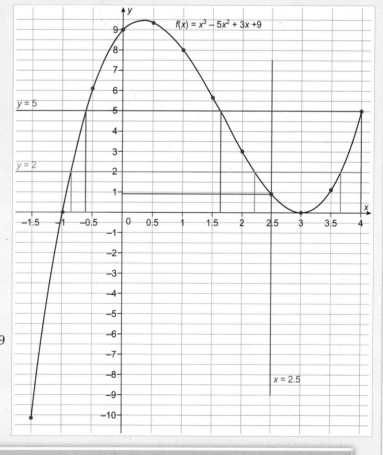

Note: Answers to parts (ii), (iv), (v), and (vi) are estimates and depend on the accuracy of the graph drawn.

Worked Example 9.7

Graph the function $g: x \rightarrow 8 - 12x + 6x^2 - x^3$ in the domain $1 \leqslant x \leqslant 3, x \in R$.

Solution

x	$8 - 12x + 6x^2 - x^3$	y	(x,y)
1	$8 - 12(1) + 6(1)^2 - (1)^3$	1	$(1,1)$
1.5	$8 - 12(1.5) + 6(1.5)^2 - (1.5)^3$	0.125	$(1.5, 0.125)$
2	$8 - 12(2) + 6(2)^2 - (2)^3$	0	$(2,0)$
2.5	$8 - 12(2.5) + 6(2.5)^2 - (2.5)^3$	−0.125	$(2.5, -0.125)$
3	$8 - 12(3) + 6(3)^2 - (3)^3$	−1	$(3,-1)$

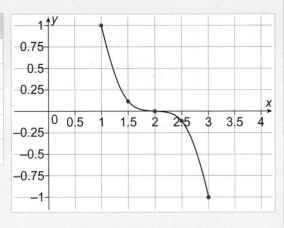

Points to note

- This function can be factorised to $g: x \rightarrow (2 - x)^3$.

- In this case, the function has three real roots. However, all three are the same ($x = 2$).

- In this case, the coefficient of x^3 is negative. Therefore, the graph starts high and finishes low.

Worked Example 9.8

Graph the function $h: x \rightarrow x^3 + x^2 - x - 10$ in the domain $-2.5 \leqslant x \leqslant 2.5, x \in R$.

Solution

x	$x^3 + x^2 - x - 10$	y	(x,y)
−2.5	$(-2.5)^3 + (-2.5)^2 - (-2.5) - 10$	−16.875	$(-2.5, -16.875)$
−2	$(-2)^3 + (-2)^2 - (-2) - 10$	−12	$(-2, -12)$
−1.5	$(-1.5)^3 + (-1.5)^2 - (-1.5) - 10$	−9.625	$(-1.5, -9.625)$
−1	$(-1)^3 + (-1)^2 - (-1) - 10$	−9	$(-1, -9)$
−0.5	$(-0.5)^3 + (-0.5)^2 - (-0.5) - 10$	−9.375	$(-0.5, -9.375)$
0	$(0)^3 + (0)^2 - (0) - 10$	−10	$(0, -10)$
0.5	$(0.5)^3 + (0.5)^2 - (0.5) - 10$	−10.125	$(0.5, -10.125)$
1	$(1)^3 + (1)^2 - (1) - 10$	−9	$(1, -9)$
1.5	$(1.5)^3 + (1.5)^2 - (1.5) - 10$	−5.875	$(1.5, -5.875)$
2	$(2)^3 + (2)^2 - (2) - 10$	0	$(2,0)$
2.5	$(2.5)^3 + (2.5)^2 - (2.5) - 10$	9.375	$(2.5, 9.375)$

Points to note

- The function can be factorised to give
$h: x \rightarrow (x - 2)(x^2 + 3x + 5)$.

- As $x^2 + 3x + 5 = 0$ has no real solutions, this indicates that the cubic function crosses the x-axis at only one point, (2,0).

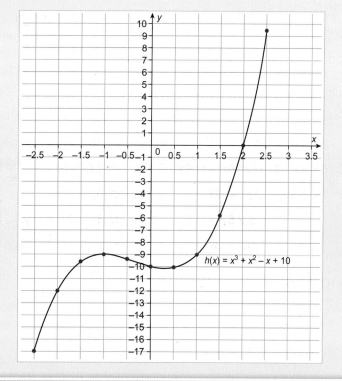

$h(x) = x^3 + x^2 - x + 10$

From these graphs, you can see why a cubic function always has at least one real root (unless the domain is restricted).

The graph of a cubic function will either:

- Start low and finish high (when the coefficient of x^3 is positive)

OR

- Start high and finish low (when the coefficient of x^3 is negative)

 ## Exercise 9.3

1. Graph the following functions in the given domain:

Function	Domain
(i) $a(x) = x^3 + x^2 - 2x + 1$	$-3 \leqslant x \leqslant 2, x \in R$
(ii) $b(x) = x^3 - x^2 - 2x + 2$	$-2 \leqslant x \leqslant 3, x \in R$
(iii) $c(x) = 2x^3 + 2x^2 - x$	$-2 \leqslant x \leqslant 2, x \in R$
(iv) $d(x) = 2x^3 - 3x^2 - 6x + 2$	$-2 \leqslant x \leqslant 3, x \in R$
(v) $e(x) = 2x^3 + 3x^2 - 11x - 6$	$-3 \leqslant x \leqslant 2, x \in R$
(vi) $f(x) = x^3 - 4x^2 + x + 6$	$-2 \leqslant x \leqslant 3, x \in R$
(vii) $g(x) = x^3 - 2x + 5$	$-2 \leqslant x \leqslant 2, x \in R$
(viii) $h(x) = -x^3 - 2x^2 + 4x + 2$	$-4 \leqslant x \leqslant 2, x \in R$
(ix) $i(x) = 2 + 15x + 3x^2 - 3x^3$	$-2 \leqslant x \leqslant 3, x \in R$
(x) $j(x) = 8 - 12x + 6x^2 - x^3$	$0 \leqslant x \leqslant 4, x \in R$

2. Draw the graph of the function
$f: x \rightarrow 2x^3 + x^2 - 8x - 4$ in the domain
$-2.5 \leqslant x \leqslant 2.5, x \in R$.

Estimate from your graph:

(i) The values of x for which $f(x) = 0$

(ii) The values of x for which $f(x) = 3$

3. Using the graph below, estimate:

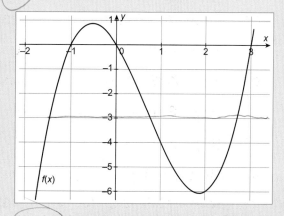

$f(x)$

(i) The values of x for which $f(x) = 0$

(ii) The values of x for which $f(x) = -3$

(iii) The range of values of x for which $f(x)$ is decreasing

4. Draw the graph of the function $f: x \to x^3 + 4x^2 + 3x - 4$ in the domain $-3 \leqslant x \leqslant 1, x \in R$.

Estimate from your graph:

(i) The value of x for which $f(x) = 0$

(ii) The values of x for which $f(x) = -3$

5. Draw the graph of the function $f: x \to x^3 + 3x^2 - x - 3$ in the domain $-4 \leqslant x \leqslant 2, x \in R$.

Estimate from your graph:

(i) The values of x for which $f(x) = 0$

(ii) The values of x for which $f(x)$ is negative and increasing

(iii) The value of x for which $x^3 + 3x^2 - x - 3 = 5$

6. Draw the graph of the function $f: x \to 2x^2 - 3x^3$ in the domain $-1.5 \leqslant x \leqslant 1.5, x \in R$.

Estimate from your graph:

(i) The values of x for which $f(x) = 0$

(ii) The value of x for which $3x^3 - 2x^2 + 5 = 0$

7. The growth model used for a new product is given by the graph below.

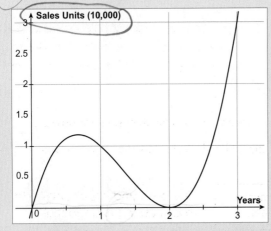

(i) What is the maximum level of sales reached in the first two years of the product's life cycle?

(ii) At approximately what time is this maximum level reached?

(iii) Two aggressive marketing campaigns are undertaken during the product's life cycle. Estimate from the graph when these two campaigns took place. Explain your answer.

(iv) If the product has an expected life of three years, what is the maximum level of sales that the product can achieve?

8. On the same axes and scales, graph the functions $f: x \to x^3 - 2x^2 - 2x + 3$ and $g: x \to 4 + 2x - x^2$ in the domain $-2 \leqslant x \leqslant 3$, $x \in R$.

Use your graph to approximate the values of x for which $f(x) = g(x)$.

9. On the same axes and scales, graph the functions
$f: x \to \frac{1}{2}x + 2$
$g: x \to x^2 - 2x + 4$
$j: x \to (x + 1)(x - 1)^2$
in the domain $-2 \leqslant x \leqslant 3$.

Use your graph to:

(i) Approximate the value of x for which $f(x) = j(x)$

(ii) Approximate the value of x for which $g(x) = j(x)$

10. The graphs of $f(x) = -5x^3 + 11x^2 - 3$ and $g(x) = 3x + 0.5$ for $-1 \leqslant x \leqslant 2, x \in R$, are shown.

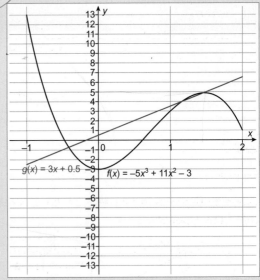

Use the graph to find:

(i) The approximate value of $f(1.5)$

(ii) The approximate value of $f(x) = 0$

(iii) The values of x for which $f(x) = g(x)$

11. The graph below models the temperature in degrees Celsius of a computer server over a four-minute period.

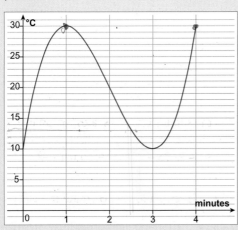

(i) What is the maximum temperature reached by the server?

(ii) At what times is this temperature recorded?

(iii) It is recommended that the temperature of the server should not exceed 28°C. Give the approximate time intervals for which the server is above the recommended temperature.

(iv) After 2.5 minutes, what is the temperature of the server?

12. The graph below shows the sales cycle for a games console. The product will be removed from the market after 5.5 years.

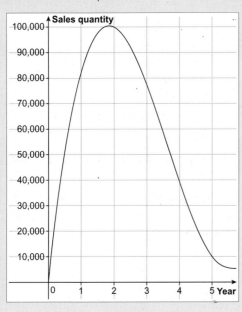

(i) At what time will sales quantity reach its peak?

(ii) At what two approximate times will sales quantity be 45,000 units?

(iii) The sales quantity can be represented by the cubic function $1,000(4x^3 - 44x^2 + 122x)$, where x is time in years. Using this function, investigate the accuracy of your answers to parts (i) and (ii).

9.4 EXPONENTIAL FUNCTIONS

Exponential functions are of the form $y = b^x$, where b is a constant and x is the exponent (or power).

When dealing with exponential functions, we take a number called the base and raise it to a power called the exponent.

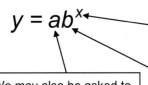

The **exponent**: For our course, this can be any real number.

The **base**: For our course, this can be any real number.

We may also be asked to multiply the exponential function by any natural number.

The base and exponent make up the exponential function.

Before dealing with exponential functions, it is essential that you know the rules for working with indices. Some key rules are shown below.

FORMULA

Rule 1: $a^p \times a^q = a^{p+q}$
Rule 2: $\dfrac{a^p}{a^q} = a^{p-q}$
Rule 3: $(a^p)^q = a^{pq}$
Rule 4: $a^0 = 1$

These formulae appear on page 21 of *Formulae and Tables*.

Graphs of Exponential Functions

The graph of an exponential function has a very distinctive shape. Exponential graphs will always pass through the point (0,1). They will never touch or cross the *x*-axis.

> **Note**
>
> ▪ The **domain** of the function is the whole real numberline or the set of all real numbers.
> ▪ The **range** of the function is $(0,\infty)$.
> ▪ The graph will **never** touch or cross the *x*-axis.

 Worked Example 9.9

Graph the function $f(x) = 10^x$ in the domain $-2 \leqslant x \leqslant 1, x \in R$.

Solution

x	10^x	*y*	*(x,y)*
−2	10^{-2}	0.01	(−2,0.01)
−1	10^{-1}	0.1	(−1,0.1)
0	10^0	1	(0,1)
1	10^1	10	(1,10)

If the exponent is *x* and the base is greater than 1, the curve slopes upwards.

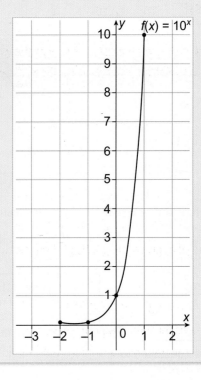

Worked Example 9.10

Graph the function $f(x) = 10^{-x}$ in the domain $-1 \leqslant x \leqslant 2, x \in R$.

Solution

x	10^{-x}	y	(x,y)
−1	$10^{-(-1)}$	10	(−1,10)
0	$10^{-(0)}$	1	(0,1)
1	10^{-1}	0.1	(1,0.1)
2	10^{-2}	0.01	(2,0.01)

If the exponent is –x and the base is greater than 1, the curve slopes downwards.

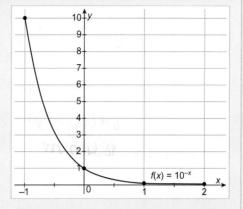

 Worked Example 9.11

Graph the function $f(x) = 2(3^x)$ in the domain $-2 \leqslant x \leqslant 2, x \in R$.

Solution

x	$2(3^x)$	y	(x,y)
−2	$2(3^{-2})$	$\frac{2}{9}$	$\left(-2,\frac{2}{9}\right)$
−1	$2(3^{-1})$	$\frac{2}{3}$	$\left(-1,\frac{2}{3}\right)$
0	$2(3^0)$	2	(0,2)
1	$2(3^1)$	6	(1,6)
2	$2(3^2)$	18	(2,18)

In this case, the graph passes through the point (0,2), as the function has been multiplied by 2.

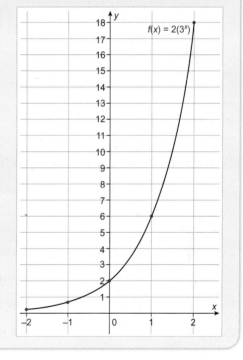

 Worked Example 9.12

Find the value of a, given the graph of the function $f(x) = ab^x$, $b > 0$.

Solution

$f(x) = b^x$ passes through the point (0,1).

This graph passes through the point (0,3).

Therefore, the function ($f(x) = b^x$) has been multiplied by 3.

$\therefore a = 3$

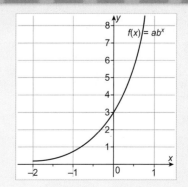

Worked Example 9.13

The growth of bacteria is modelled with an exponential function $y = 3(6^x)$, where x is time passed in seconds.

(i) Draw the graph of this function for the first 5 seconds of the bacteria's growth.

(ii) Use the graph to estimate the population of the bacteria after 3.5 seconds.

Solution

(i)

x	$3(6^x)$	y	(x, y)
0	$3(6^0)$	3	$(0, 3)$
1	$3(6^1)$	18	$(1, 18)$
2	$3(6^2)$	108	$(2, 108)$
3	$3(6^3)$	648	$(3, 648)$
4	$3(6^4)$	3,888	$(4, 3,888)$
5	$3(6^5)$	23,328	$(5, 23,328)$

(ii) Go to 3.5 on the x-axis. Draw a vertical line to meet the graph and then go across to the y-axis. Read off this value. The population of the bacteria after 3.5 seconds is approximately 1,600.

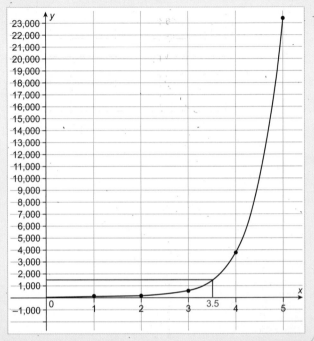

Exercise 9.4

In Questions 1–5, graph each function in the domain $-2 \leqslant x \leqslant 3, x \in R$.

1. $y = 2^x$ 4. $y = 5^{-x}$

2. $y = 4^x$ 5. $y = 3^x$

3. $y = \frac{1}{3^x}$

In Questions 6–13, graph each function in the domain $-2 \leqslant x \leqslant 2, x \in R$.

6. $y = 3(3^x)$ 10. $y = 2(0.5^x)$

7. $y = 3(2^x)$ 11. $y = 2(2^{-x})$

8. $y = 4(2^x)$ 12. $y = 3(2^{-x})$

9. $y = 2(4^x)$ 13. $y = 2(0.5^{-x})$

In Questions 14–18, identify the unknown values a and b.

14. $y = ab^x$

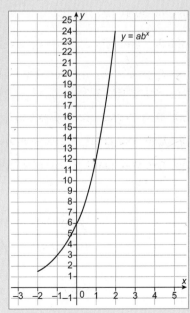

GRAPHING FUNCTIONS

15. $y = ab^x$

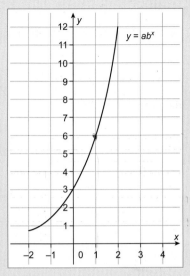

16. $y = ab^x$

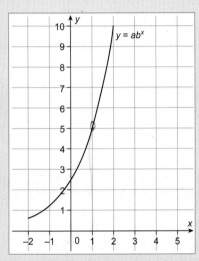

17. $y = ab^x$

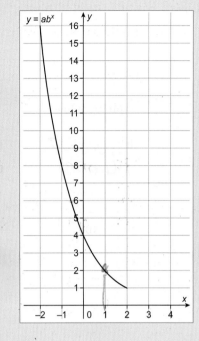

18. $y = ab^x$

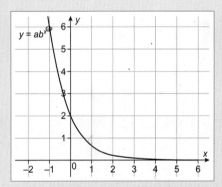

19. While making pizza dough in Home Economics class, the teacher points out that ideally the yeast mixture should be made about one hour before use. She points out that the mixture doubles in volume every hour.

Initially, Laura has 10 cm³ of the mixture.

(i) Calculate the volume of the mixture each hour for the first four hours. (Use a table to display your results.)

(ii) Draw a graph to display this data.

(iii) Use your graph to estimate the volume of the mixture after 2.5 hours.

(iv) Use your graph to estimate how long it takes for the volume of the mixture to reach 100 cm³ in size.

20. ABC Ltd purchased a delivery van costing €60,000. It is the policy of the company to depreciate all delivery vans at a rate of 20% using the reducing-balance method.

(i) Complete the schedule of depreciation below for the first five years of the asset's useful economic life:

Year	Cost (€)/NBV	Rate of depreciation	Depreciation (€)	NBV (€)
1	60,000.00	0.2	12,000.00	48,000.00
2	48,000.00	0.2	9600.00	38,400.00
3	38,400.00	0.2	7680.00	30,720.00
4	30,720.00	0.2	6,144.00	24,576.00
5	24,576.00	0.2	4,915.20	19,660.80

(ii) Verify the NBV at the end of Year 5 by using the formula for depreciation.

(iii) If F is the final value of the asset, write an exponential function in t (time passed in years) relating F (final value), P (initial cost of the asset), i (rate of depreciation), and t (time passed in years).

(iv) Graph the NBV against time passed.

21. Mustafa bought a car for €5,000. He expects the car to have a useful life of three years, at the end of which it will be worth €3,645. He will depreciate the car at a rate of 10% per annum (reducing-balance method).

(i) Using the formula for depreciation on page 30 of the *Formulae and Tables*, identify the base and the exponent in the formula.

(ii) Verify that Mustafa's residual value is in fact correct.

(iii) Graph the net value of the car from the date of purchase to the date of disposal.

(iv) From your graph, estimate the value of the car after 2.5 years.

(v) Use the depreciation formula to find the value of the car after 2.5 years.

9.5 TRANSFORMATIONS OF LINEAR FUNCTIONS

This section will cover what happens to a graph of a function when one or more parts of the function change. This is called a **transformation** of the graph of the function. When we graph a function under a transformation, the graph changes shape and/or location.

Linear Functions

When we transform a linear function, the graph can shift up or down and/or change slope.

When we are transforming graphs of linear functions, it is best if the functions are in the form $y = mx + c$, where m is the slope and c is the y-intercept (the y-value where the line crosses the y-axis).

A change in the value of the slope m will result in the slope of the line increasing or decreasing.

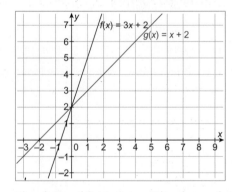

The slope of $f(x)$ is 3. The slope of $g(x)$ is 1.

A change in the value of the y-intercept c will result in the graph of the function moving vertically up or down the y-axis. This transformation will result in a line that is parallel to the original line.

For g(x), the y-intercept is 4.

For f(x), the y-intercept is 2.

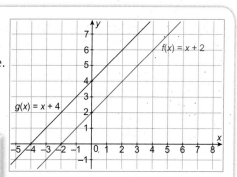

> There are two acceptable ways of writing the y-intercept:
>
> - Stating the y-value only
> - Giving the co-ordinates of the point where the graph crosses the y-axis

Worked Example 9.14

The graph of the function $y = 3x - 4$ is shown.

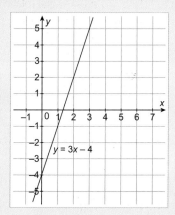

Sketch the graphs of the following functions:

   (i) $y = 3x + 2$ (ii) $y = \frac{3}{4}x - 4$

Solution

   (i) $y = 3x + 2$

The slope has not changed but the y-intercept is now (0,2).

The line will be parallel to the original line but will now be vertically higher so that it goes through the point (0,2).

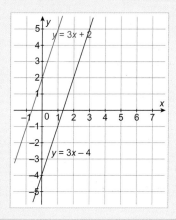

(ii) $y = \frac{3}{4}x - 4$

The y-intercept has not changed, but the slope has changed.

> Remember: Slope = $\dfrac{\text{Rise}}{\text{Run}}$

A slope of $\frac{3}{4}$ means that we move up three units for every four units we go to the right.

We draw a line which goes though the y-intercept (0,–4) with a slope of $\frac{3}{4}$.

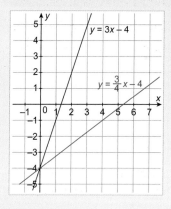

9.6 TRANSFORMATIONS OF QUADRATIC FUNCTIONS

Consider the function $y = x^2$ in the domain $-3 \leqslant x \leqslant 3, x \in R$.

x	x^2	y	(x,y)
−3	$(-3)^2$	9	(−3,9)
−2	$(-2)^2$	4	(−2,4)
−1	$(-1)^2$	1	(−1,1)
0	$(0)^2$	0	(0,0)
1	$(1)^2$	1	(1,1)
2	$(2)^2$	4	(2,4)
3	$(3)^2$	9	(3,9)

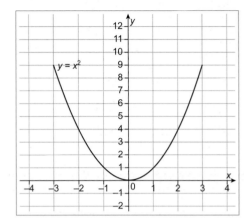

The graph of this function:

- ▪ Goes through the point (0,0)

- ▪ Has (0,0) as its lowest point

- ▪ Is symmetrical about the y-axis

Graphs of Functions of the Form $y = ax^2$, $a > 0$

Consider the function $y = 2x^2$ in the domain $-3 \leqslant x \leqslant 3, x \in R$.

x	$2x^2$	y	(x,y)
−3	$2(-3)^2$	18	(−3,18)
−2	$2(-2)^2$	8	(−2,8)
−1	$2(-1)^2$	2	(−1,2)
0	$2(0)^2$	0	(0,0)
1	$2(1)^2$	2	(1,2)
2	$2(2)^2$	8	(2,8)
3	$2(3)^2$	18	(3,18)

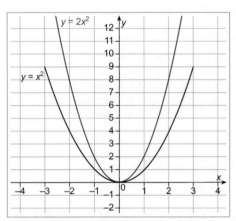

Note: For a given x-value, the y-value has been multiplied by 2.

What do we notice about the graph of $y = 2x^2$?

The graph of $y = 2x^2$:

- ▪ Still goes through the point (0,0)

- ▪ Still has (0,0) as its lowest point

- ▪ Still is symmetrical about the y-axis

- ▪ Is **narrower** than the graph of $y = x^2$

Now, consider the function $y = 3x^2$ in the same domain.

x	$3x^2$	y	(x,y)
−3	$3(−3)^2$	27	(−3,27)
−2	$3(−2)^2$	12	(−2,12)
−1	$3(−1)^2$	3	(−1,3)
0	$3(0)^2$	0	(0,0)
1	$3(1)^2$	3	(1,3)
2	$3(2)^2$	12	(2,12)
3	$3(3)^2$	27	(3,27)

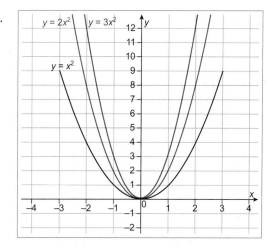

Note: For a given x-value, the y-value has been multiplied by 3.

We can see that the graph of $y = 3x^2$ is narrower than the graphs of the other two functions.

For a quadratic function $f(x) = ax^2$, $a > 0$, as the value of a increases, the graph of $f(x)$ becomes narrower.

Graphs of Functions of the Form $y = x^2 + b$

Consider the function $y = x^2 + 3$ in the domain $−3 \leqslant x \leqslant 3$, $x \in R$.

x	$x^2 + 3$	y	(x,y)
−3	$(−3)^2 + 3$	12	(−3,12)
−2	$(−2)^2 + 3$	7	(−2,7)
−1	$(−1)^2 + 3$	4	(−1,4)
0	$(0)^2 + 3$	3	(0,3)
1	$(1)^2 + 3$	4	(1,4)
2	$(2)^2 + 3$	7	(2,7)
3	$(3)^2 + 3$	12	(3,12)

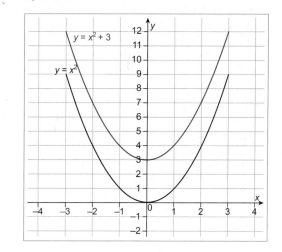

What do we notice about the graph of $y = x^2 + 3$?

The graph of $y = x^2 + 3$:

- Goes through the point (0,3)
- Is symmetrical about the y-axis
- Has (0,3) as its lowest point

In other words, the graph of $y = x^2 + 3$ is the graph of $y = x^2$ shifted (translated) three units upwards.

If b is positive, the graph of $f(x) = x^2 + b$ is the graph of $y = x^2$ shifted b units upwards.

If b is negative, the graph of $f(x) = x^2 + b$ is the graph of $y = x^2$ shifted −b units downwards.

Graphs of Functions of the Form $y = (x + b)^2$

Consider the function $y = (x + 1)^2$ in the same domain.

x	(x + 1)²	y	(x,y)
−3	$(−3 + 1)^2$	4	(−3,4)
−2	$(−2 + 1)^2$	1	(−2,1)
−1	$(−1 + 1)^2$	0	(−1,0)
0	$(0 + 1)^2$	1	(0,1)
1	$(1 + 1)^2$	4	(1,4)
2	$(2 + 1)^2$	9	(2,9)
3	$(3 + 1)^2$	16	(3,16)

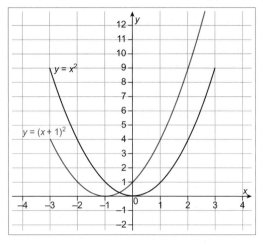

What do we notice about the graph of $y = (x + 1)^2$?

The graph of $y = (x + 1)^2$:

- Goes through the point (−1,0)
- Has (−1,0) as its lowest point
- Is symmetrical about the line $x = −1$

In other words, the graph of $y = (x + 1)^2$ is the graph of $y = x^2$ shifted (translated) one unit to the left.

What do you think the graph of $y = (x − 2)^2$ would look like?

It would be the graph of $y = x^2$ shifted (translated) two units to the right.

If b is positive, the graph of $f(x) = (x + b)^2$ is the graph of $y = x^2$ shifted b units to the left.

If b is negative, the graph of $f(x) = (x + b)^2$ is the graph of $y = x^2$ shifted $−b$ units to the right.

The y-intercept of the function $f(x) = (x + b)^2$ is $(0, (b)^2)$.

Graph the function $f(x) = (x + 2)^2$ in the domain $-5 \leqslant x \leqslant 1, x \in R$.

Use your graph to sketch the graph of:

    (i) $g(x) = (x - 1)^2$ (ii) $h(x) = (x + 2)^2 - 5$

Solution

We first draw the graph of the function $f(x) = (x + 2)^2$ in the domain $-5 \leqslant x \leqslant 1, x \in R$.

x	$(x + 2)^2$	y	(x,y)
−5	$(-3)^2$	9	(−5,9)
−4	$(-2)^2$	4	(−4,4)
−3	$(-1)^2$	1	(−3,1)
−2	$(0)^2$	0	(−2,0)
−1	$(1)^2$	1	(−1,1)
0	$(2)^2$	4	(0,4)
1	$(3)^2$	9	(1,9)

Couples: {(−5,9), (−4,4), (−3,1), (−2,0), (−1,1), (0,4), (1,9)}

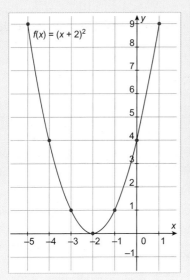

    (i) $g(x) = (x - 1)^2$

        The graph touches the x-axis at (1,0).

        The y-intercept is $(0,(-1)^2) = (0,1)$

        The graph of $g(x)$ is the graph of $f(x)$ shifted three units to the right.

Sketch the function through the point (1,0) and the point (0,1).

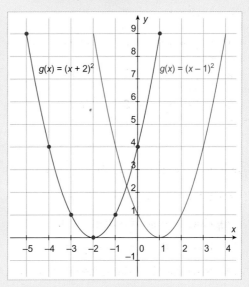

  (ii) $h(x) = (x + 2)^2 - 5$

      The graph of $h(x)$ is the graph of $f(x)$ shifted downwards by five units.

      ∴ The lowest point is (−2,−5) and the y-intercept is (0,−1).

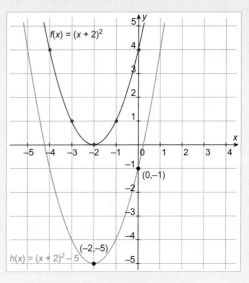

1. The graph of the linear function $f(x) = 2x + 5$ is shown. Use your graph to match the following functions with the functions shown on the graph:

   (a) $g(x) = 2x - 1$ (b) $h(x) = 2x + 2$

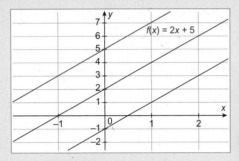

2. The graph of the linear function $f(x) = 4x - 1$ is shown. Use your graph to match the following functions with the functions shown on the graph:

   (a) $g(x) = x - 1$ (b) $h(x) = x + 3$

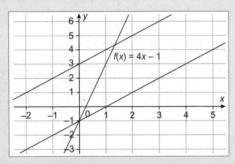

3. The graph of the function $y = 2x + 1$ is shown. Copy this graph into your copybook and sketch the graphs of the following functions:

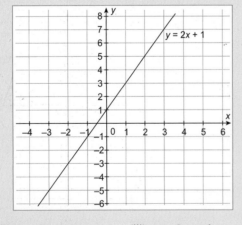

   (i) $y = 2x + 4$ (iii) $y = 3x + 1$

   (ii) $y = 2x - 3$

4. Graph the function $y = -2x + 4$ in the domain $-3 \leqslant x \leqslant 3, x \in R$.

   Hence, sketch the graph of the following functions:

   (i) $f(x) = -2x + 3$ (iii) $h(x) = x + 3$

   (ii) $g(x) = 2x + 4$

5. Graph the function $f: x \rightarrow 3x - 2$ in the domain $-5 \leqslant x \leqslant 2, x \in R$.

   Hence, sketch the graph of the following functions:

   (i) $j(x) = 3x + 3$ (iii) $h(x) = x + 6$

   (ii) $g(x) = -3x + 3$

6. The graph of the function $y = x^2$ is shown. Use this graph to match the following functions with the functions shown on the graph:

   (i) $y = 3x^2$ (ii) $y = 5x^2$

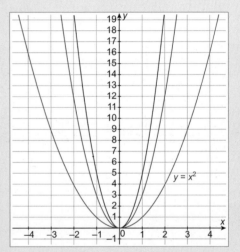

7. The graph of the function $y = x^2$ is shown. Use this graph to match the following functions with the functions shown on the graph:

   (i) $y = x^2 - 3$ (ii) $y = x^2 + 4$

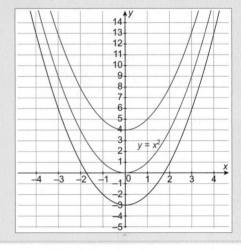

8. The graph of $f(x) = x^2 + x + 2$ is shown. Use this graph to match the following functions with the functions shown on the graph:

(i) $g(x) = 3x^2 + 3x + 6$

(ii) $h(x) = x^2 + x + 4$

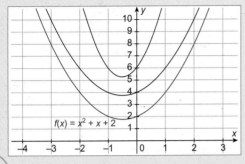

$f(x) = x^2 + x + 2$

9. The graph of the function $y = x^2$ is shown. Use this graph to match the following functions with the functions shown on the graph:

(i) $y = (x + 1)^2$ (ii) $y = (x - 5)^2$

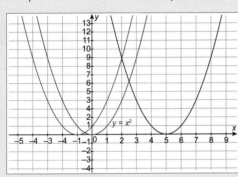

$y = x^2$

10. Graph the function $f(x) = 2x^2$ in the domain $-3 \leqslant x \leqslant 3, x \in R$.

Hence, sketch the following functions:

(i) $g(x) = 4x^2$ (ii) $h(x) = 3x^2$

11. Graph the function $f(x) = 2x^2 + 4$ in the domain $-4 \leqslant x \leqslant 3, x \in R$.

Hence, sketch the following functions:

(i) $g(x) = 2x^2 + 1$ (ii) $h(x) = 2x^2 - 2$

12. The graph of the function $f(x) = (x - 3)^2$ is shown.

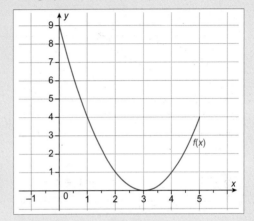

$f(x)$

Sketch the following functions:

(i) $g(x) = (x - 3)^2 + 6$ (iii) $i(x) = (x - 2)^2$

(ii) $h(x) = 2(x - 3)^2$

9.7 TRANSFORMATIONS OF CUBIC FUNCTIONS

Consider the function $y = x^3$ in the domain $-2 \leqslant x \leqslant 2, x \in R$.

x	x^3	y	(x,y)
−2	$(-2)^3$	−8	(−2,−8)
−1	$(-1)^3$	−1	(−1,−1)
0	$(0)^3$	0	(0,0)
1	$(1)^3$	1	(1,1)
2	$(2)^3$	8	(2,8)

Note the shape of this graph and how the graph passes through (0,0).

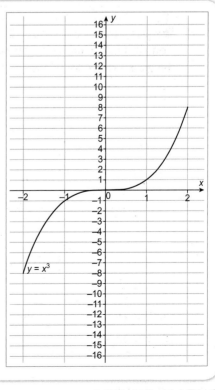

$y = x^3$

Graphs of Functions of the Form $y = ax^3$, $a > 0$

Consider the function $y = 2x^3$ in the same domain.

x	2x³	y	(x,y)
–2	$2(-2)^3$	–16	(–2,–16)
–1	$2(-1)^3$	–2	(–1,–2)
0	$2(0)^3$	0	(0,0)
1	$2(1)^3$	2	(1,2)
2	$2(2)^3$	16	(2,16)

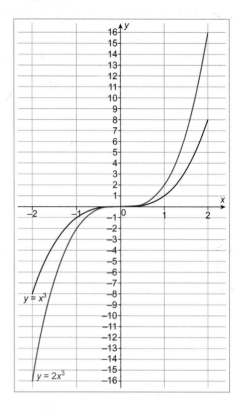

Note: For a given x-value, the y-value has been multiplied by 2.

We can see that, in comparison with the graph of $y = x^3$, the graph of $y = 2x^3$ is stretched vertically.

Now consider the function $y = 0.5x^3$ in the same domain.

x	0.5x³	y	(x,y)
–2	$0.5(-2)^3$	–4	(–2,–4)
–1	$0.5(-1)^3$	–0.5	(–1,–0.5)
0	$0.5(0)^3$	0	(0,0)
1	$0.5(1)^3$	0.5	(1,0.5)
2	$0.5(2)^3$	4	(2,4)

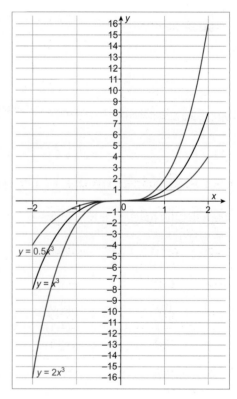

Note: For a given x-value, the y-value has been multiplied by 0.5.

We can see that, in comparison with the graph of $y = x^3$, the graph of $y = 0.5x^3$ is compressed vertically.

For a cubic function of the form $f(x) = ax^3$, $a > 0$, as a increases in value, the graph of $f(x)$ is stretched vertically. As a decreases in value, the graph of $f(x)$ is compressed vertically.

Graphs of Functions of the Form $y = x^3 + b$

Consider the function $y = x^3 + 1$ in the same domain.

x	$x^3 + 1$	y	(x,y)
-2	$(-2)^3 + 1$	-7	$(-2,-7)$
-1	$(-1)^3 + 1$	0	$(-1,0)$
0	$(0)^3 + 1$	1	$(0,1)$
1	$(1)^3 + 1$	2	$(1,2)$
2	$(2)^3 + 1$	9	$(2,9)$

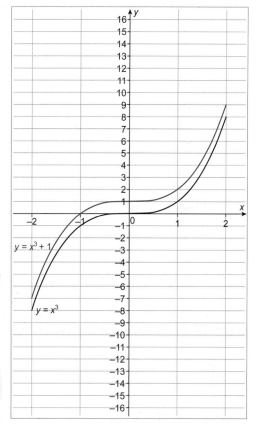

We can see that the graph of $y = x^3 + 1$ is the graph of $y = x^3$ shifted (translated) one unit upwards.

What would you expect the graph of $y = x^3 - 2$ to look like?

The graph of $y = x^3 - 2$ is the graph of $y = x^3$ shifted (translated) two units downwards.

> If b is positive, the graph of $f(x) = x^3 + b$ is the graph of $y = x^3$ shifted b units upwards.

> If b is negative, the graph of $f(x) = x^3 + b$ is the graph of $y = x^3$ shifted $-b$ units downwards.

Graphs of Functions of the Form $y = (x + b)^3$

Consider the function $y = (x + 1)^3$ in the same domain.

x	$(x + 1)^3$	y	(x,y)
-2	$(-1)^3$	-1	$(-2,-1)$
-1	$(0)^3$	0	$(-1,0)$
0	$(1)^3$	1	$(0,1)$
1	$(2)^3$	8	$(1,8)$
2	$(3)^3$	27	$(2,27)$

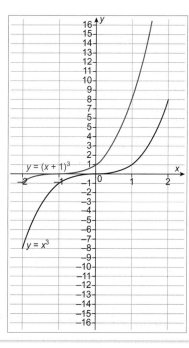

What do you notice about the graph of $y = (x + 1)^3$?

It is the graph of $y = x^3$ shifted (translated) one unit to the left.
The y-intercept is $(0, (1)^3) = (0,1)$.

What would you expect the graph of $y = (x - 2)^3$ to look like?

The graph of $y = (x - 2)^3$ is the graph of $y = x^3$ shifted (translated) two units to the right.
The y-intercept is $(0, (-2)^3) = (0, -8)$.

> If b is positive, the graph of $f(x) = (x + b)^3$ is the graph of $y = x^3$ shifted b units to the left.

> If b is negative, the graph of $f(x) = (x + b)^3$ is the graph of $y = x^3$ shifted $-b$ units to the right.

> The y-intercept of the function $f(x) = (x + b)^3$ is $(0, (b)^3)$.

Worked Example 9.16

Graph the function $f(x) = x^3 - 2x^2 - 5x + 6$ in the domain $-2 \leqslant x \leqslant 3, x \in R$.

Hence, sketch the following functions:

   (i) $g(x) = 0.5(x^3 - 2x^2 - 5x + 6)$

   (ii) $h(x) = x^3 - 2x^2 - 5x + 9$

Solution

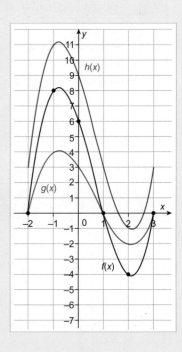

x	$x^3 - 2x^2 - 5x + 6$	y	(x, y)
-2	$(-2)^3 - 2(-2)^2 - 5(-2) + 6$	0	$(-2, 0)$
-1	$(-1)^3 - 2(-1)^2 - 5(-1) + 6$	8	$(-1, 8)$
0	$(0)^3 - 2(0)^2 - 5(0) + 6$	6	$(0, 6)$
1	$(1)^3 - 2(1)^2 - 5(1) + 6$	0	$(1, 0)$
2	$(2)^3 - 2(2)^2 - 5(2) + 6$	-4	$(2, -4)$
3	$(3)^3 - 2(3)^2 - 5(3) + 6$	0	$(3, 0)$

   (i) Multiplying the function by 0.5 causes the graph of $f(x)$ to be compressed by a factor 0.5.
Each y-value is halved.

   (ii) $h(x) = x^3 - 2x^2 - 5x + 9$

$$= x^3 - 2x^2 - 5x + 6 + 3$$

$$\therefore h(x) = f(x) + 3$$

Adding 3 to the function shifts the graph of $f(x)$ vertically upwards by three units.

Worked Example 9.17

Graph the function $y = (x - 3)^3$ in the domain $2 \leqslant x \leqslant 4, x \in R$.

Hence, sketch the following functions:

    (i) $f(x) = (x - 2)^3$

    (ii) $g(x) = (x - 3)^3 + 1$

Solution

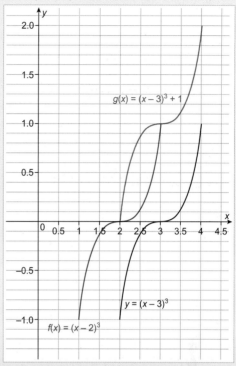

x	$(x - 3)^3$	y	(x, y)
2	$(2 - 3)^3$	-1	$(2, -1)$
2.5	$(2.5 - 3)^3$	-0.125	$(2.5, -0.125)$
3	$(3 - 3)^3$	0	$(3, 0)$
3.5	$(3.5 - 3)^3$	0.125	$(3.5, 0.125)$
4	$(4 - 3)^3$	1	$(4, 1)$

    (i) All the points on the graph of $y = (x - 3)^3$ have been shifted to the left by one unit.

    (ii) All the points on the graph of $y = (x - 3)^3$ have been shifted vertically upwards by one unit.

 Exercise 9.6

1. Shown below is the graph of the function $f(x) = x^3 - 6x + x + 1$. Use the graph to match the functions with those graphed below.

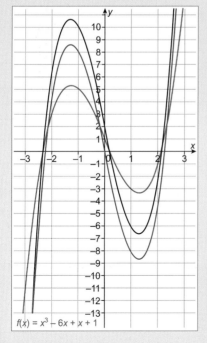

    (i) $g(x) = 2 (x^3 - 6x + x + 1)$

    (ii) $h(x) = 2 (x^3 - 6x + x + 1) - 2$

2. Shown below is the graph of the function $f(x) = (x - 4)^3$. Use the graph to match the functions with those graphed below.

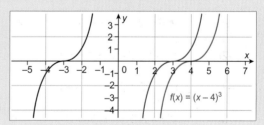

    (i) $g(x) = (x - 3)^3$ (ii) $h(x) = (x + 3)^3$

3. Graph the function $f(x) = x^3$ over the domain $-2 \leqslant x \leqslant 2, x \in R$.

    Hence, sketch the following functions:

    (i) $g(x) = x^3 + 2$ (iii) $k(x) = 2x^3 - 2$

    (ii) $h(x) = 2x^3$

4. Sketch the following functions on the same axes and scales (use a domain of $-2 \leqslant x \leqslant 2, x \in R$):

    (i) $f(x) = 2x^3$ (ii) $g(x) = -x^3$

    What do each of these graphs have in common? How are they different?

5. Graph the function $f(x) = -x^3$ over the domain $-2 \leqslant x \leqslant 2, x \in R$.
   Hence, sketch the function $g(x) = -x^3 + 4$.

6. Sketch the function $f(x) = 2(x - 2)^3 + 4$.
   Hint: Begin by graphing the function $y = x^3$, using a domain of $-2 \leqslant x \leqslant 2, x \in R$.

7. Sketch the function $h: x \to 3(x + 1)^3 + 4$.

8. The graphs of $f(x)$ and $g(x)$ are given below.

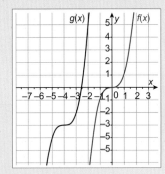

(i) Describe in your own words a transformation that would map the graph of $f(x)$ to the graph of $g(x)$.

(ii) Write the functional form of $g(x)$ in terms of x.

9. The graph of $f(x) = 2x^3$ has been vertically compressed by a factor of 0.5.
   What is the new functional form?

10. The graph of $f(x) = x^3 - 3$ has been shifted right by two units and down by three units.
    What is the new functional form?

9.8 TRANSFORMATIONS OF EXPONENTIAL FUNCTIONS

Consider the function $y = 2^x$ in the domain $-2 \leqslant x \leqslant 2, x \in R$.

x	2^x	y	(x,y)
-2	$2^{-2} = \frac{1}{2^2}$	$\frac{1}{4}$	$\left(-2, \frac{1}{4}\right)$
-1	$2^{-1} = \frac{1}{2^1}$	$\frac{1}{2}$	$\left(-1, \frac{1}{2}\right)$
0	2^0	1	$(0,1)$
1	2^1	2	$(1,2)$
2	2^2	4	$(2,4)$

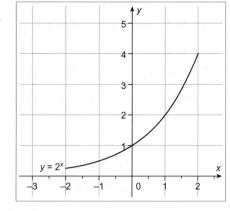

The graph of $y = 2^x$ is upward sloping and passes through the point $(0,1)$.

Graphs of Functions of the Form $y = ak^x$, $a > 0$

Consider the function $y = 2(2^x)$ in the same domain.

x	$2(2^x)$	y	(x,y)
-2	$2(2^{-2}) = 2\left(\frac{1}{2^2}\right)$	$\frac{1}{2}$	$\left(-2, \frac{1}{2}\right)$
-1	$2(2^{-1}) = 2\left(\frac{1}{2^1}\right)$	1	$(-1,1)$
0	$2(2^0) = 2(1)$	2	$(0,2)$
1	$2(2^1) = 2(2)$	4	$(1,4)$
2	$2(2^2) = 2(4)$	8	$(2,8)$

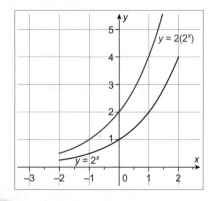

Note: For a given x-value, we multiply the y-value by 2.

What do you notice about the graph of $y = 2(2^x)$?

- The graph of $y = 2(2^x)$ is upward sloping.
- The graph passes through the point $(0,2)$.
- The graph of $y = 2(2^x)$ lies above the graph of $y = 2^x$. This is because, compared with $y = 2^x$, for a given x-value, each y-value has been multiplied by 2.

Consider the function $y = \frac{1}{2}(2^x)$ in the same domain.

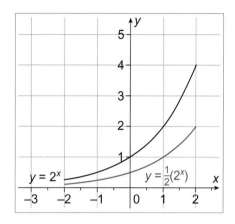

x	$\left(\frac{1}{2}\right)2^x$	y	(x,y)
-2	$\frac{1}{2}(2^{-2}) = \frac{1}{2}\left(\frac{1}{2^2}\right)$	$\frac{1}{8}$	$\left(-2,\frac{1}{8}\right)$
-1	$\frac{1}{2}(2^{-1}) = \frac{1}{2}\left(\frac{1}{2}\right)$	$\frac{1}{4}$	$\left(-1,\frac{1}{4}\right)$
0	$\frac{1}{2}(2^0) = \frac{1}{2}(1)$	$\frac{1}{2}$	$\left(0,\frac{1}{2}\right)$
1	$\frac{1}{2}(2^1) = \frac{1}{2}(2)$	1	$(1,1)$
2	$\frac{1}{2}(2^2) = \frac{1}{2}(4)$	2	$(2,2)$

Note: For a given x-value, we multiply the y-value by $\frac{1}{2}$.

What do you notice about the graph of $y = \frac{1}{2}(2^x)$?

- The graph of $y = \frac{1}{2}(2^x)$ is upward sloping.
- The graph passes through the point $\left(0,\frac{1}{2}\right)$.
- The graph of $y = \frac{1}{2}(2^x)$ lies below the graph of $y = 2^x$. This is because, compared with $y = 2^x$, for a given x-value, each y-value has been multiplied by $\frac{1}{2}$.

> The graph of $f(x) = a.k^x$, $a > 0$, lies above the graph of $y = k^x$ if $a > 1$.

> The graph of $f(x) = a.k^x$, $a > 0$, lies below the graph of $y = k^x$ if $a < 1$.

> The graph of $f(x) = a.k^x$, passes through the point $(0,a)$.

Graphs of Functions of the Form $y = k^x + b$

> The graph of the function $f(x) = k^x + b$ is the graph of $y = k^x$ shifted b units upwards if $b > 0$ **or** shifted $-b$ units downwards if $b < 0$.

Consider the function $y = 2^x + 1$ in the same domain.

x	2ˣ + 1	y	(x,y)
−2	$2^{-2} + 1 = \frac{1}{2^2} + 1$	1.25	(−2,1.25)
−1	$2^{-1} + 1 = \frac{1}{2^1} + 1$	1.5	(−1,1.5)
0	$2^0 + 1 = 1 + 1$	2	(0,2)
1	$2^1 + 1 = 2 + 1$	3	(1,3)
2	$2^2 + 1 = 4 + 1$	5	(2,5)

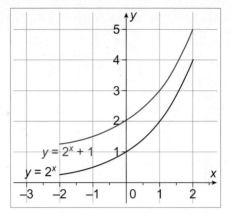

We can see that the graph of $y = 2^x + 1$ is the graph of $y = 2^x$ shifted (translated) one unit upwards.

Graphs of Functions of the Form $y = k^{x+h}$

Consider the function $y = 2^{x+1}$ in the same domain.

x	2ˣ⁺¹	y	(x,y)
−2	2^{-1}	$\frac{1}{2}$	$\left(-2,\frac{1}{2}\right)$
−1	2^0	1	(−1,1)
0	2^1	2	(0,2)
1	2^2	4	(1,4)
2	2^3	8	(2,8)

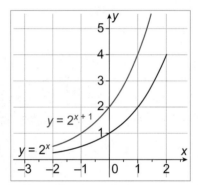

Note the position of the graph of $y = 2^{x+1}$. There are two ways of thinking about this graph:

    (1) The graph of $y = 2^{x+1}$ ($= 2(2^x)$) lies above the graph of $y = 2^x$.

    (2) The graph of $y = 2^{x+1}$ is the graph of $y = 2^x$ shifted one unit to the left.

Consider the function $y = 2^{x-1}$ in the same domain.

x	2ˣ⁻¹	y	(x,y)
−2	$2^{-3} = \frac{1}{2^3}$	$\frac{1}{8}$	$\left(-2,\frac{1}{8}\right)$
−1	$2^{-2} = \frac{1}{2^2}$	$\frac{1}{4}$	$\left(-1,\frac{1}{4}\right)$
0	$2^{-1} = \frac{1}{2^1}$	$\frac{1}{2}$	$\left(0,\frac{1}{2}\right)$
1	$2^0 = 1$	1	(1,1)
2	$2^1 = 2$	2	(2,2)

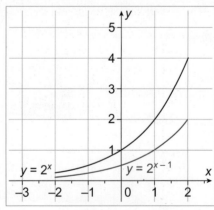

Note the position of the graph of $y = 2^{x-1}$.

    (1) The graph of $y = 2^{x-1}$ ($= 2^{-1}.2^x = \frac{1}{2}(2^x)$) lies below the graph of $y = 2^x$.

    (2) The graph of $y = 2^{x-1}$ is the graph of $y = 2^x$ shifted one unit to the right.

The graph of $f(x) = k^{x+h}$ is the graph of $y = k^x$ shifted h units to the left if $h > 0$ **or** $−h$ units to the right if $h < 0$.

GRAPHING FUNCTIONS

Worked Example 9.18

Graph the function $y = 3(3^x)$ in the domain $-3 \leqslant x \leqslant 2, x \in R$.

Hence, sketch the functions:

(i) $f(x) = 3^x$ (ii) $g(x) = 3^{x-1}$

Solution

x	$3(3^x)$	y	(x,y)
-3	$3(3^{-3})$	0.11	$(-3, 0.11)$
-2	$3(3^{-2})$	0.33	$(-2, 0.33)$
-1	$3(3^{-1})$	1	$(-1, 1)$
0	$3(3^0)$	3	$(0, 3)$
1	$3(3^1)$	9	$(1, 9)$
2	$3(3^2)$	27	$(2, 27)$

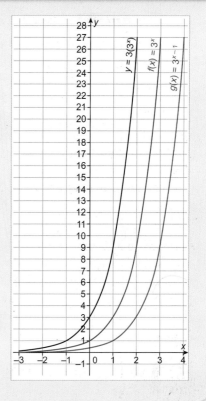

(i) $y = 3(3^x) \Rightarrow y = 3^{x+1}$

Therefore, the graph of $f(x) = 3^x$ is the graph of 3^{x+1} shifted one unit to the right.

(ii) $f(x) = 3^x$. Therefore, the graph of $g(x) = 3^{x-1}$ is the graph of 3^x shifted one unit to the right.

 Exercise 9.7

1. Shown below is the graph of the function $f(x) = 3(2^x)$. Use the graph to match the functions with those graphed below.

   (i) $g(x) = 2^x$ (ii) $h(x) = 2^{x-1}$

   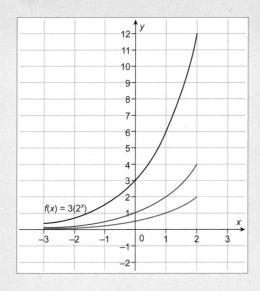

2. Shown below is the graph of the function $f(x) = 4^x$. Use the graph to match the functions with those graphed below.

   (i) $g(x) = (0.5)4^x$ (ii) $h(x) = 4^{x+1}$

   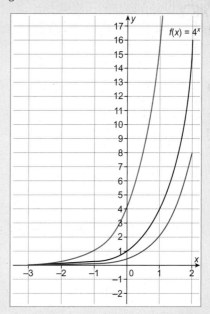

3. Shown below is the graph of the function $f(x) = 8^x$. Use the graph to match the functions with those graphed below.

(i) $g(x) = 0.5(8^x)$ (ii) $h(x) = 8^x - 2$

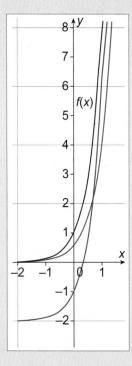

4. Graph the function $y = 2^x$ over the domain $-2 \leqslant x \leqslant 2, x \in R$.

Hence, sketch the functions:

(i) $f(x) = 2^{x+1}$ (iii) $h(x) = 3(2^x)$

(ii) $g(x) = 2^x + 2$

5. Graph the function $f(x) = \left(\frac{1}{2}\right)^x$ over the domain $-3 \leqslant x \leqslant 3, x \in R$.

Hence, sketch the functions:

(i) $g(x) = 2\left(\frac{1}{2}\right)^x$ (ii) $h(x) = \left(\frac{1}{2}\right)^x + 1$

6. The graphs of the functions $f(x) = 2^x$ and $g(x)$ are given.

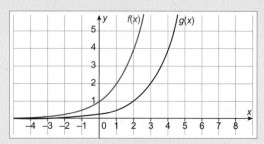

(i) Describe in your own words a transformation that would map the graph of $f(x)$ to the graph of $g(x)$.

(ii) What is the functional form of $g(x)$?

7. The graph of the function $y = 3^x$ is shifted three units to the right.
What is the new functional form?

8. The graph of the function $y = 4^x$ is stretched vertically by a factor of 3 and is shifted to the right by three units.
What is the new functional form?

9. The graph of the function $y = 2^x$ is shifted to the left by two units and is shifted upwards by three units.
What is the new functional form?

Revision Exercises

1. Draw a graph of the following functions with the given domains:

	Function	Domain
(i)	$f(x) = 3x - 4$	$-2 \leqslant x \leqslant 2, x \in R$
(ii)	$g(x) = 2 - 2.5x$	$-3 \leqslant x \leqslant 1, x \in R$
(iii)	$h(x) = 6 - 4x$	$0 \leqslant x \leqslant 5, x \in R$

2. Draw the graph of the linear function $f: x \rightarrow 3x - 2$ in the domain $-3 \leqslant x \leqslant 4, x \in R$.

Use your graph to estimate:

(i) The value of $f(x)$ when $x = 2.5$

(ii) The value of x for which $3x - 2 = 6$

(iii) The value of x for which $3x - 3 = -5$

(iv) The range of values of x for which $f(x) \geqslant 0$

3. Using the same axes and scales, draw the two graphs $f(x) = 3x - 8$ and $g(x) = 8 - 2x$ in the domain $-1 \leqslant x \leqslant 4, x \in R$. What is the point of intersection of the two graphs?

4. A student suggests that the number of times a student goes out in a six-month period and the amount of weekly disposable income a student has over that period are given by a linear function $y = 1 + 0.2x$, where x represents the weekly disposable income in euro and y represents the number of times the student goes out.

   (i) Copy and complete the following table, and hence, draw the graph for the given domain:

Income (€)	10	20	30	40	50	60	70	80	90	100
Number of times to go out										

   (ii) Estimate from your graph the number of times a student with a weekly income of €55 will go out in the six months.

   (iii) Estimate from your graph the weekly income of a student who goes out 15 times in the six months.

   (iv) Estimate from your graph the weekly income of a student who goes out at least eight times in the six months.

5. Draw the graph of the function $f: x \rightarrow x^2 - 3x - 4$ in the domain $-2 \leqslant x \leqslant 4$, $x \in R$.

   Estimate from your graph:

   (i) The value of $f(2.2)$

   (ii) The value of x for which $x^2 - 3x - 5 = 0$

   (iii) The values of x for which $x^2 - 3x - 4 \leqslant 0$

   (iv) The minimum value of $f(x)$

6. Draw the graph of the function $f: x \rightarrow 6 - 3x - x^2$ in the domain $-5 \leqslant x \leqslant 3$, $x \in R$.

   Find from your graph:

   (i) The value of $f(-1.5)$

   (ii) The values of x for which $y = 2$

   (iii) The maximum value of $f(x)$

   (iv) The range of values of k for which $f(x) = k$ has two distinct real solutions

7. Use the same scales and axes to draw the graphs of the two functions $f(x) = 3 - 2x + x^2$ and $g(x) = 5 - 2x - x^2$ in the domain $-3 \leqslant x \leqslant 2, x \in R$.

   (i) Use your graphs to estimate the values of x for which $f(x) = g(x)$.

   (ii) Use your graphs to estimate the values of x for which $f(x) \geqslant g(x)$.

   (iii) Use your graphs to estimate the values of x for which $f(x) < g(x)$.

8. The function graphed below is $f(x) = ax^2 + bx + c$,
   Find the values of a, b and c.

   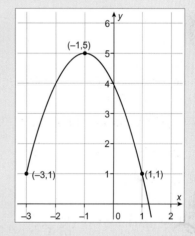

9. Graph the following functions in the given domain:

	Function	Domain
(i)	$f(x) = x^3 + x^2 - 3x + 1$	$-3 \leqslant x \leqslant 2, x \in R$
(ii)	$g(x) = x^3 - 2x^2 - 2x + 2$	$-2 \leqslant x \leqslant 3, x \in R$
(iii)	$h(x) = 2x^3 + 4x^2 - x$	$-3 \leqslant x \leqslant 1, x \in R$
(iv)	$p(x) = 3x^3 - 6x^2 - 6x + 2$	$-1 \leqslant x \leqslant 3, x \in R$

10. Draw the graph of the cubic function $f: x \rightarrow x^3 + 3x^2 + 2x - 3$ in the domain $-3 \leqslant x \leqslant 1, x \in R$.

    Estimate from your graph:

    (i) The value of x for which $f(x) = 0$

    (ii) The values of x for which $f(x) = -3$

    (iii) The number of real roots of the function

11. On the same axes and scales, graph the functions $f: x \rightarrow x^3 - 3x^2 + 2x + 3$ and $g: x \rightarrow 5 + 2x - x^2$ in the domain $-1.5 \leqslant x \leqslant 3.5, x \in R$.

Use your graph to approximate the value of x for which $f(x) = g(x)$.

12. On the same axes and scales, graph the functions

$f: x \rightarrow \frac{1}{2}x + 2$

$g: x \rightarrow 2x^2 - 2x + 1$

$h: x \rightarrow x^3 - 3x^2 - x + 3$

in the domain $-2 \leqslant x \leqslant 3, x \in R$.

Using your graph, approximate:

(i) The values of x for which $f(x) = h(x)$

(ii) The values of x for which $g(x) = h(x)$

13. The graph of $f(x) = x^2 + 2x + 3$ is shown. Use this graph to match the following functions with the functions shown on the graph:

(i) $g(x) = 2x^2 + 4x + 6$

(ii) $h(x) = x^2 + 2x + 4$

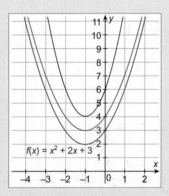

14. The graph of the function $y = 3^x$ is stretched vertically by a factor of 2. What is the new functional form?

15.

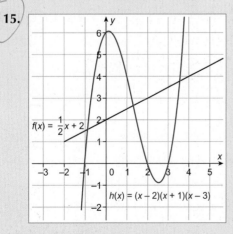

(i) Use the diagram to estimate the approximate value of $f(1.5)$

(ii) Use the diagram to estimate the approximate value of x if $f(x) = 3.5$

(iii) Use the diagram to estimate the value of x for which $f(x) = g(x)$

16. Graph the following exponential functions in the domain $-3 \leqslant x \leqslant 2, x \in R$:

(i) $f(x) = 2(3^x)$ (iii) $h(x) = 3(2^x)$

(ii) $g(x) = 2(1.5^x)$ (iv) $p(x) = 3(0.5^x)$

17. Identify the a-value in the function $y = ab^x$ graphed below.

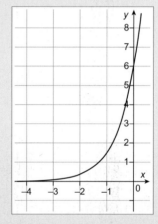

18. Identify the values of a and b in the function $y = ab^x$ graphed below.

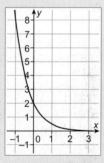

19. Charlie puts a proposal to his parents. He asks for his pocket money to be paid in the following way:

Week 1: he will receive €1;

Week 2: he will receive €2;

Week 3: he will receive €4, and so on.

(i) Set up a table to show the amount of pocket money Charlie will receive each week for the first eight weeks.

(ii) Graph the data in the table, placing the week number on the x-axis.

(iii) What type of function is this?
Explain your answer.

(iv) Is it possible that the pattern of payments is different to the pattern you described in part (i)?
Explain your answer.

20. Label each function on the graph below.

    (i) $f(x) = 2^x$

  (ii) $g(x) = x^2 + 3x - 4$

 (iii) $h(x) = x^3 - 2x^2 - 5x + 6$

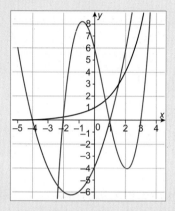

21. An investment follows the following growth model: $F = P(1 + i)^t$, where P is the initial amount invested, i is the rate of interest, and t is the length of time in years.

Consider an initial investment of €400 invested at 12% per annum for five years.

  (i) Calculate the value of the investment at the end of each year for the first five years of the investment.

 (ii) Using the number of years as the x-variable and the final value as the y-variable, graph the growth of the investment over a five-year period.

(iii) Clearly identify the base and the exponent in the formula $F = P(1 + i)^t$.

(iv) Use your graph to estimate the value of the investment after three years and three months.

22. A pension fund started to decline following an exponential decay model given by the function $y = 100{,}000(4^{-x})$, where x is years passed and y is value in euros.

  (i) What was the initial value of the pension fund before the decline in value?

 (ii) Graph the value of the pension fund over a five-year period.

(iii) How long does it take for the value of the fund to decay to €50,000?

(iv) Will the pension fund ever reach a value of €0?

23. Two functions f and g are defined for $x \in R$ as follows:

$f: x \mapsto 2^x$
$g: x \mapsto 9x - 3x^2 - 1$

(a) Complete the table below, and use it to draw the graphs of f and g for $0 \leqslant x \leqslant 3$.

x	0	0.5	1	1.5	2	2.5	3
f(x)							
g(x)							

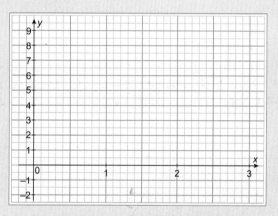

(b) Use your graphs to estimate the value(s) of x for which $2^x + 3x^2 - 9x + 1 = 0$.

(c) Let k be the number such that $2^k = 6$. Using your graph(s), or otherwise, estimate $g(k)$.

SEC Project Maths Sample Paper 1, Leaving Certificate Ordinary Level, 2012

GRAPHING FUNCTIONS

NADA	CAD	0.9512
A	CNY	7.3169
EURO	EUR	0.6644
JAPAN	JPY	109.00
SINGAPORE	SGD	1.3712
		7.0043

Arithmetic II

Learning Outcomes

In this chapter you will learn to:

- ➲ Use the equivalence of fractions, decimals and percentages to compare proportions

- ➲ Round off a result

- ➲ Make and justify estimates and approximations of calculations and calculate percentage error and tolerance

- ➲ Accumulate error (by addition or subtraction only)

- ➲ Calculate average rates of change (with respect to time)

- ➲ Solve problems involving:
  - ➲ Domestic bills and charges
  - ➲ Currency transactions
  - ➲ Metric system, change of units, everyday imperial units (conversion factors provided)
  - ➲ Costing: materials, labour and wastage

10.1 INTRODUCTION

Proportional Parts – Dividing Quantities in a Given Ratio

Ratios are often used to divide or share quantities.

 ## Worked Example 10.1

A pizza is cut into 14 equal slices and is shared between Alan, Brian and Ciara in the ratio 2 : 2 : 3, respectively.

How many slices does each person get?

Solution

Step 1   Write down the total number of parts.

$2 + 2 + 3 = 7$

Step 2   Express each person's share as a fraction of the total number of parts.

Alan	Brian	Ciara
$\frac{2}{7}$	$\frac{2}{7}$	$\frac{3}{7}$

Step 3   Multiply each fraction by the amount to be shared.

Alan $\frac{2}{7} \times 14 = 4$ slices

Brian $\frac{2}{7} \times 14 = 4$ slices

Ciara $\frac{3}{7} \times 14 = 6$ slices

 ## Worked Example 10.2

Ben and Niall are the owners of a company. Ben has 30,000 shares and Niall has 20,000 shares. After taxes, the company has made a profit of €150,000 this year. The profit is divided between them in the ratio of their shareholdings.

(i)   In what ratio will the profits be divided?

(ii)   How much will Niall receive?

(iii)   Who receives the bigger share of the profits?

Solution

(i)   Ben : Niall

30,000 : 20,000

Ratio = 3 : 2

> Write ratios as whole numbers in their simplest form.

(ii) $3 + 2 = 5$ parts

Niall receives $\frac{2}{5}$:

$\frac{2}{5} \times €150,000 = €60,000$

∴ Niall's share of the profits = €60,000.

(iii) Ben's share = €150,000 − €60,000

= €90,000

∴ Ben receives the bigger share of the profits.

Worked Example 10.3

In making road grit, rock salt and sand are mixed together in the ratio 6 : 11, respectively. The amount of rock salt used is 312 kg. How many kilograms of sand are used?

Solution

Step 1 Rock salt = 6 parts = 312 kg

Step 2 Find what 1 part is.

$1 \text{ part} = \frac{312}{6}$

$= 52 \text{ kg}$

Step 3 Find the amount of sand used.

11 parts = $52 \times 11 = 572$

∴ Sand used = 572 kg

Exercise 10.1

1. Simplify each of the following ratios:

(i) 2 : 4

(ii) 20 : 15

(iii) 72 : 120

(iv) 14 : 28 : 42

(v) 27 : 63 : 108

(vi) $\frac{1}{2} : \frac{3}{4}$

(vii) $\frac{1}{3} : 1$

(viii) $\frac{1}{2} : \frac{1}{4} : 2$

(ix) $\frac{1}{2} : \frac{3}{4} : \frac{3}{8}$

(x) $\frac{1}{5} : \frac{3}{15} : \frac{2}{10}$

2.
(i) Divide 450 g in the ratio 7 : 2.

(ii) Divide €132 in the ratio 7 : 4.

(iii) Divide 169 cm in the ratio 9 : 4.

(iv) Divide €4,500 in the ratio 6 : 9.

(v) Divide 156 kg in the ratio 8 : 5.

(vi) Divide 90 m in the ratio 1 : 2 : 3.

(vii) Divide 840 g in the ratio 5 : 1 : 1.

(viii) Divide €900 in the ratio 7 : 8 : 3.

(ix) Divide 221 g in the ratio 8 : 1 : 4.

(x) Divide 552 cm in the ratio 3 : 5 : 4.

3.
(i) Divide 450 g in the ratio $1 : \frac{1}{2}$.

(ii) Divide €150 in the ratio $\frac{1}{2} : \frac{3}{4}$.

(iii) Divide 132 mm in the ratio $\frac{1}{3} : 1$.

(iv) Divide 4,400 g in the ratio $\frac{1}{2} : \frac{1}{4} : 2$.

(v) Divide 156 kg in the ratio $\frac{1}{2} : \frac{3}{4} : \frac{3}{8}$.

(vi) Divide 900 m in the ratio $\frac{1}{5} : \frac{3}{15} : \frac{2}{10}$.

(vii) Divide 444 g in the ratio $\frac{1}{2} : \frac{5}{6} : \frac{2}{3}$.

(viii) Divide €1,425 in the ratio $\frac{2}{3} : \frac{3}{4} : \frac{1}{6}$.

(ix) Divide 222 g in the ratio $\frac{1}{3} : \frac{2}{9} : \frac{3}{27}$.

(x) Divide 700 cm in the ratio $\frac{3}{14} : \frac{6}{7}$.

4. In a salad dressing, the ratio of oil to vinegar is 3 : 1. If James makes 200 ml of dressing, how many millilitres of vinegar are used?

5. A school is given a grant of €4,800 for sports equipment for its volleyball and soccer teams. In the school, 184 students play volleyball and 296 play soccer. It is decided to divide the money in the ratio of players playing each sport.

How much does each team receive?

6. A teacher gives a prize of €24 to the three students who have made the biggest effort in her class. She decides to divide the money in the ratio of their results.

If the results of the winners are 94%, 83% and 63%, how will the €24 be divided?

7. (i) A prize is divided between Alan and Niall in the ratio 1 : $\frac{1}{2}$. If Alan receives €400, what is the total prize?

(ii) Two lengths of pipe are in the ratio $\frac{1}{2}$: $\frac{3}{4}$. If the longer piece is 45 cm, what length is the shorter piece of pipe?

(iii) Colin has two children aged 9 years and 4 years. He won a sum of money playing the lottery and decided to divide it between his two children in the ratio of their ages. If his youngest child gets €340, how much did Colin win?

(iv) Ross makes biscuits mixing sugar and flour in the ratio 6 : 9. If he uses 180 g of sugar, how much flour is used?

(v) A piece of wood is cut in the ratio 5 : 2 : 1. If the shortest piece is 120 cm, what is the length of each of the other two pieces?

(vi) A sum of money is divided between three people in the ratio 7 : 8 : 3.

If the largest amount is €400, what is the smallest amount?

(vii) Three people A, B and C eat a tin of sweets, each getting the following fraction: $\frac{1}{5}$, $\frac{7}{15}$ and $\frac{1}{3}$.

If A gets 30 sweets, how many sweets do B and C each get?

8. 720 g of detergent is made up of bleach and soap in the ratio 3 : k.

If there are 270 g of bleach in the detergent, what is the value of k?

9. Angie is reading a novel for school. She has read 160 pages and her teacher tells her that she has read $\frac{5}{8}$ of the book.

How many pages are in the book?

10. Bryan and Niamh are given €70 to share. Bryan tells Niamh that her options are either to share the money in the ratio of their ages (19 and 16, respectively) or to share the money in the ratio $\frac{5}{9}$: $\frac{4}{9}$.

What is the better option for Niamh?

10.2 APPROXIMATION, PERCENTAGE ERROR AND TOLERANCE

Recall that:

- 9% = $\frac{9}{100}$, as a fraction
- 9% = 0.09, as a decimal

To write a fraction or a decimal as a percentage, multiply by 100 and add the % symbol.

Write $\frac{3}{5}$ as a percentage:

$\frac{3}{5} \times 100 = 60\%$

Write 0.58 as a percentage:

$0.58 \times 100 = 58\%$

Estimates and Approximations of Calculations

When performing rough calculations or estimates, we often round off numbers to make our calculations easier and quicker.

Sometimes it is necessary for us to make estimates and approximations of calculations. This can be to save time or money, or simply for convenience.

If a hardware store were doing a stocktake (count of all stock in the shop), it would be far too time-consuming and costly for the staff to count every single screw. Equally, if a shop owner had a pick-and-mix stand for sweets, they would rarely count every sweet. They would simply make estimates.

Rounding is often used when we are estimating or approximating calculations.

Error

Humans are bound to make errors from time to time. Using estimates and approximations can also lead to errors. To improve our precision, it is good practice to have an idea of how much we have possibly erred. In addition, small errors left unchecked can grow over time. That is why we calculate percentage error.

Calculating percentage error:

Step 1 Get the observed value and the accurate value.

Step 2 Subtract the observed value from the accurate value and take the positive.

Error = |Accurate – Observed|

Step 3 Divide the error by the accurate value.

Relative error = $\dfrac{\text{Error}}{\text{Accurate value}}$

Step 4 Multiply by 100 to calculate the percentage error.

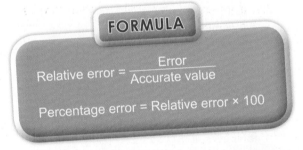

FORMULA

Relative error = $\dfrac{\text{Error}}{\text{Accurate value}}$

Percentage error = Relative error × 100

Worked Example 10.4

Find the percentage error in taking 1 cm for 0.8 cm.

Solution

Step 1 Observed value = 1 cm

Accurate value = 0.8 cm

Step 2 Error = |0.8 – 1|

= 0.2

Step 3 Relative error = $\dfrac{0.2}{0.8}$

Step 4 Percentage error = $\dfrac{0.2}{0.8} \times 100$

= 25%

ARITHMETIC II

Tolerance

Any measurement made with a measuring device is approximate. If two students were asked to measure an object, they might very well come back with two different measurements. The difference between the two measurements is called a **variation**.

It is important to note that variations and errors due to approximations are not the same as 'mistakes'.

> **Tolerance** is the greatest range of variation that can be allowed.

> To determine the tolerance in a measurement, **add** and **subtract one half** of the precision of the measuring instrument that is being used.

For example, a metric ruler is used to measure the length of an object. The result is 10.5 cm and the ruler has a precision of 0.1 cm (i.e. the ruler gives measurement to the nearest millimetre). The **tolerance interval** is 10.5 ± 0.05 cm.

Any measurements within the tolerance interval are accepted as correct or acceptable.

Worked Example 10.5

Yousef works as a quality control officer in a factory that manufactures 14-cm-long pencils. He uses a metric ruler to check the length of pencils he randomly samples. The ruler has a precision of 0.5 cm.

(i) What is the tolerance interval for a pencil in this factory?

(ii) If Yousef picks a pencil at random and it is 14.06 cm long, will it be accepted or rejected?

Solution

(i) Tolerance interval $= 14 \pm \frac{1}{2}(0.5) = 14 \pm 0.25$ cm

(ii) The pencil will be accepted, as its length (14.06 cm) is inside the tolerance interval, ie $13.75 \leqslant 14.06 \leqslant 14.25$.

Accumulated Error

> **Accumulated error** is the collected inaccuracy that can occur when multiple errors are combined.

If the solution of a problem requires many arithmetic operations, each of which is performed using rounded numbers, the **accumulated error** may significantly affect the result.

Worked Example 10.6

ABC Ltd has a policy of rounding its invoices to the nearest euro when billing clients.
If ABC had the following invoices in the last month, calculate the accumulated error.

Invoice 1   Amount before rounding = €1,560.46

Invoice 2   Amount before rounding = €950.32

Invoice 3   Amount before rounding = €144.52

Solution

Step 1   Calculate the actual amount billed.

Invoice 1   Rounded amount = €1,560

Invoice 2   Rounded amount = €950

Invoice 3   Rounded amount = €145

Amount billed = €2,655

Step 2   Calculate the amount that would be billed if rounding were not applied.

Total bill = 1,560.46 + 950.32 + 144.52

= €2,655.30

Step 3   Calculate the accumulated error.

Error = |2,655.30 − 2,655|

= €0.30

Exercise 10.2

1. Find the error, relative error and percentage error (correct to two decimal places) for the following values:

(i) Accurate value 150, Observed value 149

(ii) Accurate value 36, Observed value 36.9

(iii) Accurate value 180, Observed value 183

(iv) Accurate value 4.8, Observed value 5

(v) Accurate value 6.7, Observed value 7

(vi) Accurate value 54.15, Observed value 55

(vii) Accurate value 1.36, Observed value 1.5

(viii) Accurate value 502, Observed value 500

(ix) Accurate value 360, Observed value 359

(x) Accurate value 58.6, Observed value 60

2. If 56 is taken as an approximation for 55.4, calculate to two decimal places the percentage error.

3. If 2.3 is taken as an approximation for 2.33, calculate to two decimal places the percentage error.

4. The mass of a bag of flour should be 1 kg. A quality control inspector misreads the weight of one bag and finds it to be 1,010 g. What is the percentage error?

5. The depth of water in a reservoir is estimated to be 1.6 m. The true depth is 1.56 m. What is the percentage error, correct to one decimal place?

6. The value of $\dfrac{49.27 + 11.15}{15.24 - 3.06}$ was estimated to be 5. Calculate:

(i) The error

(ii) The percentage error, correct to one decimal place

7. The value of $\dfrac{40.354}{\sqrt{16.45}}$ was estimated to be 10. Calculate:

(i) The error

(ii) The percentage error, correct to one decimal place

8. A statement arrives to an office showing four invoices that have to be paid.

Invoice 1   €245.45

Invoice 2   €364.78

Invoice 3   €1,445.12

Invoice 4   €4,500.25

The office manager checks the statement quickly to make sure the final figure is accurate. She ignores the cent amount on each invoice.

(i) What is the total that she arrives at?

(ii) What is the correct amount owed?

(iii) What is the accumulated error?

9. Calculate the tolerance interval for each of the following measurements:

	Observed measurement	Level of accuracy/ precision
(i)	320 g	5 g
(ii)	640 cm	0.5 cm
(iii)	1.8 m	0.1 cm
(iv)	1.96 m	0.5 cm
(v)	3.4 kg	100 g
(vi)	5,300 kg	0.25 kg
(vii)	1.4 cm	0.1 mm
(viii)	25 kg	0.2 g

10. A company produces tiles measuring 16.5 cm × 18.4 cm. When passed through quality control, the tiles are rejected if they fall outside the tolerance interval.

If a tile measures 16.6 cm × 18.8 cm, will it pass quality control?
(Accuracy of measurement 1 mm)

11. Mr O'Brien gives his class an exam on graphing functions. He asks his students to use the graph to find the value of x, for which the graph $f(x) = 2.5$.

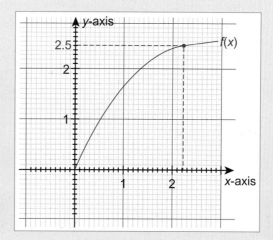

What range of values of x should Mr O'Brien accept?

12. A door is measured with a measuring tape of accuracy 0.1 cm. The observed measurement is 54 cm. What is the tolerance interval on this measurement?

13. A coffee producer sells coffee in 450 g bags. Packets of coffee are randomly picked and weighed with a precision of 5 g.

(i) What is the tolerance interval for the weight of a bag of coffee?

(ii) If a bag of coffee is picked at random and is found to be 453 g, should the packet be rejected?

ACTIVITY 10.1

10.3 AVERAGE RATES OF CHANGE (WITH RESPECT TO TIME)

The most common rate of change with respect to time that we use is speed, the change in distance with respect to time. Rates of change are used in many other areas also; for example, the change in price with respect to time and the change in quantity produced with respect to time.

FORMULA

$$\text{Rate of change} = \frac{\text{Change in quantity}}{\text{Change in time}}$$

Worked Example 10.7

Rebecca completes a 10 km fun run in 1 hour 20 minutes.
What is her average speed in kilometres per hour?

Solution

Step 1 Convert the time to hours.

$$1 \text{ hr } 20 \text{ mins} = 1\frac{1}{3} \text{ hours}$$

$$= \frac{4}{3} \text{ hours (leaving as a fraction avoids error created by rounding decimals)}$$

Step 2 Calculate average speed.

$$\text{Speed} = \frac{\text{Distance}}{\text{Time}}$$

$$= 10 \text{ km} \div \frac{4}{3} \text{ hr}$$

$$= 7.5 \text{ km/hr}$$

Worked Example 10.8

A TY student is selling bags of grit door-to-door during a cold spell of weather. He starts his door-to-door sales at 10 a.m., charging €5 for a bag of grit. He is surprised by the demand for the grit and so he puts his price up several times during the day. At 1 p.m. he is charging €8 per bag.

What is the rate of change of the price, per hour?

Solution

Step 1 Find the change in price.

€8 – €5 = €3

Step 2 Calculate the change in time.

$$
\begin{array}{rl}
1 \text{ p.m.} = & 13.00 \\
10 \text{ a.m.} = & -10.00 \\
\hline
& 3.00
\end{array}
$$

Step 3 Calculate the rate of change.

$$\frac{€3}{3 \text{ hr}}$$

$$\frac{€1}{\text{hr}}$$

The price he charges increases (on average) by €1 per hour.

Note that a rate of change can also be **negative**.

When a new games console is launched, for example, the price might be €300. As time passes, the price of the games console goes down. This may mean that demand for the product is lower, perhaps because newer and more advanced consoles have been introduced.

Worked Example 10.9

A new HD television was launched with a selling price of €1,200.
Eighteen months later, the same television could be purchased for €900.

   (i) What is the rate of change per month for the price of the television (correct to two decimal places)?

   (ii) What does this rate of change mean?

Solution

   (i) Change in price: €900 − €1200 = −€300

      Change in time: 18 months

      Rate of change in price: $\dfrac{-€300}{18 \text{ months}}$

$$= \dfrac{-€16.6667}{\text{month}}$$

$$\approx \dfrac{-€16.67}{\text{month}} \quad \text{OR} \quad -€16.67 \text{ per month}$$

   (ii) This means the price has fallen by approximately €16.67 per month since the launch of the TV onto the market.

Exercise 10.3

1. Calculate the missing values in the following table:

	Time of departure	Time of arrival	Distance travelled (km)	Average speed (km/hr)
(i)	10:35	12:55	36	
(ii)	09:00	10:30	150	
(iii)	12:15	14:45		95
(iv)	08:02	14:47		108

2. Ian runs a marathon (26.2 miles) in 3 hours 45 mins.
Find his average speed in miles per hour.

3. A cyclist travelled 40 km. She started at 11:47 and arrived at her destination at 13:14.
Calculate her speed to the nearest kilometre per hour.

4. Calculate the missing values in the following table:

	Time of departure	Time of arrival	Distance travelled (km)	Average speed (km/hr)
(i)	10:35		455	105
(ii)		10:30	90	90
(iii)	12:15		265.5	118
(iv)	08:02		104.5	95

5. David commutes from his home to Limerick city, a distance of 85 km. His commute usually takes 1 hr 15 mins.

   (i) Find his average speed in kilometres per hour.

   (ii) His average speed was reduced to 35 km/hr during heavy snow on his journey home. How long did the commute take, to the nearest minute?

   (iii) What was his total commute time to and from the city that day?

6. A car journey of 560 km took 6 hrs 45 mins.

   (i) Calculate the average speed for this journey in kilometres per hour.

   (ii) Average diesel consumption was 7 km per litre. How many litres were consumed on the journey?

   (iii) If the cost of a litre of diesel is €1.48 per litre, inclusive of VAT at 21%, what is the cost of diesel excluding VAT?

7. During a housing boom, the price of houses increased steadily over an 18-month period. A house that cost €240,000 at the start of the period had a sale value of €276,000 at the end of the period. What was the average rate of change in the price per month?

8. A new game costing €60 is released on 1 December. At the end of March, the same game costs €48.

What is the rate of change in the price of this game over the period?

9. Management accountants for a firm forecast the following projections for sales over a six-month period: sales are expected to increase at a rate of 200 units per month. If sales at the start of the period are 240,000 units, what are the expected sales at the end of the period?

10. The price of a barrel of oil is expected to increase at an average rate of $0.50 per month over a 15-month period. A barrel costs $52 at present.

   (i) What is the expected price at the end of the 15-month period?

   (ii) Is an option (right to buy or sell a product/ stock) to buy oil at $60 per barrel a good deal? Why?

11. Two lorry drivers, Niall and John, are talking about their recent trips. Niall says he travelled 4,500 km over the past week, spending a total of 48 hours driving. John says, 'That is nothing. I travelled 4,000 km and spent a total of 33 hours driving.' Whose story is more believable? Justify your answer.

Graphs Without Formulae

There are many types of graphs that may be used to represent various situations and problems.
When numbers are used in the graph, it is referred to as a **quantitative** graph.

This section deals with graphs where we do not know the formulae used to produce them.
One of the most common examples of this type of graph is the **distance–time** graph.

 ## Worked Example 10.10

Áine completed a fun run on a particular day. She started the run at 10:00 and finished it at 11:30. The graph below shows her run.

> It is important to remember that in distance–time graphs, the speed can be represented by the slope (gradient) between two points.

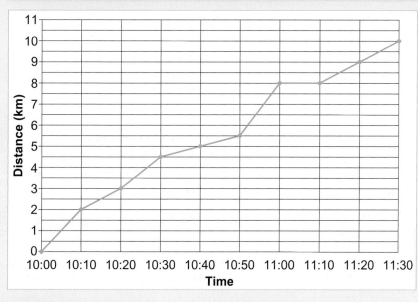

(i) What distance was the fun run?

(ii) Áine took a break at one point during the run. At what time was this?

(iii) What was Áine's average speed in km per hour between 10:30 and 10:50?

(iv) When was Áine running at her fastest speed?

Solution

(i) Reading from the graph, we see that the run was 10 km.

(ii) From the graph, we see that she did not move from 11:00 to 11:10.
This is the time she took her break.

(iii) At 10:30 she had run 4.5 km.

At 10:50 she had run 5.5 km.

In 20 minutes she ran 1 km.

In one hour (3 × 20 mins), she would have run 3 km.

Her speed was 3 km/hr.

(iv) From the graph we can see that the greatest slope is between 10:50 and 11:00.
This is when she was running her fastest.

> It is important to realise the role of **slope** or rate of change in graphs.
>
> ■ Remember that Slope = $\frac{\text{Rise}}{\text{Run}}$, i.e the rate of change of the y's with respect to the x's.
>
> ■ It is also important to note what the x-axis and y-axis represent.
>
> ■ In distance–time graphs, the steeper the slope, the faster the average speed.

Describe the speed of each of the following graphs.

Figure A

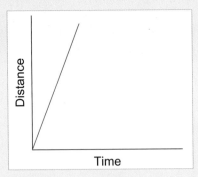

Figure B

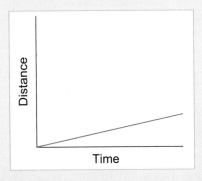

Figure C

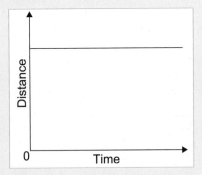

Figure D

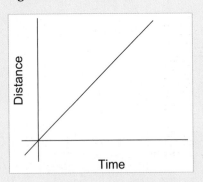

Figure E

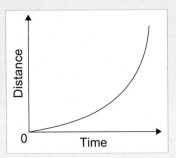

Solution

> Faster-moving objects travel a greater distance over a given time.

Figure A: The slope of this graph is positive (going up from left to right) and quite steep.

The y-value (distance) is increasing quickly with respect to time.

∴ The graph represents an object moving at a fast speed.

Figure B: The slope of this graph is positive and shallow.

The y-value (distance) is increasing slowly with respect to time.

∴ The graph represents an object moving at a slow speed.

Figure C: The slope of this graph is flat, i.e = 0.

The y-value (distance) does not change with respect to time.

∴ The graph represents an object that is not moving.

Figure D: The slope of this graph is roughly 1.

It increases one unit of distance for every one unit of time.

∴ The graph represents an object moving at a steady, moderate speed.

Figure E: As this is a non-linear graph, the rate of change varies. At the start, the gradient appears to be shallow, but further on it becomes steeper.

∴ The graph represents an object moving slowly at the start but then speeding up.

Exercise 10.4

1. Dolores is part of a cycling group. Her group leave on their journey at 8 a.m. and return to their departure point at 12.30 p.m. The graph below represents Dolores's journey.

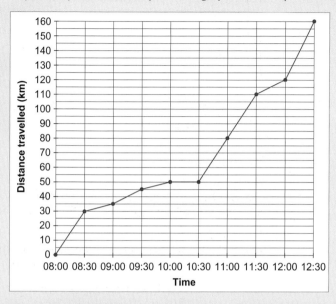

   (i) How far did Dolores cycle?

   (ii) At one point Dolores stopped for a rest. Where is this represented on the graph?

   (iii) What was her average speed for the journey?

   (iv) When was Dolores cycling at her fastest speed?

   (v) There were several parts of the journey which were downhill.
   Identify once such part, and explain your answer.

2. The graph below was generated following analysis of a share price over 10 days.

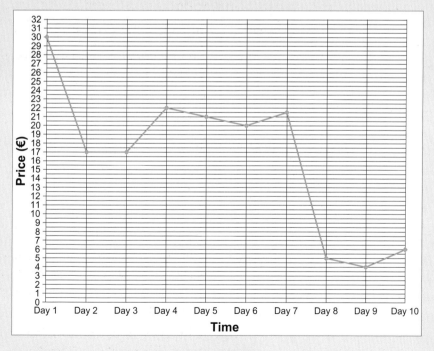

   (i) What day was the stock price highest?

   (ii) What was the lowest price the stock fell to?

(iii) During the 10-day period, information was leaked regarding the management of the company this stock was for. What day do you think this was? Explain why.

(iv) What day(s) was best to buy shares in this particular company? Give a reason.

(v) Could the graph given be used to predict future share prices (for this particular stock)? Explain why or why not.

3. Angela brings her poodle for a walk. While out walking, she meets her friend Robert and goes for a coffee. She takes her eye off the poodle for a split second. She turns around and finds her poodle is gone. Robert remembers last seeing her at 11:30, as he had just checked his watch.

The following describes the poodle's journey:

- At 11:30 the poodle strolled away from Angela, travelling 0.5 km in 10 minutes until she reached a playground.

- She then played with some children for 30 minutes until one of the children kicked a ball towards her and frightened her; she then ran off, travelling 0.75 km in 15 minutes.

- When she was resting, people from the dog pound spotted her. They put her into their van and brought her to the pound. This journey was 10.25 km and took 15 minutes.

- The staff in the pound immediately noticed Angela's number on the poodle's collar and called Angela to collect her. After 30 minutes Angela arrived and brought the poodle home.

Graph the poodle's journey from the time she went missing until she was collected by Angela.

4. The following graphs show different representations of a bath filling with water. Match each statement with the correct graph.

Statement	Graph
Statement 1: A bath that is empty and is being filled up with water from a tap.	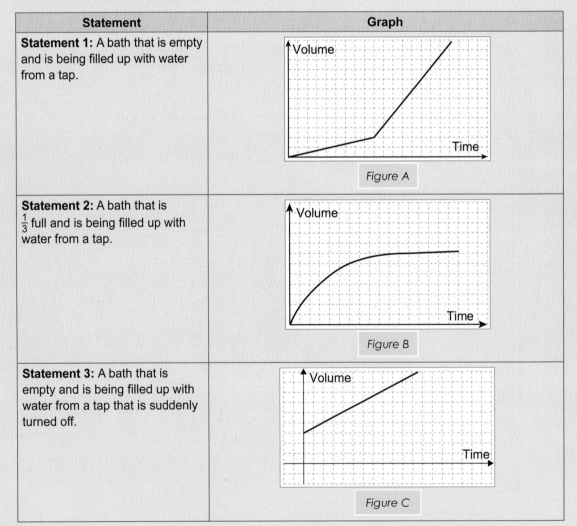 Figure A
Statement 2: A bath that is $\frac{1}{3}$ full and is being filled up with water from a tap.	Figure B
Statement 3: A bath that is empty and is being filled up with water from a tap that is suddenly turned off.	Figure C

Statement 4: A bath that is empty and is being filled up with water from a tap that is slowly losing water pressure.	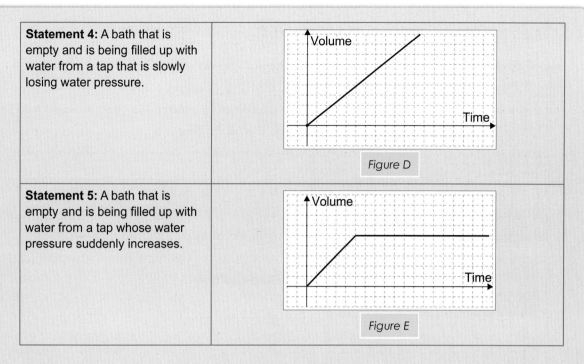*Figure D*
Statement 5: A bath that is empty and is being filled up with water from a tap whose water pressure suddenly increases.	*Figure E*

5. The graph below represents the number of products produced by a factory worker over a 10-day period:

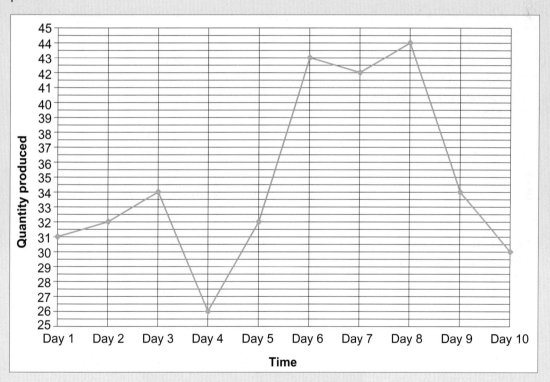

(i)   On which day did the worker have his highest performance?

(ii) On one particular day, the supervisor was out sick. Which day do you think this was? Explain your answer.

(iii) A bonus incentive was introduced for those who had the highest productivity levels. What day do you think this incentive was mentioned to staff?

(iv) Did this incentive have a long-lasting effect on this particular worker? Explain your answer.

10.4 HOUSEHOLD BILLS

Households have bills for many things, from groceries and TV licences to utilities such as electricity and gas. Two regular bills in households are electricity and gas bills.

The amount of electricity or gas used by a household is recorded by a meter. The meter is usually read every two months. Bills show the present and previous meter readings.

Worked Example 10.12

Calculate the values of A, B, C, D, E and F on the following electricity bill.

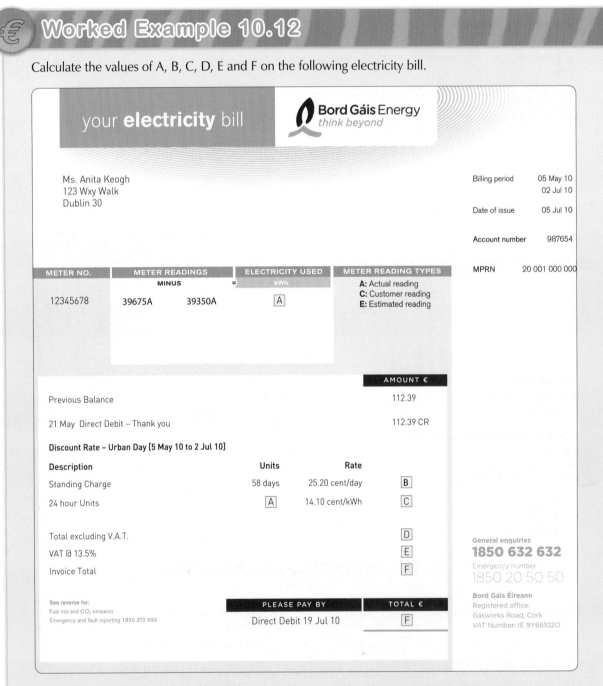

| your **electricity** bill | **Bord Gáis** Energy *think beyond* |

Ms. Anita Keogh
123 Wxy Walk
Dublin 30

Billing period	05 May 10
	02 Jul 10
Date of issue	05 Jul 10
Account number	987654
MPRN	20 001 000 000

METER NO.	METER READINGS			ELECTRICITY USED	METER READING TYPES
	MINUS		=	kWh	A: Actual reading
12345678	39675A	39350A		[A]	C: Customer reading
					E: Estimated reading

	AMOUNT €
Previous Balance	112.39
21 May Direct Debit – Thank you	112.39 CR

Discount Rate – Urban Day [5 May 10 to 2 Jul 10]

Description	Units	Rate	
Standing Charge	58 days	25.20 cent/day	[B]
24 hour Units	[A]	14.10 cent/kWh	[C]
Total excluding V.A.T.			[D]
VAT @ 13.5%			[E]
Invoice Total			[F]

See reverse for:
Fuel mix and CO$_2$ emission
Emergency and fault reporting 1850 372 999

PLEASE PAY BY	TOTAL €
Direct Debit 19 Jul 10	[F]

General enquiries
1850 632 632
Emergency number
1850 20 50 50

Bord Gáis Éireann
Registered office:
Gasworks Road, Cork
VAT Number: IE 9Y661020

Solution

Step 1 Find the number of units used.

Present meter reading – Previous meter reading

39675 – 39350 = 325 units [A]

> On an electricity bill, units are measured in kilowatt hours (kWh).

Step 2 Calculate charges based on units used.

Standing charge = 25.20 cent for 58 days	= €14.62	B
Unit rate = 14.10 cent for 325 kWh	= €45.83	C
Total excluding VAT	= €60.45	D
VAT @ 13.5%	= €8.16	E
Total including VAT	= €68.61	F

> The standing charge is a charge that you must pay regardless of the amount of electricity used. It is based on the number of days you have the service.

Worked Example 10.13

Calculate the values of A, B, C, D, E, F, G and H on the following gas bill.

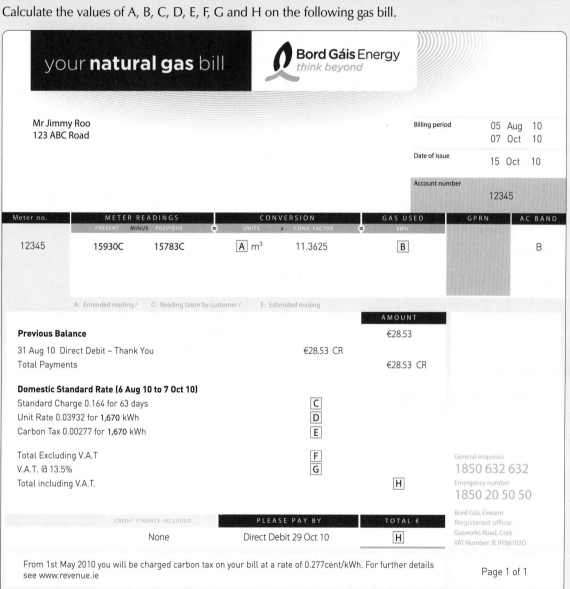

> The amount of gas that is used is measured by volume and recorded in units.

Solution

Step 1 Find the number of units used.

Present meter reading – Previous meter reading

15930 –15783 = 147 units A

Step 2 Convert the units to kilowatt hours.

Units × conversion factor = kWh

147 × 11.3625 = 1,670 (rounded to nearest kWh) $\boxed{B}$

Step 3 Calculate charges based on units used.

> The standing charge is a charge you must pay regardless of the amount of gas used. It is based on the number of days you have the service.

Standing charge = 0.164 for 163 days	= €10.33 $\boxed{C}$
Unit rate = 0.03932 for 1,670 kWh	= €65.66 $\boxed{D}$
Carbon tax = 0.00277 for 1,670 kWh	= €4.63 $\boxed{E}$
Total excluding VAT	= €80.62 $\boxed{F}$
VAT @ 13.5%	= €10.88 $\boxed{G}$
Total including VAT	= €91.50 $\boxed{H}$

When calculating bills for various services, it is important to remember the following:

- Measure the amount of the service or product used (in units).
- Calculate the cost of the total units used.
- Include any standing charges for the service or product.
- Calculate the VAT using the correct rate.
- Amounts are normally rounded to the nearest cent.
- kWh are rounded to the nearest whole number.

Worked Example 10.14

Ed has his telephone service with Digicell. His monthly standing charge is €50. This includes 200 minutes of calls and 150 text messages. If he exceeds the number of minutes allowed, he is charged 15c per minute. Every additional text message costs 12c.

During the month of December, Ed sends 160 text messages and the duration of all his calls is 220 minutes.
VAT is charged at 21%. What is the total cost of his bill this month?

Solution

Standing charge		= €50.00
Text messages (160) = 150 × 0		= €0.00
	10 × €0.12	= €1.20
Calls (220 minutes) = 200 × 0		= €0.00
	20 × €0.15	= €3.00
Total (excluding VAT)		= €54.20
VAT @ 21%		= €11.38
Total (including VAT)		= €65.58

Exercise 10.5

1. Calculate the values of A, B, C, D, E and F on the following electricity bill.

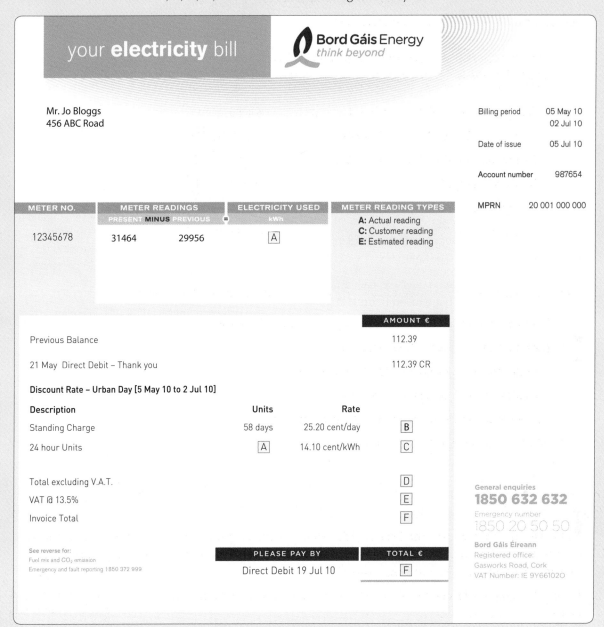

your **electricity** bill

Bord Gáis Energy
think beyond

Mr. Jo Bloggs
456 ABC Road

Billing period	05 May 10
	02 Jul 10
Date of issue	05 Jul 10
Account number	987654
MPRN	20 001 000 000

METER NO.	METER READINGS			ELECTRICITY USED	METER READING TYPES
	PRESENT	MINUS PREVIOUS	=	kWh	**A:** Actual reading
					C: Customer reading
12345678	31464	29956		[A]	**E:** Estimated reading

	AMOUNT €
Previous Balance	112.39
21 May Direct Debit – Thank you	112.39 CR

Discount Rate – Urban Day [5 May 10 to 2 Jul 10]

Description	Units	Rate	
Standing Charge	58 days	25.20 cent/day	[B]
24 hour Units	[A]	14.10 cent/kWh	[C]
Total excluding V.A.T.			[D]
VAT @ 13.5%			[E]
Invoice Total			[F]

See reverse for:
Fuel mix and CO₂ emission
Emergency and fault reporting 1850 372 999

PLEASE PAY BY	TOTAL €
Direct Debit 19 Jul 10	[F]

General enquiries
1850 632 632
Emergency number
1850 20 50 50

Bord Gáis Éireann
Registered office:
Gasworks Road, Cork
VAT Number: IE 9Y661020

2. Study the following meter readings taken from electricity bills and calculate for **each** bill:

(i) The number of units used

(ii) The cost of electricity used if each unit costs 12 cent

	Present	Previous
Bill 1	9,625	9,556
Bill 2	11,455	10,004
Bill 3	5,150	4,492
Bill 4	12,978	12,345

(iii) If the standing charge is €12 and VAT is charged at 13.5%, calculate the total cost of each bill in part (ii).

3. Calculate the cost of gas used for each of the following households if gas costs €0.06 for every kilowatt hour used (exclusive of VAT).

	kWh used
Bill 1	1,580
Bill 2	1,794
Bill 3	1,782
Bill 4	1,970

4. Michaela has the following bill pay option on her phone:

   ■ For €60 per month, she has unlimited calls to numbers within Ireland and 300 free text messages.

   ■ All calls to destinations outside of Ireland are charged at 45c per minute.

   Last month, she made an overseas call lasting 20 minutes. She did not exceed her quota for text messages.

   (i) How much did her overseas call cost?

   (ii) How much was her bill before VAT was added?

   (iii) If VAT is charged at 21%, what was the total of her bill?

5. Nicki hears an ad on the radio:

   New iPhone 5! €250, Pay as you go, 500 MB download, 100 minutes and 100 free text messages when you top up by €30 each month. Additional calls cost €0.13 per minute and texts cost €0.09 to any network.

Nicki avails of this deal. In the first month of her contract, she makes calls amounting to 124 minutes, sends 98 text messages and downloads 188 MB.

   (i)   What is her total cash outflow for the first month?

   (ii) What is the cost of her calls and texts for the month?

   (iii) How much credit has she left at the end of the month?

   (iv) The €30 is inclusive of VAT at 21%. What is the cost exclusive of VAT?

6. Danny recently had Sky installed in his apartment. The entertainment package he chose costs €25 per month with no sports channels included. If he orders a match on pay-per-view, he is charged €7.50 per game.

   (i)   Let x be the number of games Danny orders in any given month. Write an expression in terms of x for his monthly bill.

   (ii) Draw a graph to represent the monthly cost of Danny's bill.

   (iii) If Danny orders six games in a particular month, what will his bill for that month amount to?

   (iv) Use the graph from part (ii) to find the cost of the bill if Danny orders eight games in a month.

7. Jackie pays a standing charge of €20 per month for her phone. Her calls cost €0.11 per minute. If Jackie does not want to spend more than €40 on her next phone bill, what is the maximum number of minutes she can use this month? (Ignore VAT.)

8. Aaron and Robbie are thinking of changing networks. Each researches the different networks. Robbie says network A will cost less and Aaron says network B is the better option.

	Network A	Network B
Standing charge	€20	€15
Free minutes	100	100
Texts	10c per text	12c per text
Cost per minute for calls	15c	25c

   (i)   If Aaron and Robbie send text messages only, at what number of text messages will their bills be the same? (Assume that Aaron uses Network B and Robbie uses Network A, and that both send the same number of texts.)

   (ii) If they make calls only, at what number of minutes will their bills be the same?

   (iii) If both boys make calls for 120 minutes each month and send 150 text messages, which is the better network to choose?

9. The following is a gas meter reading for Jack's apartment.

| Present = 19,841 units |
| Previous = 18,679 units |
| Conversion factor = 10.9856 |
| Unit rate = €0.03 per kWh used |

Calculate:

(i) The number of units used

(ii) The number of kilowatt hours used

(iii) The cost of the gas used before VAT

(iv) The total cost of the bill if VAT is charged at 13.5%

10. Heating oil is delivered to the Hogan household. Before the delivery, there were 120 litres of oil in the oil tank. After the delivery, there were 4,320 litres.

(i) Calculate the cost of oil delivered if 1 litre costs 78.9c.

(ii) VAT is charged at 13.5%. What is the total bill inclusive of VAT?

11. The present meter reading on Denise's electricity meter is 63,892 units. The previous reading was 63,042 units.

(i) How many units of electricity have been used since the last reading?

(ii) What is the cost of electricity used if electricity costs 14.3c per unit?

(iii) A standing charge of €12 is added and VAT is then charged on the full amount. The total bill comes to €150.91. Calculate the rate at which VAT was charged.

10.5 MATERIALS, LABOUR AND WASTAGE

Managers need to know the costs involved in providing their products to the market for a number of reasons:

- **Planning:** Having an accurate cost for a product allows managers to set an accurate price.
- **Control:** By comparing the budgeted cost of a product with the actual cost of the product, managers can identify areas of the business that are underperforming or doing very well.
- **Stock valuation:** At the end of the financial year, all stocks need to be valued for accounting purposes. It is also important that businesses that manufacture their own products have a value for their goods for insurance purposes.

To have an accurate value, all costs involved in getting the product to its finished state must be included in the valuation. The table below shows examples of both direct and indirect costs for a company manufacturing school desks.

Direct costs (costs directly linked to production)	Materials	Raw materials used in the manufacture of the product	Wood, metal frames
	Labour	Wages of those who work directly in the manufacture of the product	Saw operators who cut table tops, workers who assemble the desks, workers who spray the desk frames and varnish the table tops
	Direct expenses	Any expenses that may be attributed directly to the product	Hire of special equipment
Indirect costs (costs not directly linked to production)			Factory rent, rates, light and heat

■ **Wastage:** A manager will try to minimise wastage where possible in a business, as it reduces any profit that the company will make. Human error and machine faults mean, however, that there will inevitably be some wastage in almost all businesses.

■ **Variable costs:** These are costs that vary directly with the level of output or activity, for example, sales commission based on unit sales.

■ **Fixed costs:** These are costs that are not affected by the level of activity (within a given range of activity). For example, the rent for the factory is fixed regardless of the amount of product produced. If production exceeds the level the factory can cope with, however, additional space may need to be rented, causing the cost to rise.

Worked Example 10.15

A company budgets to manufacture 5,000 units of its product. Materials required are 50 kg per unit at €0.50 per kg. Each unit produced requires six hours of direct labour at €7 per hour. Indirect costs are €15,000. Calculate:

(i) The cost of manufacture of the 5,000 units

(ii) The unit cost of manufacture

Solution

(i) Cost of manufacture of 5,000 units

5,000 units @ 50 kg = 250,000 kg

Cost per kg = €0.50

Cost of materials = 250,000 × 0.50

= €125,000

5,000 units @ 6 hrs = 30,000 hrs

Cost per hour = €7

∴ Total labour cost = €210,000

Indirect costs = €15,000

∴ Total cost of manufacture = €125,000
+ €210,000
+ €15,000

= €350,000

(ii) The unit cost of manufacture = $\dfrac{350,000}{5,000}$

= €70

Worked Example 10.16

A confectionary company receives an order for 250 custom-made products for Christmas hampers. The production team has given the following breakdown for the product.

Material requirements

■ Material A: 25 g per unit

■ Material B: 100 g per unit

■ Labour Hours: 0.05 per unit

Costs

■ Variable costs: €0.75 per unit

■ Fixed costs allocated to the product: €500

■ Material A: €0.01 per g

■ Material B: €0.05 per g

■ Labour rate: €7 per hour

(i) Find the total cost of the order and the cost per unit.

(ii) Find the price the company should charge per unit to make a profit on cost of 25% on each unit produced.

(iii) If on average 5% of the finished goods are damaged in the warehouse, how many units should the company produce to ensure that the order is covered?

Solution

(i)

Costs		Cost (€)
Material A	25 g × 250 × €0.01	62.50
Material B	100 g × 250 × €0.05	1,250.00
Labour	0.05 × 250 × €7	87.50
Variable costs	250 × €0.75	187.50
Fixed costs		500.00
Total cost		2,087.50

The total cost of the order is €2,087.50.

$$\text{Unit cost} = \frac{€2087.50}{250}$$

$$= €8.35$$

(ii) A profit on cost of 25%

Profit: €8.35 × 0.25 = €2.0875

Selling price: €8.35 + €2.0875

$$= €10.4375$$

$$\approx €10.44$$

∴ The company should charge approximately €10.44 per unit to make a profit on cost of 25% on each unit produced.

(iii) On average 5% of goods are damaged.

So the 250 units represent 95% of the required production.

$$95\% = 250 \text{ units}$$

$$1\% = \frac{250}{95}$$

$$100\% = \frac{250}{95} \times 100$$

$$= 263.1579 \text{ units}$$

∴ The company should produce 264 units to ensure that there will be enough stock to meet the order.

 Exercise 10.6

1. Distinguish between:

   (i) Direct and indirect costs

   (ii) Fixed and variable costs

2. Jimmy Jeans received an order from a retail outlet for a batch of 10,000 pairs of jeans. The production costs of the jeans are as follows:

	€
Direct materials	25,000
Factory rent	11,000
Wages of material cutters	4,000
Wages of machinists	€0.75 per unit produced
Factory overheads	20,000

   (i) Calculate the total manufacturing costs of the batch.

   (ii) Calculate the unit cost of a pair of jeans

3. A deli recently received an order for 135 mini-quiches.

(i) If wastage of the finished product is assumed to be 10%, how many quiches should the deli prepare?

The production costs of the quiches are as follows:

Direct materials	€250
Labour	€11 per hour
Labour hours required	4
Deli overheads allocated to this job	€100

(ii) Calculate the cost of the batch (based on units calculated in (i)).

(iii) Calculate the cost per unit.

(iv) If the deli wishes to make a profit of 20%, what price should it charge per quiche?

4. Townsend Ltd manufactures two products, X and Y. Both products use the same raw materials. The production costs are as follows:

	Product X	Product Y
Units produced	6,000	5,000
Materials in each product	8 kg	9 kg
Production time per unit	6 hours	5 hours
Wages	€5 per hour	
Cost of materials per kg	€3	

(i) Calculate the materials required for the production of product X.

(ii) Calculate the materials required for the production of product Y.

(iii) Calculate the cost of materials for product X and product Y.

(iv) Calculate the total cost of labour for products X and Y.

5. Nolan Plc is a boat manufacturing company. Two materials are used in the manufacture of the boat. An order is placed for 60 units.

The following table gives the production costs for 1 unit:

Material A	36 metres
Material B	108 metres
Expected price per metre	€7
Labour hours required	60
Labour rate	€7 per hour

There is approximate wastage of 10% on all materials used.

(i) How many metres of material A should be purchased to meet the requirements of the order?

(ii) How many metres of material B should be purchased to meet the requirements of the order?

(iii) Calculate the cost price of this order.

(iv) Calculate the selling price per unit this company should charge if they wish to make a profit of 15%.

6. SIOAL Ltd manufactures two products, Primary and Superb. It expects to sell Primary at €190 and Superb at €230.

Sales demand is expected to be 6,000 units of Primary and 4,500 units of Superb.

Both products use the same raw materials and skilled labour but in different quantities per unit as follows:

	Primary	Superb
Material W	6 kg	5 kg
Material X	4 kg	7 kg
Skilled labour	7 hours	8 hours

The expected prices for raw materials during 2011 are:

- Material W: €3 per kg
- Material X: €5 per kg

The skilled labour rate is expected to be €11.00 per hour.

The company's production overhead costs are expected to be:

- Variable: €4.50 per skilled labour hour
- Fixed: €116,000 per annum

If SIOAL produces all units required for sale, find:

(i) The amount of material W needed

(ii) The amount of material X needed

(iii) The total labour hours used in production

(iv) The total labour cost of production

(v) The total cost of production (including variable and fixed costs)

(vi) The profit made if the company sells at the expected prices

(vii) The profit made if the prices are to be reduced by 10%

10.6 CURRENCY EXCHANGE

In the eurozone, the unit of currency is the euro. If you travel to any country within the eurozone, there is no need to change your money. However, if you travel to any country outside the eurozone, you will need to change your money. For example, if you travel to Japan, you will need to convert your money from euro into Japanese yen.

Worked Example 10.17

On a certain day, €1 = £0.84. Liam is travelling to London and wants to change €200 into sterling (£). How much sterling will he get?

Solution

$$€1 = £0.84$$

$$€1 × 200 = £0.84 × 200$$

$$€200 = £168$$

Liam will get £168.

 Worked Example 10.18

On a particular day, €1 = $1.36. How much would you receive in euro in exchange for $129.20?

Solution

$$\$1.36 = €1$$

$$\$1 = \frac{€1}{1.36}$$

$$\$1 × 129.20 = \frac{€1}{1.36} × 129.20$$

$$\$129.20 = €95$$

You would receive €95.

> Always arrange the exchange rate to have the currency you are looking for on the right-hand side.

Foreign currency can be bought and sold at a **bureau de change**. Many banks, building societies and department stores offer this service. However, they do not all offer the same exchange rates.

At a bureau de change you will see the following signs:

- If you are going on holiday and want to buy foreign currency, the bank is selling it to you. So use the 'SELL at' exchange rate.

- If you have returned from holiday and want to sell back the currency you have left over, it is the 'BUY at' rate that you must use.

Bureau de Change

WE BUY AT	WE SELL AT

These two different rates are used in order for the operators of the bureau de change to make a profit. Another cost that you should consider is the **commission** the bureau de change will charge you. This is an extra charge for the service they have provided.

 Worked Example 10.19

Carol is going on holidays to America. She wants to change €450 into dollars. She goes to her local bank. At the bureau de change counter, she sees a sign that says:

	We buy	We sell
US dollars	1.36	1.29

(i) How much will she get in dollars for €450?

(ii) If commission is charged at 2% of the euro value, how much will Carol pay in total?

Solution

(i) First ask the question: Is Carol buying or selling US dollars?

She is buying dollars – therefore, the bank is selling.

So, the exchange rate is €1 = $1.29 (the rate the bank sells at).

$$€1 = \$1.29$$

$$€1 × 450 = \$1.29 × 450$$

$$€450 = \$580.50$$

Carol will get $580.50.

(ii) Commission is always charged in addition to the cost of the currency.

Carol will pay €450 + 2% commission

Commission = €450 × 2%

= €9

∴ Total cost = €450 + €9

= €459

Exercise 10.7

1. On a day when €1 = $1.34, find:

   (i) The value in dollars of €225

   (ii) The value in euro of $313.56

2. On a day when €1 = £0.67 and £1 = $1.52, find:

   (i) The value in dollars of €350 (to the nearest cent)

   (ii) The value in euro of $871 (to the nearest cent)

3. Tickets to a gig at the O₂ in London are £38. Tickets to see the same artist at the O₂ in Dublin are €48. If the exchange rate is €1 = £0.84, which ticket is cheaper?

4. If €1 = $1.48 (Australian dollars), €1 = ¥116.84 (Japanese yen) and €1 = £0.89:

   (i) How many Australian dollars would you get for €560?

   (ii) How many Japanese yen would you get for €850?

   (iii) How many pounds would you get for €400?

   (iv) How many euro would you get for ¥67,122?

   (v) How many euro would you get for $106.50?

   (vi) Are you better off if you get ¥432,308 or £3,248.50?

5. A bank quotes the following exchange rates for euro:

	We buy	We sell
Sterling £	0.87	0.82
Yen ¥	111	108

(a) Mark has €900 and wants to exchange it for sterling.

   (i) How much will he get?

   (ii) Commission is charged at €0.75 for every €200 or part thereof converted. How much will he pay in total for this transaction?

   (iii) What percentage of the total was the commission?

(b) Alison has ¥5,994.

   (i) How much will she get in euro if no commission is charged?

   (ii) There is a bureau de change next to the bank that offers a buy rate of 108 but charges a €1.25 commssion. Which offer is better for Alison?

6. Ursula is importing wine for her restaurant. She is charged $3.66 (New Zealand dollars) for each bottle of wine. There are 12 bottles in each case.

If she imports 10 cases, how much will she pay in euro if €1 = $1.83?

7. A part for a computer costs €250 in Ireland. The same part costs $265 in North America. If $1 = €0.78, is it cheaper to buy the part in America or Ireland? Ignore cost of delivery.

8. Mohamed buys IDR9,960,500 (Indonesian rupiah). The exchange rate is €1 = IDR12,450.50. Commission is charged on this transaction.

  (i) How much is the commission charge, in euro, if Mohamed pays €820?

  (ii) What is the rate of commission?

9. An importer buys goods for £442 sterling when the exchange rate is €1 = £0.82. He sells the goods at cost price plus 20%.

Calculate, in euro, the price at which he sells the goods.

10.7 METRIC SYSTEM – IMPERIAL SYSTEM

The metric system is an international decimalised system of measurement, first adopted by France in 1791. It is the common system of measuring units used by most of the world.

Since the 1960s the International System of Units ('Système International d'Unités' in French, hence SI) has been the internationally recognised standard metric system.

Metric units are universally used in scientific work and are widely used around the world for personal and commercial purposes.

The USA and UK still use the imperial system of measurement. All UK road signs must by law be shown in imperial measurement. It is often necessary for us to be able to convert from metric to imperial and from imperial to metric.

This conversion is done in a similar way to foreign exchange conversions.

Below is a table with some conversion rates:

Conversion factors					
From	*To*	*Multiply by*	*From*	*To*	*Multiply by*
Inches	Millimetres	25.4	Hectares	Acres	2.471
Millimetres	Inches	0.0394	Pints	Litres	0.5682
Inches	Centimetres	2.54	Litres	Pints	1.76
Centimetres	Inches	0.3937	US pints	Litres	0.47311
Feet	Metres	0.3048	Litres	US pints	2.114
Metres	Feet	3.281	US gallons	Litres	3.785
Yards	Metres	0.9144	Gallons	Litres	4.546
Metres	Yards	1.094	Litres	US gallons	0.2642
Miles	Kilometres	1.609	Litres	Gallons	0.22
Kilometres	Miles	0.6214	Grains	Grams	0.0648
Inches^2	Centimetres^2	6.452	Grams	Grains	15.43
Centimetres^2	Inches^2	0.155	Ounces	Grams	28.35
Metres^2	Feet^2	10.76	Grams	Ounces	0.03527
Feet^2	Metres^2	0.0929	Pounds	Grams	453.6
Yards^2	Metres^2	0.8361	Grams	Pounds	0.002205
Metres^2	Yards^2	1.196	Pounds	Kilograms	0.4536
Miles^2	Kilometres^2	2.589	Kilograms	Pounds	2.205
Kilometres^2	Miles^2	0.3861	Tonnes	Kilograms	1016.05
Acres	Hectares	0.4047	Kilograms	Tonnes	0.0009842

Worked Example 10.20

Convert 15 kg to pounds (lb), given 1 kg = 2.205 lb.

Solution

Step 1 Write down the conversion rate with the units needed on the right-hand side (RHS).

1 kg = 2.205 lb

Step 2 Multiply both sides of the equation by the number of kilograms that are to be converted.

(1×15) kg $= (2.205 \times 15)$ lb

$\therefore$ 15 kg = 33.075 lb

Worked Example 10.21

If Greg is 6 feet tall, what height is he in metres (correct to one decimal place), given 1 m = 3.281 feet?

Solution

Step 1 Write down the conversion rate with the desired units on the RHS.

3.281 feet = 1 m

Step 2 Find out what 1 foot is in metres by dividing both sides of the equation by 3.281.

$$\frac{3.281}{3.281} \text{ feet} = \frac{1}{3.281}\text{m}$$

$$1 \text{ foot} = \frac{1}{3.281}\text{m}$$

Step 3 Calculate the height you are looking for by multiplying both sides of the equation.

$$(1 \times 6) \text{ feet} = \left(\frac{1}{3.281} \times 6\right)\text{m}$$

$$6 \text{ feet} = 1.8287$$

$\therefore$ Greg is approximately 1.8 m tall.

Worked Example 10.22

Eoin is on holidays and wants to go on a ride in a theme park. He reads a sign that says the minimum height is 1.4 m. He knows he is 4 feet 10 inches tall and that the conversion rate from metres to feet is 1 m = 3.281 feet.

(i) Find Eoin's height in metres (correct to one decimal place).

(ii) Is he tall enough to go on the ride?

Solution

(i) ■ First, convert 4′ 10″ to feet.

> Note: 4 feet 10 inches can also be written as 4′ 10″.

Conversion rate: 12″ = 1′
■ Divide both sides by 12.
$$\frac{12''}{12} = \frac{1'}{12}$$
■ Multiply both sides by 10.
$$10'' = \frac{1'}{12} \times 10$$
$$10'' = 0.8333'$$
$\therefore$ 4′ 10″ = 4.8333′

■ Convert feet to metres.

Conversion rate: 3.281′ = 1 m
■ Divide both sides by 3.281.
$$\frac{3.281'}{3.281} = \frac{1}{3.281}\text{m}$$
$$1' = \frac{1}{3.281}\text{m}$$
■ Multiply both sides by 4.8333.
$$4.8333' = \left(\frac{1}{3.281} \times 4.8333\right)\text{m}$$
$$= 1.4731 \text{ m}$$
$\therefore$ 4′10″ $\approx$ 1.5 m

(ii) Yes, as 1.5 m > 1.4 m.

Exercise 10.8

1. Complete the conversions in the table below using the conversion rates provided at the start of this section (to two decimal places).

From	To
6 inches	cm
4.5 feet	m
5 miles	km
13 inches	mm
6 pints	litres
5 ounces	g
6 lbs	kg
3.5 tonnes	kg
22 yards	m
2 feet 3 inches	m

2. Jessie is making a cake in Home Economics class. The recipe says that 4 lb of flour are needed. The weighing scale gives measurements in grams. How many grams will Jessie need, given that 1 lb = 453.6 g?

3. When a cyclist has travelled a distance of 12.6 km, she has completed $\frac{4}{7}$ of her journey.

   (i) What is her total journey length in kilometres?

   (ii) What is the length of her journey in miles, correct to two decimal places? (1 mile = 1.609 km)

Use the conversion rates given at the start of this section to answer the following questions.

4. Which is heavier, 10 tonnes of feathers or 10,200 kg of bricks?

5. Sailing rope is sold by the metre in a local marina shop. Eric needs a rope 20 feet long. What length of rope to the nearest metre must he buy to ensure he has enough rope?

6. There are two DIY stores in a business park. Both stores have a special offer on electrical wire.

   ■ Store A is selling wire at a reduced rate of €1.50 per yard.

   ■ Store B is selling the same type of wire at €1.25 per metre.

   Which store is offering the better deal?

Revision Exercises

1. The length and breadth of a rectangle are in the ratio 4 : 3, respectively. The length of the rectangle is 12.8 cm. Find the breadth of the rectangle.

2. Divide 714 g in the ratio $\frac{1}{2} : \frac{1}{4} : 1$. Convert the largest share to ounces (correct to one decimal place).

3. Conor and Dylan have a business together. Conor claims that he does 85% of the work and Dylan does the rest. Profits are shared on the basis of Conor's claim. If the business makes €6,500 this quarter, how much will Dylan receive (correct to two decimal places)?

4. A grandfather gives his three grandchildren €150 to share. The children decide to share the money in the ratio of their ages. The six-year-old gets €30, the second child is 15 years old, and the third child gets €45. What age is the third child?

5. The value of $\dfrac{36.354}{\sqrt{4.45}}$ was estimated to be 18. Calculate:

   (i) The error

   (ii) The percentage error, correct to one decimal place

6. A statement arrives at an office showing three invoices that have to be paid.

Invoice 1	€ 2405.65
Invoice 2	€364.92
Invoice 3	€45.49

The office manager checks the statement quickly to make sure the final figure is accurate. She rounds each invoice to the nearest cent.

   (i) What is the total that she arrives at?

   (ii) What is the correct amount owed?

   (iii) What is the accumulated error?

7. A bag of peanuts is weighed on weighing scales with an accuracy of 1 gram. The observed value is 26 g. What is the tolerance interval on this measurement?

8. A chocolate producer sells cooking chocolate in 477 g bars. Bars are randomly picked and weighed with a precision of 5 g.

   (i) What is the tolerance interval for the weight of a bar of chocolate?

   (ii) If a bar of chocolate is picked at random and is found to be 481 g, should the bar be rejected?

9. A games console was released at the start of 2006 with a retail price of €300. By the end of 2009, the average retail price was €200.

   (i) What was the rate of price decrease per year in this time period (assuming the rate was constant)?

   (ii) If the rate remains constant, what price would you expect to pay for the games console in 2012?

   (iii) Draw a suitable graph to represent the information in parts (i) and (ii).

10. James travelled from Dublin to London, a distance of approximately 460 km. If his flight time was 50 minutes:

   (i) What was the average speed of the plane in kilometres per hour?

   (ii) What was the distance travelled in miles? (Use the conversion factors given in this chapter.)

11. The following is a gas meter reading for Alan's apartment.

Present	12,444 units
Previous	12,138 units
Conversion factor	11.3625
Unit rate	€0.035 per kWh used

Calculate:

   (i) The number of units used

   (ii) The number of kilowatt hours used

   (iii) The cost of the gas used before VAT

   (iv) The total cost of the bill if VAT is charged at 13.5% (correct to two decimal places)

12. Heating oil is delivered to the Moore household. One litre costs 80c and VAT is charged at 13.5%. The total cost of the bill, inclusive of VAT, is €1,470.96.

If there were 110 litres in the Moore's oil tank before the delivery, how many litres are there after the delivery?

13. A bank quotes the following exchange rates for euro:

	We buy	We sell
Sterling £	0.86	0.81
US dollar $	1.38	1.34
Yen ¥	191	111

   (i) Jack has €950 and wants sterling. How much will he get in sterling?

  (ii) Nico has ¥5884. How much will he get in euro if his bank charges a 2% commission?

 (iii) Anna has £154 and she wants to change this sum to euro. How much will she receive in euro?

 (iv) Henry has $1,200. How much will he get in euro in exchange if commission is set at €1.75 per €100 received or part thereof?

14. SVC Ltd has recently completed its sales forecasts for the year to 31 December 2012. It expects to sell two products: Product 1 @ €125 and Product 2 @ €145.

Its budgeted sales are 12,000 units for Product 1 and 5,000 units for Product 2.

Both products use the same materials but in different quantities per unit as follows:

	Product 1	**Product 2**
Material X	10 kg	5 kg
Material Y	5 kg	7 kg
Skilled labour	5 hours	4 hours

- Material X: €1.50 per kg
- Material Y: €3.50 per kg
- Skilled labour: paid at €7.50 per hour
- Variable costs: €7 per unit
- Fixed costs: €180,000

Calculate:

  (i) The amount of material X needed

  (ii) The amount of material Y needed

 (iii) The total labour hours used in production

 (iv) The total labour cost of production

  (v) The total cost of production (including variable and fixed costs)

 (vi) The profit made if the company sells at the expected prices

(vii) The profit made if the prices are increased by 10%

chapter 11

Complex Numbers

Learning Outcomes

In this chapter you will learn:

- About the origins of complex numbers
- How to plot complex numbers on an Argand diagram
- How to add, subtract, multiply and divide complex numbers
- How to do transformations using complex numbers

- How to find the modulus of a complex number
- How to find the argument of a complex number
- How to find the conjugate of a complex number
- How to solve quadratic equations with complex roots

The Italian mathematicians Gerolamo Cardano (1501–1576) and Niccolò Tartaglia (1500–1557) were the first to encounter complex numbers.

Gerolamo Cardano *Niccolò Tartaglia*

While working on the solutions to cubic equations, they came upon some unusual solutions involving the square root of –1. Today we call such solutions **complex** solutions.

Complex numbers have many applications in the modern world in such diverse areas as electronic engineering, aircraft design, computer-generated imaging in the film industry and medicine.

Complex numbers have been introduced to allow for the solutions of certain equations that have no real solutions.

The equation $x^2 + 1 = 0$ has no real solution, since the square of a real number, x, is either 0 or positive.

Therefore, $x^2 + 1$ cannot be zero.

To find a solution to such an equation we need to introduce a new number whose square is –1. We call this number i (the Greek letter iota).

Let us check that i is a solution to $x^2 + 1 = 0$.

Substitute i into the equation.

$(i)^2 + 1 = 0$

$-1 + 1 = 0$

$0 = 0$

$\therefore i$ is a solution.

This allows as to solve equations of the type $x^2 - 2x + 5 = 0$.

Using the quadratic formula $\Rightarrow x = \dfrac{2 \pm \sqrt{-16}}{2}$

$= \dfrac{2 \pm \sqrt{16} \cdot \sqrt{-1}}{2}$

$= \dfrac{2 \pm 4\sqrt{-1}}{2}$

$= 1 \pm 2\sqrt{-1}$

$= 1 \pm 2i$

$i = \sqrt{-1}$ and $i^2 = -1$

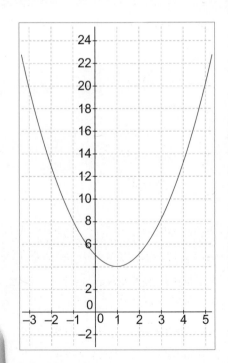

YOU SHOULD REMEMBER…

- The rules of indices
- The distributive properties of the real numbers
- How to use the quadratic formula to solve equations

KEY WORDS

- **Complex number**
- **Argand diagram**
- **Real part**
- **Imaginary part**
- **Translation**
- **Dilation**
- **Modulus**
- **Conjugate**

If both $a < 0$ and $b < 0$, then $\sqrt{a}.\sqrt{b} \neq \sqrt{ab}$ $(a, b \in R)$.

But if $a < 0$ and $b > 0$, or if $a > 0$ and $b < 0$, then $\sqrt{a}.\sqrt{b} = \sqrt{ab}$ $(a, b \in R)$.

√-1 Worked Example 11.1

Simplify:

    (i) $\sqrt{-4}$ (iii) $\sqrt{-48} + \sqrt{-27}$
    (ii) $\sqrt{-72}$

Solution

    (i) $\sqrt{-4} = \sqrt{4}\sqrt{-1}$

             $= 2i$

    (ii) $\sqrt{-72} = \sqrt{72} \cdot \sqrt{-1}$

               $= \sqrt{36} \cdot \sqrt{2} \cdot \sqrt{-1}$

               $= 6\sqrt{2}i$

    (iii) $\sqrt{-48} + \sqrt{-27}$

          $= \sqrt{48}\sqrt{-1} + \sqrt{27}\sqrt{-1}$

          $= \sqrt{16 \times 3}i + \sqrt{9 \times 3}i$

          $= 4\sqrt{3}i + 3\sqrt{3}i$

          $= 7\sqrt{3}i$

√-1 Worked Example 11.2

Simplify the following:

    (i) i^3 (iii) i^{49}
    (ii) i^4

Solution

    (i) $i^3 = (i^2)(i)$

             $= (-1)(i)$

      $\therefore i^3 = -i$

    (ii) $i^4 = (i^2)^2$

             $= (-1)^2$

      $\therefore i^4 = 1$

    (iii) $i^{49} = (i^{48})(i)$

             $= (i^2)^{24}(i)$

             $= (-1)^{24}(i)$

             $= (1)i$

      $\therefore i^{49} = i$

√-1 Worked Example 11.3

Solve the equation $z^2 + 64 = 0$.

Solution

$z^2 + 64 = 0$

    $z^2 = -64$

    $z = \pm\sqrt{-64}$

    $z = \pm\sqrt{64}\sqrt{-1}$

    $z = \pm 8i$

Exercise 11.1

1. Write the following in the form ki, $k \in R$, $i^2 = -1$:

    (i) $\sqrt{-100}$ (vi) $\sqrt{-49}$

    (ii) $\sqrt{-81}$ (vii) $\sqrt{-64}$

    (iii) $\sqrt{-25}$ (viii) $\sqrt{-169}$

    (iv) $\sqrt{-36}$ (ix) $\sqrt{-144}$

    (v) $\sqrt{-121}$ (x) $\sqrt{-16}$

2. Write the following in the form pi, $p \in R$, $i^2 = -1$:

    (i) $\sqrt{-17}$ (vi) $\sqrt{-23}$

    (ii) $\sqrt{-31}$ (vii) $\sqrt{-29}$

    (iii) $\sqrt{-14}$ (viii) $\sqrt{-43}$

    (iv) $\sqrt{-19}$ (ix) $\sqrt{-5}$

    (v) $\sqrt{-21}$ (x) $\sqrt{-3}$

3. Write the following in the form $a\sqrt{b}i$, $a, b \in R$, b is square free and $i^2 = -1$:

    (i) $\sqrt{-8}$ (vi) $\sqrt{-32}$

    (ii) $\sqrt{-98}$ (vii) $\sqrt{-500}$

    (iii) $\sqrt{-45}$ (viii) $\sqrt{-54}$

    (iv) $\sqrt{-300}$ (ix) $\sqrt{-27}$

    (v) $\sqrt{-12}$ (x) $\sqrt{-125}$

4. Simplify the following in the form $a\sqrt{b}i$, $a, b \in R$, b is square free and $i^2 = -1$:

   (i) $\sqrt{-50} + \sqrt{-8}$ (iii) $\sqrt{-125} + \sqrt{-20}$

   (ii) $\sqrt{-27} - \sqrt{-12}$ (iv) $\sqrt{-44} + \sqrt{-99}$

5. Solve the following equations, giving your answer in the form $\pm pi$, $p \in N$, $i^2 = -1$:

   (i) $z^2 + 9 = 0$ (iv) $z^2 + 36 = 0$

   (ii) $z^2 + 4 = 0$ (v) $z^2 + 49 = 0$

   (iii) $z^2 + 25 = 0$ (vi) $z^2 + 100 = 0$

6. Solve the following equations, giving your answer in the form $\pm \sqrt{p}i$, $p \in N$, $i^2 = -1$.

   (i) $z^2 + 7 = 0$ (iv) $z^2 + 17 = 0$

   (ii) $z^2 + 11 = 0$ (v) $z^2 + 14 = 0$

   (iii) $z^2 + 15 = 0$ (vi) $z^2 + 26 = 0$

7. Simplify each of the following:

   (i) i^3 (iv) i^{12}

   (ii) i^6 (v) i^{13}

   (iii) i^5 (vi) i^{45}

8. Simplify the following, giving your answer in the form pi, $p \in N$, $i^2 = -1$:

   (i) $(2i)^7$ (iv) $(4i)^5$

   (ii) $(3i)^3$ (v) $(2i)^8$

   (iii) $(5i)^4$ (vi) $(5i)^3$

9. Match the numbers in Column A with those in Column B.

A	B
i^4	$1 - i$
$2i^3$	-3
$i^8 + i^3$	$-128i$
i^{98}	$1 + i$
$3(i)^2$	0
$i^4 - i^8$	$-64i$
$(2i)^7$	1
$i^4 - i^7$	$9i$
$(4i)^3$	$-2i$
$5i + 4i$	-1

10. A spinner has eight equal sectors and on each sector is a different power of i.

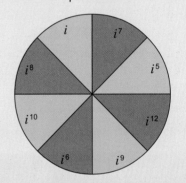

i	-1	$-i$	1
$-€5$	$€2$	$€10$	$€2$

The table gives possible winnings or losses for one spin of the spinner. By simplifying the powers of i on the spinner, find the probability of:

   (i) Winning €10 on one spin

   (ii) Losing €5 on one spin

11.1 COMPLEX NUMBERS AND THE ARGAND DIAGRAM

A **complex number**, z, is any number of the form $z = a + ib$, $a, b \in R$, $i^2 = -1$.

a is called the **real part** of z (Re(z)) and b is called the **imaginary part** of z (Im(z)).

$2 + 3i$, $5 - 2i$, $\frac{1}{2} + \frac{3}{4}i$, and $\sqrt{2} - 3i$ are all examples of complex numbers.

√−1 **Worked Example 11.4**

$z = 7 - 8i$ is a complex number. Write down Re(z) and Im(z).

Solution

Re(z) = 7 and Im(z) = −8

Do not include i in Im(z).

The Argand Diagram

Just as a real number can be represented on a real numberline, a complex number can be represented on a diagram called the **Argand diagram**, also known as the **complex plane**. The Argand diagram is a two-dimensional plane with two perpendicular axes. The horizontal axis is the real axis and the vertical axis is the imaginary axis.

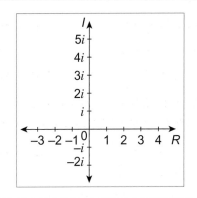

Here is the complex number $3 + 2i$ represented on an Argand diagram.

The Argand diagram was devised by the Swiss mathematician, Jean-Robert Argand (1768–1822).

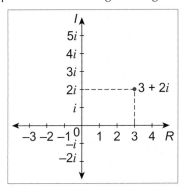

OR

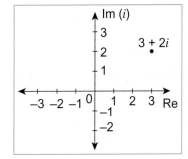

√−1 **Worked Example 11.5**

Represent the following numbers on an Argand diagram:

    (i) −1 + 2i   (ii) 2 + 3i   (iii) −3 − 2i   (iv) 3 − i

Solution

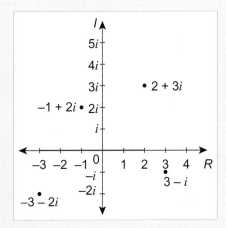

Exercise 11.2

1. Plot the following complex numbers on an Argand diagram:

   (i) $3 + 2i$ (iii) $-6 + 2i$ (v) $2 - 3i$

   (ii) $5 - 2i$ (iv) $-3 - 2i$ (vi) $4 + i$

2. Show the following complex numbers on the complex plane:

   (i) -2 (iii) 4 (v) $2 + 0i$

   (ii) $3i$ (iv) $-5i$ (vi) i

3. Study the Argand diagram given and complete the grid to spell the name of a famous mathematician.

$3 + i$	$-2 - 2i$	$3 - i$	$-2 + 5i$	$-2 - 2i$	$4 + 3i$	$-3 - i$

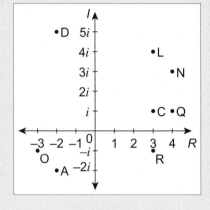

4. Study the Argand diagram given and complete the grid to spell the name of a famous composer.

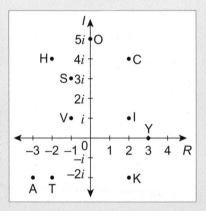

$-2 - 2i$	$2 + 4i$	$-2 + 4i$	$-3 - 2i$	$2 + i$	$2 - 2i$	$5i$	$-1 + i$	$-1 + 3i$	$2 - 2i$	$3 + 0i$

5. Say whether the following numbers lie on the real axis or the imaginary axis:

   (i) 2 (v) $0 + 2i$ (viii) i^3

   (ii) $3i$ (vi) $-1 + 0i$ (ix) i^4

   (iii) $-2i$ (vii) i^2 (x) $(2i)^4$

   (iv) -4

6. Plot the following numbers on an Argand diagram:

   (i) $3 + \sqrt{-4}$ (iv) $8 - \sqrt{-25}$

   (ii) $5 + \sqrt{-49}$ (v) $10 - \sqrt{-36}$

   (iii) $-4 + \sqrt{-9}$ (vi) $-2 + \sqrt{-1}$

7. Show the following numbers on the complex plane:

   (i) $1 - \sqrt{-144}$ (iv) $\frac{1}{2} + \sqrt{-\frac{1}{16}}$

   (ii) $-4 - \sqrt{-1}$

   (iii) $7 - \sqrt{-81}$ (v) $\frac{3}{2} + \sqrt{-\frac{1}{25}}$

8. For each of the following complex numbers (z), write down Re(z) and Im(z), the real and imaginary parts of the complex number z:

   (i) $\frac{1}{2} - \frac{3}{2}i$ (iv) $3 - \frac{1}{\sqrt{3}}i$

   (ii) $\sqrt{2} - 3i$ (v) $-\frac{5}{6} + 3i$

   (iii) $\frac{22}{7} - 3.14i$

9. Using the data in the box below, form six different complex numbers in the form $a + bi$, where a and b are non-zero integers and $a \neq \pm b$.

For example: $-3 + 2i$

$$3, 2, i, +, -$$

Then plot the complex numbers on an Argand diagram.

10. Using the data in the box, form 12 different complex numbers in the form $a + bi$ where a and b are integers and $a \neq \pm b$.

For example: $4 + 5i$

$$0, 3, 4, 5, i, +, -$$

Plot the complex numbers on an Argand diagram.

11.2 ADDING AND SUBTRACTING COMPLEX NUMBERS; MULTIPLICATION BY A REAL NUMBER

We can add, subtract, multiply and divide complex numbers provided we follow certain well-defined steps.

Addition of Complex Numbers

 ACTIVITY 11.1

In Activity 11.1 you discovered how to add complex numbers.

So, to add two complex numbers, we add the real parts to the real parts and the imaginary parts to the imaginary parts.

If z_1 and z_2 are two complex numbers, then $z_1 + z_2 = \text{Re}(z_1 + z_2) + \text{Im}(z_1 + z_2)i$.

Add the Reals and add the Imaginaries.

√−1 Worked Example 11.6

$z_1 = 2 + 3i$ and $z_2 = 1 + 5i$. Evaluate $z_1 + z_2$.

Solution

$z_1 + z_2 = (2 + 3i) + (1 + 5i)$

$= (2 + 1) + (3 + 5)i$

$\therefore z_1 + z_2 = 3 + 8i$

We use z_1 and z_2 to distinguish between different complex numbers.

In Activity 11.1 you learned how to subtract complex numbers.

If z_1 and z_2 are two complex numbers, then $z_1 - z_2 = \text{Re}(z_1 - z_2) + \text{Im}(z_1 - z_2)i$.

$z_1 = 8 + 6i$ and $z_2 = 4 + 2i$. Find $z_1 - z_2$.

Solution

$z_1 - z_2 = (8 + 6i) - (4 + 2i)$

$= (8 - 4) + (6 - 2)i$

$\therefore z_1 - z_2 = 4 + 4i$

Multiplying a Complex Number by a Real Number

While this section focuses on addition and subtraction, we will also deal with multiplying a complex number by a real number.

If z is a complex number and a is a real number, then $az = a\,\text{Re}(z) + a\,\text{Im}(z)i$.

If $z = 4 + 2i$, find $3z$.

Solution

$3z = 3(4 + 2i)$

$= 3(4) + 3(2i)$

$\therefore 3z = 12 + 6i$

ACTIVITY 11.2

Transformations 1

In Activity 11.2 you learned that addition of complex numbers is the equivalent of a **translation** on the complex plane. You also discovered that multiplication by a real number is the equivalent of a **dilation** (stretching, contraction) on the complex plane.

$z_1 = 2 + 4i$, $z_2 = 2 + 3i$, $z_3 = -1 + 2i$ and $\omega = 1 + i$.

(i) Plot z_1, z_2 and z_3 on an Argand diagram.

(ii) Evaluate $z_1 + \omega$, $z_2 + \omega$ and $z_3 + \omega$.

(iii) Plot the answers to part (ii) on an Argand diagram.

(iv) Describe the transformation that is the addition of ω.

Solution

(i)

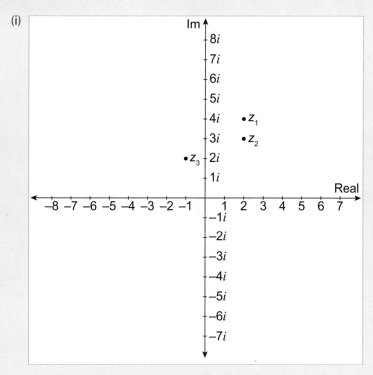

(ii) $z_1 + \omega = (2 + 4i) + (1 + i)$
$= 3 + 5i$

$z_2 + \omega = (2 + 3i) + (1 + i)$
$= 3 + 4i$

$z_3 + \omega = (-1 + 2i) + (1 + i)$
$= 0 + 3i$

(iii)

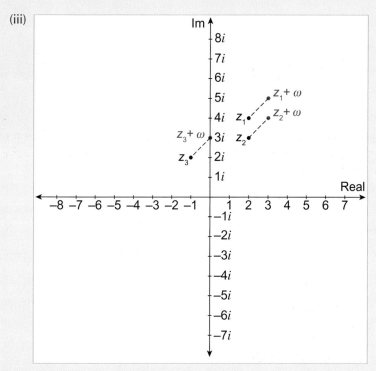

(iv) From the Argand diagram, the numbers z_1, z_2 and z_3 are moved the same distance and in the same direction. We call such a transformation a translation.

$\sqrt{-1}$ Worked Example 11.10

$z_1 = 2 + 4i$, $z_2 = 2 + 3i$, $z_3 = -1 + 2i$ and $a = 2$.

(i) Plot z_1, z_2 and z_3 on an Argand diagram.

(ii) Evaluate az_1, az_2 and az_3.

(iii) Plot the answers to part (ii) on an Argand diagram.

(iv) Describe the transformation that is multiplication by a.

Solution

(i)

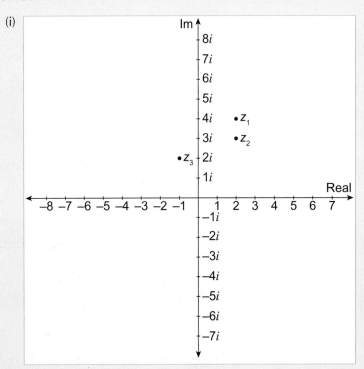

(ii) $az_1 = 2(2 + 4i)$

$= 4 + 8i$

$az_2 = 2(2 + 3i)$

$= 4 + 6i$

$az_3 = 2(-1 + 2i)$

$= -2 + 4i$

(iii)

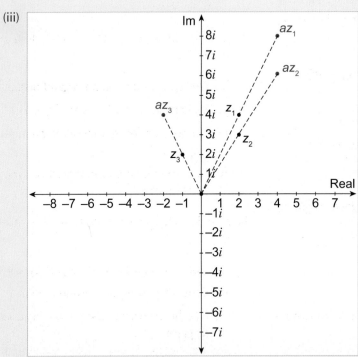

(iv) From the diagram we see that all the points are moved further from the origin by a factor of 2. We call such a transformation a dilation by a factor of 2.

- If F is the dilation factor and if $F > 1$ or $F < -1$, the dilation is sometimes referred to as a **stretching** on the complex plane.
- If $-1 < F < 1$, the dilation is sometimes referred to as a **contracting** on the complex plane.

Exercise 11.3

1. Let $z_1 = 7 + 5i$ and $z_2 = 2 + i$.
Evaluate each of the following:

  (i) $z_1 + z_2$ (iii) $3z_1 + 2z_2$

  (ii) $z_1 - z_2$ (iv) $2z_1 - 3z_2$

2. Let $z_1 = 3 - 2i$ and $z_2 = 2 + 4i$.
Evaluate each of the following:

  (i) $z_1 + z_2$ (iii) $z_1 + 3z_2$

  (ii) $z_1 - z_2$ (iv) $2z_1 - 5z_2$

3. Let $z_1 = -1 + 2i$ and $z_2 = 2 + 3i$.
Evaluate each of the following:

  (i) $2z_1 + z_2$ (iii) $2z_2 - 3z_1$

  (ii) $2z_1 - z_2$ (iv) $z_2 - z_1$

4. Let $z = 2 + i$. Find:

  (i) $z + 3$ (iv) $2z + 5z$

  (ii) $z + 3i$ (v) $2z + 3 - 3i$

  (iii) $z - 3z$

5. Let $z = 2 - 3i$. Show the following on an Argand diagram:

  (i) $z + 3$ (iii) $1 - z$

  (ii) $2z + 6i$ (iv) $\frac{1}{2}(z + i)$

6. Let $z = 1 + i$.

  (a) Show the following on an Argand diagram:

    (i) z (iv) $4z$

    (ii) $2z$ (v) $5z$

    (iii) $3z$

  (b) Describe the transformation of z in parts (ii) to (v) above.

7. Let $z = -1 + i$.

  (a) Show the following on an Argand diagram:

    (i) z (iv) $4z$

    (ii) $2z$ (v) $5z$

    (iii) $3z$

  (b) Describe the transformation of z in parts (ii) to (v) above.

8. Let $z = -24 + 48i$.

  (a) Show the following on an Argand diagram:

    (i) z (iv) $\frac{1}{4}z$

    (ii) $\frac{1}{2}z$ (v) $\frac{1}{6}z$

    (iii) $\frac{1}{3}z$

  (b) Describe the transformation of z in parts (ii) to (v) above.

9. $z_1 = 2 + 3i$, $z_2 = -2 + 5i$, $z_3 = -1 + 4i$ and $\omega = 1 + i$.

  (i) Plot z_1, z_2 and z_3 on an Argand diagram.

  (ii) Evaluate $z_1 + \omega$, $z_2 + \omega$ and $z_3 + \omega$.

  (iii) Plot the answers to part (ii) on an Argand diagram.

  (iv) Describe the transformation that is the addition of ω.

10. $z_1 = 3 + 2i$, $z_2 = -1 + 4i$, $z_3 = -3 + 5i$ and $\omega = 1 - i$.

  (i) Plot z_1, z_2 and z_3 on an Argand diagram.

  (ii) Evaluate $z_1 + \omega$, $z_2 + \omega$ and $z_3 + \omega$.

  (iii) Plot the answers to part (ii) on an Argand diagram.

  (iv) Describe the transformation that is the addition of ω.

11. Copy the Argand diagram and label the complex numbers z_1, z_2, z_3, z_4 and z_5, using the information given below.

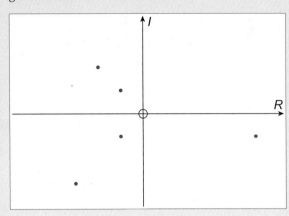

(i) $z_1 = 2z_2$

(ii) $z_4 = \frac{1}{3}z_3$

(iii) $\text{Re}(z_5) > 0$

12. Copy the Argand diagram and label the complex numbers z_1, z_2, z_3 and z_4, using the information given below.

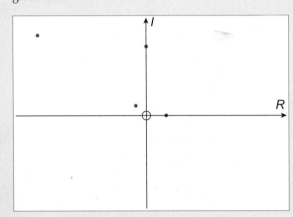

(i) $\text{Im}(z_1) > 0$

(ii) $z_2 = 10z_1$

(iii) $\text{Re}(z_3) = 0$

(iv) $\text{Im}(z_4) = 0$

11.3 MODULUS OF A COMPLEX NUMBER

The **modulus** of a complex number, $a + bi$, is its distance from the origin.

ACTIVITY 11.3

In Activity 11.3 you found that the modulus of a complex number, $a + bi$, is $\sqrt{a^2 + b^2}$.

The modulus of $a + bi$ is written $|a + bi|$.

If $z = a + bi$, $a, b \in R$ and $i^2 = -1$, then
$|z| = |a + bi| = \sqrt{a^2 + b^2}$.

√−1 Worked Example 11.11

$z_1 = 12 + 16i$ and $z_2 = -12 + 5i$. Find:

(i) $|z_1|$

(ii) $|z_2|$

(iii) $|z_1 + z_2|$

(iv) Hence show that $|z_1 + z_2| < |z_1| + |z_2|$

Solution

(i) $\quad |z_1| = \sqrt{(12)^2 + (16)^2}$

$= \sqrt{144 + 256}$

$= \sqrt{400}$

$\therefore |z_1| = 20$

Do not use i in the square root.

(ii) $\quad |z_2| = \sqrt{(-12)^2 + (5)^2}$

$\quad\quad\quad = \sqrt{144 + 25}$

$\quad\quad\quad = \sqrt{169}$

$\quad\quad \therefore |z_2| = 13$

(iii) $\quad |z_1 + z_2| = |(12 + 16i) + (-12 + 5i)$

$\quad\quad\quad\quad\quad = |0 + 21i|$

$\quad\quad\quad\quad\quad = \sqrt{(0)^2 + (21)^2}$

$\quad\quad\quad\quad\quad = \sqrt{441}$

$\quad\quad \therefore |z_1 + z_2| = 21$

(iv) $\quad |z_1| + |z_2| = 20 + 13 = 33$

$\quad\quad\quad |z_1 + z_2| = 21$

$\quad\quad\quad\quad\quad 21 < 33$

$\quad\quad \therefore |z_1 + z_2| < |z_1| + |z_2|$

$\sqrt{-1}$ Worked Example 11.12

$z_1 = 8 - i$ and $z_2 = 7 + ki$ are two complex numbers. Find:

(i) $|z_1|$

(ii) $|z_2|$ in terms of k

(iii) If $|z_1| = |z_2|$, two possible values for k

Solution

(i) $\quad |z_1| = \sqrt{(8)^2 + (-1)^2}$

$\quad\quad\quad = \sqrt{64 + 1}$

$\quad\quad \therefore |z_1| = \sqrt{65}$

(ii) $\quad |z_2| = \sqrt{(7)^2 + (k)^2}$

$\quad\quad \therefore |z_2| = \sqrt{49 + k^2}$

(iii) If $|z_1| = |z_2|$, then:

$\quad\quad \sqrt{65} = \sqrt{49 + k^2}$

Square both sides:

$\quad\quad 65 = 49 + k^2$

$\quad 65 - 49 = k^2$

$\quad\quad 16 = k^2$

$\quad\quad \pm 4 = k$

Exercise 11.4

1. Evaluate each of the following:

   (i) $|8 - 6i|$

   (ii) $|5 - 12i|$

   (iii) $|7 - 24i|$

   (iv) $|8 + 15i|$

   (v) $|9 - 40i|$

   (vi) $|-3 + 4i|$

2. Evaluate each of the following:

   (i) $|11 + 60i|$

   (ii) $|3 - 4i|$

   (iii) $|12 + 35i|$

   (iv) $|13 - 84i|$

   (v) $|-33 + 56i|$

   (vi) $|6 - 8i|$

3. Evaluate each of the following.
   Give your answer in simplest surd form.

   (i) $|1 + 2i|$

   (ii) $|2 + 2i|$

   (iii) $|3 - i|$

   (iv) $|1 - i|$

   (v) $|3 - 10i|$

   (vi) $|-7 + 3i|$

4. Evaluate each of the following:

   (i) $|3 + \sqrt{2}i|$

   (ii) $|1 + \sqrt{8}i|$

   (iii) $|3 + 2\sqrt{10}i|$

   (iv) $|-3 - \sqrt{7}i|$

   (v) $|2\sqrt{6} - i|$

   (vi) $|7 - 2\sqrt{5}i|$

5. If $|11 + 2i| = |10 + ki|$, then find two possible values of k, where $k \in R$.

6. If $|8 + ki| = 10$, then find two possible values of k, where $k \in R$.

7. If $\frac{1}{2}|6 - 8i| = |4 + ki|$, then find two possible values of k, where $k \in R$.

8. If $|p + pi| = |7 - i|$, then find two possible values of p, where $p \in R$.

9. Show that $|3 + 4i| = |0 + 5i|$.

10. If $z_1 = 2 + 3i$ and $z_2 = -2 + 5i$, then verify that $|z_1 + z_2| < |z_1| + |z_2|$.

11.4 MULTIPLYING COMPLEX NUMBERS

First we will look at multiplication of a complex number whose real part is zero, i.e. a number of the form qi, $q \in R$, by a second complex number.

√−1 Worked Example 11.13

If $z = 4 + i$, find iz.

Solution

$$iz = i(4 + i)$$
$$= 4i + i^2$$
$$= 4i - 1 \text{ (as } i^2 = -1)$$
$$\therefore iz = -1 + 4i$$

 **ACTIVITY 11.4**

Transformations 2

In Activity 11.4 you discovered that multiplication of a complex number by i is the equivalent of rotating the complex number **anti-clockwise** through 90° about the origin. You also learned that multiplication by $-i$ is the equivalent of rotating the complex number **clockwise** through 90° about the origin.

√−1 Worked Example 11.14

$z_1 = 2 + i$

(i) Find z_2, if $z_2 = iz_1$.

(ii) Plot z_1 and z_2 on an Argand diagram.

(iii) Describe the transformation that maps z_1 onto z_2.

Solution

(i) $z_2 = i(2 + i)$

$\quad\ = 2i + i^2$

$\therefore z_2 = -1 + 2i$

(ii)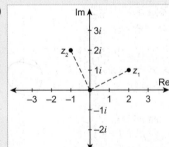

(iii) z_1 is mapped onto z_2 by an anti-clockwise rotation of 90° about the origin.

Worked Example 11.15

(i) $z_1 = 2 - 7i$ and $z_2 = 3 + 7i$. Find z_1z_2.

(ii) $z_1 = \frac{1}{2} - \frac{3}{2}i$ and $z_2 = 4 + 6i$. Find $z_1 z_2$.

Solution

(i)
$$z_1z_2 = (2 - 7i)(3 + 7i)$$
$$= 2(3 + 7i) - 7i(3 + 7i)$$
$$= 6 + 14i - 21i - 49i^2$$
$$= 6 - 7i - 49(-1)$$
$$\therefore z_1z_2 = 55 - 7i$$

(ii)
$$z_1z_2 = \left(\frac{1}{2} - \frac{3}{2}i\right)(4 + 6i)$$
$$= \frac{1}{2}(4 + 6i) - \frac{3}{2}i(4 + 6i)$$
$$= 2 + 3i - 6i - 9i^2$$
$$= 2 - 3i - 9(-1)$$
$$\therefore z_1z_2 = 11 - 3i$$

Multiplication of complex numbers is a closed operation, i.e. the product of two complex numbers is itself a complex number.

Exercise 11.5

1. Evaluate the following products:

   (i) $7i(3 + 5i)$ (iii) $2(7 + i)$ (v) $7(2 - i)$

   (ii) $i(3 - i)$ (iv) $3(1 + 5i)$ (vi) $-2(4 + i)$

2. Write the following products in the form $a + bi$:

   (i) $(2 + 7i)(3 - 5i)$ (iv) $(2 + 3i)(2 - 3i)$

   (ii) $(1 + 4i)(2 + 5i)$ (v) $(3 + 4i)(3 - 4i)$

   (iii) $(6 + i)(-2 + 3i)$ (vi) $(1 + i)(7 - 3i)$

3. Write the following products in the form $a + bi$:

   (i) $3i(2 + 4i)$ (iv) $(-2 - 2i)(-2 + 2i)$

   (ii) $(1 - i)(1 + i)$ (v) $(7 + 5i)(2 + i)$

   (iii) $5(6 - i)$ (vi) $(3 - 2i)(7i)$

4. Write the following products in the form $a + bi$:

   (i) $\left(\frac{1}{2} + \frac{3}{2}i\right)\left(\frac{1}{2} - \frac{1}{4}i\right)$ (iv) $\left(\frac{1}{2} + \frac{1}{2}i\right)\left(\frac{1}{2} - \frac{1}{2}i\right)$

   (ii) $\left(\frac{1}{5} + \frac{3}{5}i\right)\left(\frac{1}{5} - \frac{3}{5}i\right)$ (v) $\left(\frac{2}{9} + \frac{3}{5}i\right)\left(\frac{3}{4} - \frac{1}{5}i\right)$

   (iii) $\left(\frac{3}{8} + \frac{2}{11}i\right)\left(\frac{1}{4} - \frac{2}{5}i\right)$ (vi) $\left(\frac{1}{3} + \frac{2}{3}i\right)\left(-\frac{3}{5} - \frac{1}{7}i\right)$

5. Evaluate the following products in the form $a + bi$:

   (i) $(\sqrt{3} + 2i)(\sqrt{3} - 2i)$

   (ii) $(3\sqrt{7} + 5i)(3\sqrt{7} - 5i)$

   (iii) $(\sqrt{2} + \sqrt{3}i)(\sqrt{8} - \sqrt{3}i)$

   (iv) $(3 - \sqrt{3}i)(2 + 3\sqrt{3}i)$

   (v) $(5 - \sqrt{2}i)(5 + \sqrt{2}i)$

6. $z_1 = 3 + i$

   (i) Find z_2 if $z_2 = iz_1$.

   (ii) Plot z_1 and z_2 on an Argand diagram.

   (iii) Describe the transformation that maps z_1 onto z_2.

7. $z_1 = -3 + 2i$

   (i) Find z_2 if $z_2 = iz_1$.

   (ii) Plot z_1 and z_2 on an Argand diagram.

   (iii) Describe the transformation that maps z_1 onto z_2.

8. $z_1 = -3 + 4i$

   (i) Find z_2 if $z_2 = -iz_1$.

   (ii) Plot z_1 and z_2 on an Argand diagram.

   (iii) Describe the transformation that maps z_1 onto z_2.

 9. $z_1 = 3 + 4i$ and $z_2 = 10 - 24i$.

   (i) Write, in the form $a + bi$, the product z_1z_2.

   (ii) Evaluate $|z_1|$, $|z_2|$ and $|z_1z_2|$.

   (iii) Show that $|z_1||z_2| = |z_1z_2|$.

10. $z_1 = -9 + 40i$ and $z_2 = 33 + 5i$.

   (i) Evaluate z_1z_2.

   (ii) Show that $|z_1||z_2| = |z_1z_2|$.

11. $z_1 = -2 - 3i$

    (i) Find z_2 if $z_2 = -iz_1$.

    (ii) Plot z_1 and z_2 on an Argand diagram.

    (iii) Describe the transformation that maps z_1 onto z_2.

12. Copy the diagram below.

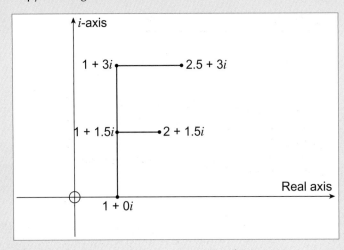

    (i) Multiply each complex number on the diagram by i.

    (ii) Plot your answers from part (i).

    (iii) Describe the transformation of the shape.

13. Copy the diagram below.

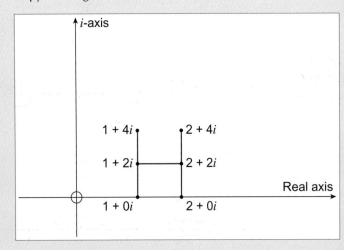

    (i) Multiply each complex number on the diagram by $-i$.

    (ii) Plot your answers from part (i).

    (iii) Describe the transformation of the shape.

14. Copy the diagram below.

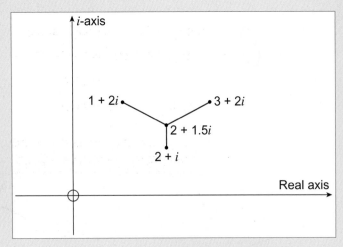

    (i) Multiply each complex number on the diagram by $2i$.

    (ii) Plot your answers from part (i).

    (iii) Describe the transformation of the shape.

Transformations 3

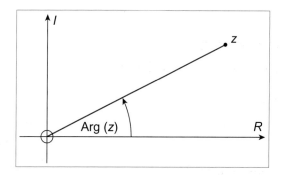

The **argument** of a complex number, z, is the angle that the line joining the complex number to the origin makes with the positive side of the real axis. We use Arg(z) to denote the argument of z.

$\sqrt{-1}$ Worked Example 11.16

$z_1 = 1 + i$ and $z_2 = -1 + i$.

(i) Evaluate z_3 if $z_3 = z_1 z_2$.

(ii) Plot z_1 and z_2 on an Argand diagram. Using a protractor, find the angles that z_1 and z_2 make with the positive side of the real axis, i.e. $Arg(z_1)$ and $Arg(z_2)$.

(iii) Plot z_3 on an Argand diagram.

(iv) What is $Arg(z_3)$?

(v) How is $Arg(z_3)$ related to $Arg(z_1)$ and $Arg(z_2)$?

Solution

(i) $z_3 = z_1 z_2 = (1 + i)(-1 + i)$

$\Rightarrow z_3 = 1(-1 + i) + i(-1 + i)$

$= -1 + i - i + i^2$

$= -1 + (-1)$

$= -2$

$\therefore z_3 = -2 + 0i$

(ii)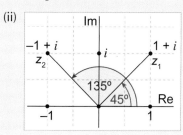

(iii)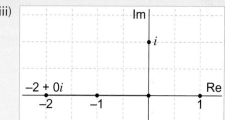

(iv)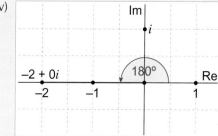

$Arg(z_3) = 180°$ [a straight angle]

(v) $Arg(z_1) + Arg(z_2) = 135° + 45°$

$= 180°$

$\therefore Arg(z_1) + Arg(z_2) = Arg(z_3)$

If z_1 and z_2 are complex numbers, then $Arg(z_1) + Arg(z_2) = Arg(z_1 z_2)$.

Worked Example 11.17

$z_1 = 3 + 4i$ and $z_2 = 5 + 12i$.

(i) Find $|z_1|$ and $|z_2|$.

(ii) Evaluate $z_1 z_2$.

(iii) Find $|z_1 z_2|$.

(iv) How are $|z_1||z_2|$ and $|z_1 z_2|$ related?

Solution

(i) $|z_1| = \sqrt{(3)^2 + (4)^2}$

$= \sqrt{9 + 16}$

$= \sqrt{25}$

$\therefore |z_1| = 5$

$|z_2| = \sqrt{(5)^2 + (12)^2}$

$= \sqrt{25 + 144}$

$= \sqrt{169}$

$\therefore |z_2| = 13$

(ii) $z_1 z_2 = (3 + 4i)(5 + 12i)$

$= 3(5 + 12i) + 4i(5 + 12i)$

$= 15 + 36i + 20i + 48i^2$

$= 15 + 56i + 48(-1)$

$\therefore z_1 z_2 = -33 + 56i$

(iii) $|z_1 z_2| = |-33 + 56i|$

$= \sqrt{(-33)^2 + (56)^2}$

$= \sqrt{1{,}089 + 3{,}136}$

$= \sqrt{4{,}225}$

$\therefore |z_1 z_2| = 65$

(iv) $|z_1||z_2| = (5)(13)$

$= 65$

$= |z_1 z_2|$

Therefore, $|z_1||z_2| = |z_1 z_2|$.

Exercise 11.6

1. $z_1 = 1 + 2i$ and $z_2 = 3 + 4i$.

(i) Evaluate z_3 if $z_3 = z_1 z_2$.

(ii) Plot z_1 and z_2 on an Argand diagram. Using a protractor, find the angles that z_1 and z_2 make with the positive side of the real axis, i.e. $\text{Arg}(z_1)$ and $\text{Arg}(z_2)$.

(iii) Plot z_3 on the Argand diagram.

(iv) What is $\text{Arg}(z_3)$?

(v) Using the measurements from earlier parts investigate if $\text{Arg}(z_3) = \text{Arg}(z_1) + \text{Arg}(z_2)$.

2. $z_1 = 2 + i$ and $z_2 = -3 + 2i$.

(i) Evaluate z_3 if $z_3 = z_1 z_2$.

(ii) Plot z_1 and z_2 on an Argand diagram. Using a protractor, find the angles that z_1 and z_2 make with the positive side of the real axis, i.e. $\text{Arg}(z_1)$ and $\text{Arg}(z_2)$.

(iii) Plot z_3 on the Argand diagram.

(iv) What is $\text{Arg}(z_3)$?

(v) Using the measurements from earlier parts investigate if $\text{Arg}(z_3) = \text{Arg}(z_1) + \text{Arg}(z_2)$.

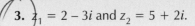3. $z_1 = 2 - 3i$ and $z_2 = 5 + 2i$.

(i) Find $|z_1|$ and $|z_2|$ correct to three decimal places.

(ii) Evaluate $z_1 z_2$.

(iii) Find $|z_1 z_2|$ correct to two decimal places.

(iv) Evaluate $|z_1||z_2|$ to two decimal places. Hence, verify that $|z_1||z_2| = |z_1 z_2|$.

4. $z_1 = 3 - 2i$ and $z_2 = 2 - 4i$.

(i) Find $|z_1|$ and $|z_2|$ correct to three decimal places.

(ii) Evaluate $z_1 z_2$.

(iii) Find $|z_1 z_2|$ correct to one decimal place.

(iv) Evaluate $|z_1||z_2|$ to one decimal place. Hence, verify that $|z_1||z_2| = |z_1 z_2|$.

11.5 CONJUGATE OF A COMPLEX NUMBER

If $z = a + bi$, $a, b \in R$ and $i^2 = -1$, then the **conjugate** of z (writen as $\bar{z}$) = $a - bi$.

For example, if $z = -2 - 12i$, then $\bar{z} = -2 + 12i$.

Rule: Change the sign of the Imaginary part.

$\sqrt{-1}$ Worked Example 11.18

$z = -2 + 3i$. Find $\bar{z}$.

Solution

$\bar{z} = -2 - 3i$

$\sqrt{-1}$ Worked Example 11.19

$z = 2 - 2i$

   (i) Find $\bar{z}$.   (ii) Plot z and $\bar{z}$ on the Argand diagram.

Solution

   (i) $\bar{z} = 2 + 2i$

   (ii)

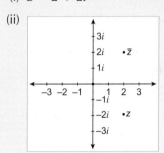

$\bar{z}$ is the image of z by an axial symmetry in the real axis.

$\sqrt{-1}$ Worked Example 11.20

If $z = 13 + 2i$, find:

   (i) $\bar{z}$ (ii) $z + \bar{z}$ (iii) $z - \bar{z}$ (iv) $z\bar{z}$

Solution

   (i) $\bar{z} = 13 - 2i$

   (ii) $z + \bar{z} = (13 + 2i) + (13 - 2i)$

               $= 26$ (a real number)

   (iii) $z - \bar{z} = (13 + 2i) - (13 - 2i)$

                $= 13 + 2i - 13 + 2i$

                $= 4i$

   (iv) $z\bar{z} = (13 + 2i)(13 - 2i)$

           $= 13(13 - 2i) + 2i(13 - 2i)$

           $= 169 - 26i + 26i - 4i^2$

           $= 169 - 4(-1)$

           $= 169 + 4$

           $= 173$ (a real number)

Exercise 11.7

1. $z_1 = 7 + 5i$ and $z_2 = 2 + i$. Find:

(i) $\bar{z}_1$ $7 - 5i$ (iii) $z_1 + \bar{z}_1$

(ii) $\bar{z}_2$ $2 - i$ (iv) $z_2 + \bar{z}_2$

2. $z_1 = 5 + 2i$ and $z_2 = 3 - 4i$. Find:

(i) $\bar{z}_1$ (iv) $z_1 + z_2$

(ii) $\bar{z}_2$ (v) $\overline{z_1 + z_2}$

(iii) $\bar{z}_1 + \bar{z}_2$

3. $z_1 = -1 + 2i$ and $z_2 = 2 + 3i$. Find:

(i) $\bar{z}_1$ (iv) $z_1 + z_2$

(ii) $\bar{z}_2$ (v) $\overline{z_1 + z_2}$

(iii) $\bar{z}_1 + \bar{z}_2$

4. $z_1 = a + bi$ and $z_2 = c - di$. Find, in terms of a, b, c, and d:

(i) $\bar{z}_1$ (iv) $z_1 + z_2$

(ii) $\bar{z}_2$ (v) $\overline{z_1 + z_2}$

(iii) $\bar{z}_1 + \bar{z}_2$ (vi) Verify that
$\overline{z_1 + z_2} = \bar{z}_1 + \bar{z}_2$.

5. $z_1 = 5 + 6i$ and $z_2 = 3 - i$. Find:

(i) $\bar{z}_1$ (iii) $z_1 z_2$ (v) $\bar{z}_1 \bar{z}_2$

(ii) $\bar{z}_2$ (iv) $\overline{z_1 z_2}$

6. Identify z_1, z_2, z_3 and z_4 on the Argand diagram using the following information:

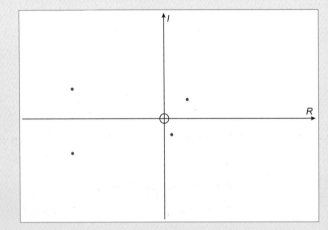

(i) $z_3 = \bar{z}_4$

(ii) $\text{Im}(z_3) > 0$

(iii) $z_1 = 2i z_2$

7. Identify z_1, z_2 and z_3 using the following information:

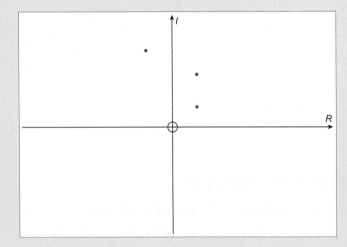

(i) $\text{Im}(z_2) < \text{Im}(z_3)$

(ii) $z_1 = z_2 z_3$

8. Identify z_1, z_2, z_3 and z_4 using the following information:

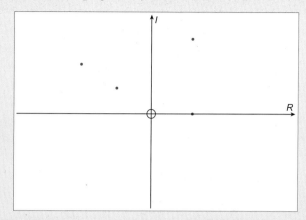

(i) $z_2 = 2z_1$

(ii) $z_3 = -iz_2$

(iii) $z_4 = \mathrm{Re}(z_3)$

9. Identify z_1, z_2, z_3, z_4 and z_5 on the Argand diagram using the following information:

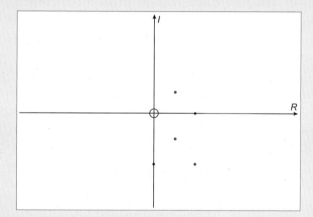

(i) $z_1 = \bar{z}_2$

(ii) $z_3 = 2z_2$

(iii) $z_4 = \mathrm{Im}(z_3)$

(iv) $z_5 = z_1 + \bar{z}_1$

10. Identify z_1, z_2, z_3, z_4 and z_5 on the Argand diagram using the following information:

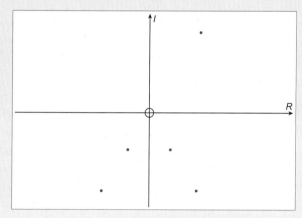

(i) $z_2 = -z_1$

(ii) $z_3 = \mathrm{Re}(z_2) + i\,\mathrm{Im}(z_1)$

(iii) $z_4 = \frac{1}{2}z_3$

(iv) $z_5 = -\frac{1}{2}z_2$

11.6 DIVIDING COMPLEX NUMBERS

In the real number system, if $a \div b = c$, then $a = b \times c$, where $a, b, c \in R$.

Similarly, in the complex number system, if $a \div b = c$, then $a = b \times c$, where $a, b, c \in C$.

However, in the complex number system, we need to follow certain well-defined steps to divide one complex number by another.

$\sqrt{-1}$ Worked Example 11.21

Calculate $\dfrac{15 + 10i}{5}$.

Solution

When we multiply a complex number z by a real number a, we multiply a by Re(z) and a by Im(z). Similarly, when we divide a complex number by a real number a, we divide Re(z) and Im(z) by a.

$$\frac{15 + 10i}{5} = \frac{15}{5} + \frac{10}{5}i$$

$$= 3 + 2i$$

$\sqrt{-1}$ Worked Example 11.22

Calculate $\dfrac{2 + 11i}{2 + i}$.

Solution

In this question we are dividing a complex number by a complex number. If we could reduce the denominator to a real number, then our task would be much easier, as we know how to divide a complex number by a real number. Fortunately, if we multiply a complex number by its conjugate, the result is a real number.

Step 1

Write down the conjugate of the denominator:
$\overline{2 + i} = 2 - i$.

Step 2

Multiply the denominator by $2 - i$.

$(2 + i)(2 - i) = 2(2 - i) + i(2 - i)$

$= 4 - 2i + 2i - i^2$

$= 4 + 1$

$= 5$

Step 3

Multiply the numerator by $2 - i$.

$(2 + 11i)(2 - i) = 2(2 - i) + 11i(2 - i)$

$= 4 - 2i + 22i - 11i^2$

$= 4 + 20i + 11$

$= 15 + 20i$

Step 4

$\dfrac{2 + 11i}{2 + i} = \dfrac{15 + 20i}{5}$

$= \dfrac{15}{5} + \dfrac{20}{5}i$

$= 3 + 4i$

> When dealing with division by a complex number, multiply both the numerator and the denominator by the conjugate of the denominator.

Exercise 11.8

1. Write the following in the form $p + qi$, $p, q \in Q$:

(i) $\dfrac{6 + 3i}{2}$

(ii) $\dfrac{15 - 20i}{5}$

(iii) $\dfrac{24 + 12i}{4}$

(iv) $\dfrac{16 - 8i}{8}$

(v) $\dfrac{5 + 12i}{7}$

2. Write the following in the form $p + qi$, $p, q \in R$:

(i) $\dfrac{5 + 5i}{1 + 2i}$

(ii) $\dfrac{1 - 5i}{1 - i}$

(iii) $\dfrac{10}{1 - 3i}$

(iv) $\dfrac{5}{1 + 2i}$

(v) $\dfrac{1 + 3i}{1 + i}$

3. Write the following in the form $p + qi$, $p, q \in R$:

(i) $\dfrac{5 - 5i}{2 + i}$

(ii) $\dfrac{6}{1 - i}$

(iii) $\dfrac{1 + 5i}{i}$

(iv) $\dfrac{6 + 8i}{2i}$

(v) $\dfrac{-7 + 24i}{3 + 4i}$

4. Write the following in the form $p + qi$, $p, q \in Q$:

(i) $\dfrac{1}{1 + i}$

(ii) $\dfrac{1 + 2i}{1 + 3i}$

(iii) $\dfrac{1 + 5i}{2 - i}$

(iv) $\dfrac{11 + 10i}{2(2 + 3i)}$

(v) $\dfrac{1 - 9i}{2i}$

5. Write the following in the form $p + qi$, $p, q \in Q$:

(i) $\dfrac{2 + i}{i}$

(ii) $\dfrac{8 - 4i}{2i}$

(iii) $\dfrac{27 - 18i}{3i}$

(iv) $\dfrac{-16 + 48i}{-4i}$

(v) $\dfrac{1 + i}{5i}$

6. Write in the form $p + qi$, $p, q \in Q$:

(i) $\dfrac{16}{i}$

(ii) $\dfrac{10}{2i}$

(iii) $\dfrac{25}{3i}$

(iv) $\dfrac{17}{5i}$

(v) $\dfrac{33}{12i}$

7. If $z = 1 - 3i$, write $\dfrac{\bar{z}}{z}$ in the form $a + bi$, $a, b \in Q$.

8. Let $z_1 = -1 + 5i$ and let $z_2 = 2 + 3i$.
   Investigate whether $\overline{\left(\dfrac{z_1}{z_2}\right)} = \dfrac{\bar{z}_1}{\bar{z}_2}$.

9. Let $z_1 = -15 + 16i$ and let $z_2 = 6 + i$.
   Investigate whether $\overline{\left(\dfrac{z_1}{z_2}\right)} = \dfrac{\bar{z}_1}{\bar{z}_2}$.

10. Let $z_1 = 11 - 10i$ and let $z_2 = 4 + i$.
   (i) Find $\dfrac{z_1}{z_2}$.
   (ii) Calculate $|z_1|$ and $|z_2|$.
   (iii) Investigate whether $\left|\dfrac{z_1}{z_2}\right| = \dfrac{|z_1|}{|z_2|}$.

11.7 QUADRATIC EQUATIONS WITH COMPLEX ROOTS

From your knowledge of algebra, you already know that the solutions to a quadratic equation, $ax^2 + bx + c = 0$, $a, b, c \in R$, are given by the formula $x = \dfrac{-b \pm \sqrt{b^2 - 4ac}}{2a}$.

In this formula we refer to $b^2 - 4ac$ as the **discriminant**.

If $b^2 - 4ac < 0$, then the solutions (roots) will be complex.

Worked Example 11.23

Solve the equation $z^2 - 6z + 13 = 0$.

Solution

$z = \dfrac{6 \pm \sqrt{(-6)^2 - 4(1)(13)}}{2(1)}$ $a = 1, b = -6, c = 13$

$= \dfrac{6 \pm \sqrt{36 - 52}}{2}$

$= \dfrac{6 \pm \sqrt{-16}}{2}$

$= \dfrac{6 \pm \sqrt{16}\sqrt{-1}}{2}$

$= \dfrac{6 \pm 4i}{2}$

$= \dfrac{6}{2} \pm \dfrac{4i}{2}$

$= 3 \pm 2i$ The roots are $3 + 2i$ and $3 - 2i$.

Exercise 11.9

1. Solve the equation $z^2 + 4z + 13 = 0$, giving your answers in the form $a + bi$, $a, b \in R$.

2. Evaluate the following:

   (i) $(1 - 2i)^2$ (ii) $-2(1 - 2i)$

   Hence, show that $1 - 2i$ is a root of the equation $z^2 - 2z + 5 = 0$.

3. Show that the roots of the equation $z^2 - 2z + 10 = 0$ are complex.

4. Solve the equation $z^2 - 8z + 17 = 0$, giving your answers in the form $a + bi$, $a, b \in R$.

5. Show that the roots of the equation $z^2 + 6z + 25 = 0$ are complex.

6. Evaluate the following:

   (i) $(-7 + i)^2$ (ii) $14(-7 + i)$

   Hence, show that $-7 + i$ is a root of the equation $z^2 + 14z + 50 = 0$.

7. Solve the equation $z^2 - 12z + 40 = 0$. Give your answers in the form $a + bi$, $a, b \in R$.

8. Find the complex roots of the equation $z^2 = -2(5z + 17)$.

9. Solve the following equations and show your solutions on an Argand diagram:

   (i) $z^2 - 4z + 5 = 0$

   (ii) $z^2 - 8z + 25 = 0$

   (iii) $z^2 + 2z + 17 = 0$

   (iv) $z^2 + 4z + 40 = 0$

10. Solve the following equations and show your solutions on an Argand diagram:

   (i) $z^2 + 16 = 0$

   (ii) $4z^2 - 12z + 25 = 0$

   (iii) $9z^2 - 6z + 5 = 0$

   (iv) $z^2 - 8z + 25 = 0$

 Revision Exercises

1. $z_1 = 3 + i$ and $z_2 = 4 - 2i$. Evaluate:

   (i) $z_1 + z_2$ (iv) $\bar{z}_2$

   (ii) $z_1 - z_2$ (v) $\dfrac{z_1}{z_2}$

   (iii) $z_1 z_2$ (vi) $|z_2|$

2. $z_1 = 7 + i$ and $z_2 = -5 - 4i$. Evaluate:

   (i) $z_1 + z_2$ (iv) $\bar{z}_2$

   (ii) $z_1 - z_2$ (v) $\dfrac{z_1}{z_2}$

   (iii) $z_1 z_2$ (vi) $|z_1 z_2|$

3. $z_1 = 2 + i$ and $z_2 = 11 + 9i$. Evaluate:

   (i) $z_1 - z_2$ (iv) $|z_2|$

   (ii) $\dfrac{z_1}{z_2}$ (v) $\left|\dfrac{z_1}{z_2}\right|$

   (iii) $|z_1|$ (vi) $\overline{z_1 z_2}$

4. $z_1 = 21 + 28i$ and $z_2 = 9 - 40i$. Evaluate:

   (i) $z_1 z_2$ (iii) $\bar{z}_1$ (v) $\bar{z}_1 \bar{z}_2$

   (ii) $\overline{z_1 z_2}$ (iv) $\bar{z}_2$ (vi) $3z_1 - 2z_2$

5. $z_1 = 48 + 14i$ and $z_2 = 33 + 56i$. Evaluate:

   (i) $z_1 z_2$ (iii) $|z_1|$ (v) $|z_1||z_2|$

   (ii) $|z_1 z_2|$ (iv) $|z_2|$ (vi) $-2z_1 + 3z_2$

6. $z_1 = 16 - 63i$ and $z_2 = 39 + 52i$. Evaluate:

   (i) $\dfrac{z_1}{z_2}$ (iii) $|z_2|$ (v) $2z_1 - z_2$

   (ii) $\dfrac{z_2}{z_1}$ (iv) $|z_1|$ (vi) $2(z_1 - z_2)$

   Show that $\left|\dfrac{z_1}{z_2}\right| = \left|\dfrac{z_2}{z_1}\right|$.

7. $\omega = 1 - i$, $z_1 = 2 + i$, $z_2 = 3 - i$ and $z_3 = -2 - 4i$.

   (i) Plot z_1, z_2 and z_3 on an Argand diagram.

   (ii) Evaluate $\omega + z_1$, $\omega + z_2$, $\omega + z_3$ and plot your answers on the Argand diagram.

   (iii) Describe the transformation that is the addition of ω.

8. If $z_1 = -3 - i$ and $z_2 = 1 - i$, write the following in the form $a + bi$, $a, b \in R$:

   (i) $3z_1 - z_2$ (ii) $\bar{z}_2$ (iii) $\dfrac{z_1}{z_2}$

9. Solve the equation $z^2 - 4z + 5 = 0$.

10. Evaluate the following:

   (i) i^5 (ii) i^6 (iii) i^7

   Hence, show that $z = i$ is a solution to the equation $4z^7 - 6z^6 + 4z^5 - 6 = 0$.

11. Identify z_1, z_2, z_3, z_4 and z_5 on the Argand diagram using the following information:

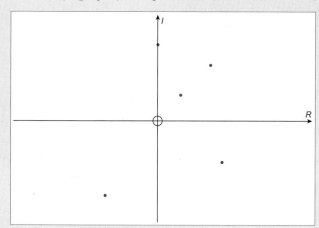

   (i) $\text{Im}(z_1) < 0$

   (ii) $z_5 = -iz_1$

   (iii) $\text{Re}(z_3) = 0$

   (iv) $z_4 = \frac{1}{2}z_2$

12. Find z by completing the pyramid shown. Each number is evaluated by adding the numbers from the two boxes directly below.

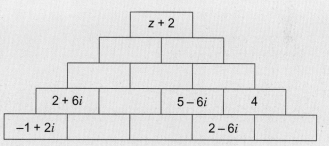

13. Find z by completing the pyramid. Each number is evaluated by adding the numbers from the two boxes directly below.

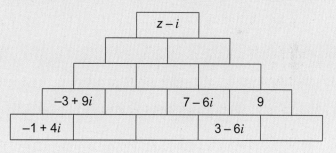

14. z is the complex number $1 + i$, where $i^2 = -1$.

   (a) (i) Find z^2 and z^3.

      (ii) Verify that $z^4 = -4$.

      (iii) Show z, z^2, z^3 and z^4 on the Argand diagram.

      (iv) Make one observation about the pattern of points on the diagram.

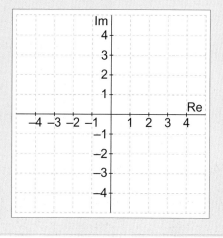

(b) Using the value of z^4, or otherwise, find the values of z^8, z^{12} and z^{16}, and insert their values in the table below.

z^4	z^8	z^{12}	z^{16}
-4			

(c) Based on the pattern of values in parts (b), or otherwise, state whether z^{40} is positive or negative. Explain how you got your answer.

(d) Write z^{40} as a power of 2.

(e) Find z^{41}.

(f) On an Argand diagram, how far from the origin is z^{41}?

SEC Project Maths Paper 1, Leaving Certificate Ordinary Level, 2011

chapter 12

Calculus

Learning Outcomes

In this chapter you will learn:

- ➲ To investigate the concept of the limit of a function

- ➲ The meaning of a derivative

- ➲ How to differentiate by rule

- ➲ How to find the slope of a tangent to a curve

- ➲ How to find the equation of a tangent to a curve

- ➲ The meaning of the second derivative

- ➲ How to find stationary points

- ➲ How to solve maximum–minimum problems or how to solve optimisation problems

- ➲ How to solve problems involving rates of change

12.1 CALCULUS

The discovery of calculus is often attributed to two men, Isaac Newton (1642–1727) and Gottfried Leibniz (1646–1716). They independently developed its foundations.

Isaac Newton
(1642–1727)

Gottfried Leibniz
(1646–1716)

Newton was an English physicist, mathematician, astronomer and theologian. Many people consider him to be the greatest and most influential scientist who ever lived.

Leibniz was a German philosopher and mathematician. He wrote in many languages, including Latin, French and German.

Leibniz was very conscious of the importance of notation. He put a lot of thought into the symbols he used. Newton, on the other hand, wrote more for himself than for anyone else. As a result, much of the notation we use in calculus today was developed by Leibniz.

12.2 LIMITS

The concept of the limit of a function was central to the development of calculus.

Consider the function $f(x) = 2x + 3$ for values of x near 2.

The table below gives values of x close to 2.

x	$f(x)$	x	$f(x)$
1.0	5	3.0	9
1.5	6	2.5	8
1.8	6.6	2.2	7.4
1.9	6.8	2.1	7.2
1.95	6.9	2.05	7.1
1.99	6.98	2.01	7.02
1.995	6.99	2.005	7.01
1.999	6.998	2.001	7.002

Graph of $f(x) = 2x + 3$

The table and graph of f show that when x is close to 2, $f(x)$ is close to 7. In fact we can make values of $f(x)$ as close as we like to 7, by taking x sufficiently close to 2. We express this by saying, 'The limit of the function $f(x) = 2x + 3$ as x approaches 2 is equal to 7.' In mathematical notation, this is expressed as $\lim_{x \to 2} f(x) = 7$.

Worked Example 12.1

The function $f(x) = 2x - 8$ is defined for all $x \in R$.
By drawing a graph of the function for values of x close to 5, find $\lim\limits_{x \to 5} f(x)$.

Solution

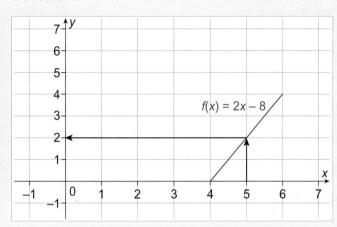

A graph of $f(x)$ in the domain $4 \leqslant x \leqslant 6$ is shown. From the graph, we can see that as x approaches 5, $f(x)$ approaches 2.

Also, it is clear that $\lim\limits_{x \to 5} f(x) = f(5) = 2$.

Worked Example 12.2

$f(x) = \dfrac{x^2 - 25}{x - 5}, x \in R, x \neq 5.$

(i) Explain why $f(x)$ is not defined for $x = 5$.

(ii) Find $\lim\limits_{x \to 5} f(x)$.

Solution

(i) Directly, $f(5) = \dfrac{5^2 - 25}{5 - 5}$

$= \dfrac{25 - 25}{5 - 5}$

$= \dfrac{0}{0}$, which is not defined.

(ii) $\dfrac{x^2 - 25}{x - 5}$ can be factorised as $\dfrac{(x - 5)(x + 5)}{(x - 5)}$.

If $x \neq 5$, we can simplify this fraction to $x + 5$.

So, $\lim\limits_{x \to 5} f(x) = \lim\limits_{x \to 5} (x + 5)$

$= 5 + 5$

$= 10$

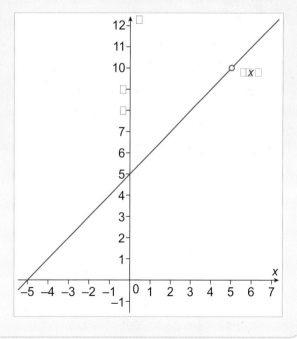

CALCULUS

Exercise 12.1

1. The function $f(x) = 2x - 4$, is defined for all $x \in R$.

   (i) Copy and complete the following table:

x	f(x)	x	f(x)
1.0	−2	3.0	2
1.5		2.5	
1.8	−0.4	2.2	
1.9		2.1	0.2
1.95		2.05	
1.99		2.01	
1.995		2.005	
1.999		2.001	

   (ii) Hence, find $\lim\limits_{x \to 2} f(x)$.

2. The function $g(x) = 2x^2 - 4$ is defined for all $x \in R$.

   (i) Copy and complete the following table:

x	g(x)	x	g(x)
4.0	28	6.0	68
4.5		5.5	
4.8	42.08	5.2	
4.9		5.1	48.02
4.95		5.05	
4.99		5.01	
4.995		5.005	
4.999		5.001	

   (ii) Hence, find $\lim\limits_{x \to 5} g(x)$.

3. Use the graph of each function to find the required limit.

   (i) $\lim\limits_{x \to 2} f(x)$

   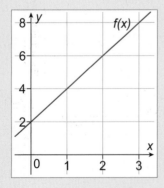

   (ii) $\lim\limits_{x \to 0} m(x)$

   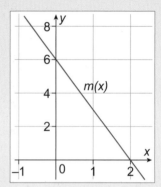

   (iii) $\lim\limits_{x \to 3} g(x)$

   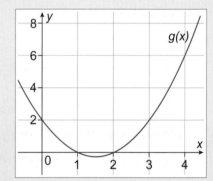

   (iv) $\lim\limits_{x \to 2} h(x)$

   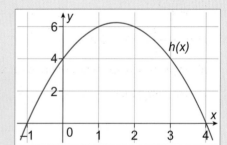

   (v) $\lim\limits_{x \to 3} p(x)$

   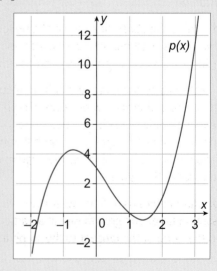

(vi) $\lim_{x\to 0} k(x)$

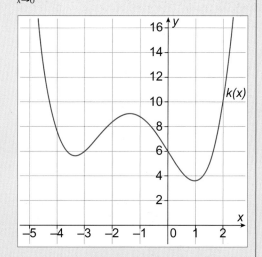

4. Evaluate each of the following limits:

(i) $\lim_{x\to 3} (x + 4)$

(iv) $\lim_{x\to 1} (x^2 - 2x + 4)$

(ii) $\lim_{x\to 1} (2x - 3)$

(v) $\lim_{x\to 5} (x^3)$

(iii) $\lim_{x\to 2} (x^2)$

5. Evaluate each of the following limits:

(i) $\lim_{x\to 3} (2x + 3)$

(iv) $\lim_{x\to 1} (5 - 6x - x^2)$

(ii) $\lim_{x\to -1} (2 - 3x)$

(v) $\lim_{x\to 3} (x^3 - 1)$

(iii) $\lim_{x\to 2} (5x^2)$

6. $f(x) = \dfrac{x^2 - 9}{x - 3}, x \in R, x \neq 3$

(i) Explain why $f(x)$ is not defined for $x = 3$.

(ii) Find $\lim_{x\to 3} f(x)$.

7. $f(x) = \dfrac{x^2 - 16}{x + 4}, x \in R, x \neq -4$

(i) Explain why $f(x)$ is not defined for $x = -4$.

(ii) Find $\lim_{x\to -4} f(x)$.

8. $f(x) = \dfrac{x^2 - 2x - 8}{x - 4}, x \in R, x \neq 4$

(i) Explain why $f(x)$ is not defined for $x = 4$.

(ii) Find $\lim_{x\to 4} f(x)$.

9. If $f(x) = x + 5, x \in R$, and $g(x) = x - 2$, $x \in R$, then show that each of the following statements is true:

(i) $\lim_{x\to 2} f(x) + \lim_{x\to 2} g(x) = \lim_{x\to 2} (f(x) + g(x))$

(ii) $\lim_{x\to 2} f(x) - \lim_{x\to 2} g(x) = \lim_{x\to 2} (f(x) - g(x))$

(iii) $\lim_{x\to 2} f(x) \times \lim_{x\to 2} g(x) = \lim_{x\to 2} (f(x) \times g(x))$

(iv) $\lim_{x\to 3} f(x) \div \lim_{x\to 3} g(x) = \lim_{x\to 3} (f(x) \div g(x))$

10. If $f(x) = x^2 - 3, x \in R$, and $g(x) = x - 2$, $x \in R$, then show that each of the following statements is true:

(i) $\lim_{x\to 1} f(x) + \lim_{x\to 1} g(x) = \lim_{x\to 1} (f(x) + g(x))$

(ii) $\lim_{x\to 3} f(x) - \lim_{x\to 3} g(x) = \lim_{x\to 3} (f(x) - g(x))$

(iii) $\lim_{x\to 2} f(x) \times \lim_{x\to 2} g(x) = \lim_{x\to 2} (f(x) \times g(x))$

(iv) $\lim_{x\to 4} f(x) \div \lim_{x\to 4} g(x) = \lim_{x\to 4} (f(x) \div g(x))$

12.3 DERIVATIVES

Calculus is **the study of rates of change** and has applications in all the natural sciences, as well as in engineering, finance, economics and medicine.

In mathematics, we can use graphs to illustrate the rate at which things grow or decay. Graph A shows the growth of bacteria in a culture over a short interval of time. The graph indicates that the rate of growth is relatively small at the beginning but increases as time goes by.

Calculus enables us to find the growth rate at any instant in time. The growth rate at a particular time, t, is the slope of the tangent to the graph at t (Graph B).

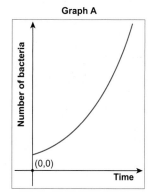

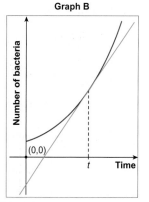

If a tangent is drawn at a point P on a curve, then the gradient (slope) of this tangent is said to be the **gradient of the curve** at P. In the diagram, the gradient of the curve at P is equal to the gradient of the tangent PQ.

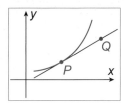

The process of finding a general expression for the gradient of a curve at any point is known as **differentiation**.

The general expression for the gradient of a curve $y = f(x)$ is itself a function, so it is called the gradient function. In practice, it is more often called the **derived function** or the **derivative**.

For any curve $y = f(x)$, $\dfrac{dy}{dx}$ is the notation used for the gradient.

$\dfrac{dy}{dx}$ represents the gradient of the curve, i.e. the rate of change of y with respect to x.

> The slope of the tangent to a curve $y = f(x)$ at any point $(x, f(x))$ on the curve is denoted by $\dfrac{dy}{dx}$ or $f'(x)$.

Note

- $\dfrac{dy}{dx}$ is read as 'dee y dee x'.
- $f'(x)$ is read as 'f prime of x'.
- One can differentiate with respect to any variable.
  For example: $\dfrac{ds}{dt}, \dfrac{dA}{dr}$.

Rule 1
If $y = ax^2$, where $x \in R$ and a is any constant, then $\dfrac{dy}{dx} = 2ax$. [Also written as $f'(x) = 2ax$]

Rule 2
If $y = ax^3$, where $x \in R$ and a is any constant, then $\dfrac{dy}{dx} = 3ax^2$. [Also written as $f'(x) = 3ax^2$]

Rule 3
⚠ If $y = a$, where a is any constant, then $\dfrac{dy}{dx} = 0$.

Rule 4
If $y = f(x) + g(x)$, then $\dfrac{dy}{dx} = \dfrac{df}{dx} + \dfrac{dg}{dx}$.

[Differentiate both functions and add the resultant answers.]

FORMULA

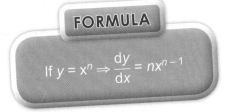

If $y = x^n \Rightarrow \dfrac{dy}{dx} = nx^{n-1}$

Formulae and Tables, page 25.

Worked Example 12.3

Differentiate the following with respect to x:

(i) $f(x) = x^2$

(ii) $f(x) = 2x$

(iii) $f(x) = 4$

(iv) $f(x) = x^2 - 2x + 5$

(v) $f(x) = x^3 + 4x^2$

Solution

(i) $f'(x) = 2x$

(ii) $f'(x) = 2$

(iii) $f'(x) = 0$

(iv) $f'(x) = 2x - 2$

(v) $f'(x) = 3x^2 + 8x$

CALCULUS

Worked Example 12.4

If $y = x^2 - 3x + 8$, find $\dfrac{dy}{dx}$ when $x = -1$.

Solution

$\dfrac{dy}{dx} = 2x - 3$ (Differentiation)

At $x = -1$:

$\dfrac{dy}{dx} = 2(-1) - 3$ (Substitution)

$= -5$

> Another way of asking this question is to find $f'(-1)$.

 Exercise 12.2

1. Differentiate with respect to x:

   (i) $y = x^3$ (iv) $y = -8x$

   (ii) $y = 3x^2$ (v) $y = -16x$

   (iii) $y = 2x^3$ (vi) $y = \frac{1}{2}x^2$

2. For each of the following, find $\dfrac{ds}{dt}$:

   (i) $s = 2t$ (iv) $s = \frac{1}{3}t^3$

   (ii) $s = 3t^2$ (v) $s = \frac{1}{2}t^2$

   (iii) $s = 5t^3$ (vi) $s = -15t$

3. Differentiate the following with respect to the letter in brackets:

   (i) $y = \frac{1}{2}x^2$ [x]   (iv) $A = \frac{1}{2}\pi r^2$ [r]

   (ii) $s = \frac{1}{3}t^3$ [t]   (v) $C = 2\pi r$ [r]

   (iii) $A = \pi r^2$ [r]   (vi) $V = x^3$ [x]

4. Differentiate the following with respect to x:

   (i) $y = 4x^2 + 2x + 6$

   (ii) $y = 3x^2 + 10x + 2$

   (iii) $y = x^2 + 9x + 12$

   (iv) $y = 3x^3 + 4x^2 - 3x + 8$

   (v) $y = 3x^2 + 4$

5. Find $\dfrac{dy}{dx}$ when:

   (i) $y = 3x$ (iv) $y = 12 - 15x$

   (ii) $y = 5 - 2x$ (v) $y = 2 - x$

   (iii) $y = 17x + 12$ (vi) $y = x^2 - 3x - 6$

6. Differentiate with respect to x:

   (i) $y = 4$ (iv) $y = \sqrt{2}$

   (ii) $y = -8$ (v) $y = 0.25$

   (iii) $y = \frac{1}{2}$ (vi) $y = 12.25$

7. Find $f'(x)$ when:

   (i) $f(x) = x^3 + x^2 + x$

   (ii) $f(x) = x^3 - x$

   (iii) $f(x) = x^3 + x$

   (iv) $f(x) = 10x^3 + 11x^2$

   (v) $f(x) = 9x^3 - 8x^2$

   (vi) $f(x) = x^3 + 6x^2 - 3x + 8$

8. Find $\dfrac{dy}{dx}$ when:

   (i) $y = x^3 + x^2 - x + 1$

   (ii) $y = 3x^3 + 2x^2 - x + 1$

9. $f(x) = x^2 - 2x + 12$

   (i) Find $f'(x)$.   (ii) Evaluate $f'(100)$.

10. $f(x) = x^3 - x^2 + 4$

   (i) Find $f'(x)$.   (ii) Evaluate $f'(-5)$.

11. $y = x^3 - 3x^2 + 2x - 8$

   (i) Find $\dfrac{dy}{dx}$.

   (ii) Evaluate $\dfrac{dy}{dx}$ when $x = 3$.

12. $y = 2x^3 + 3x^2 - 2x + 7$

   (i) Find $\dfrac{dy}{dx}$.

   (ii) Evaluate $\dfrac{dy}{dx}$ when $x = -1$.

13. $y = 5x^3 - 2x^2 - 12x + 10$

   (i) Find $\dfrac{dy}{dx}$.

   (ii) Evaluate $\dfrac{dy}{dx}$ when $x = 0$.

14. $f(x) = (x - 3)(x + 4)$, $x \in R$.

   (i) Write $f(x)$ in the form $f(x) = x^2 + mx + n$, $m, n \in Z$.

   (ii) Hence, find $f'(x)$.

15. $f(x) = (2x - 3)(x + 2)$, $x \in R$.

   (i) Write $f(x)$ in the form $f(x) = 2x^2 + ax + b$, $a, b \in Z$.

   (ii) Hence, find $f'(x)$.

12.4 SLOPES OF TANGENTS

We have already seen that the slope of the tangent to a curve $y = f(x)$ at any point $(x, f(x))$ on the curve is given by:

$$\frac{dy}{dx} \quad \textbf{OR} \quad f'(x)$$

 ## Worked Example 12.5

A graph of the cubic function $f(x) = 2x^3 + 5x^2 + x - 3$ is shown. The tangent to $f(x)$ at the point $(0,-3)$ is also shown on the diagram.

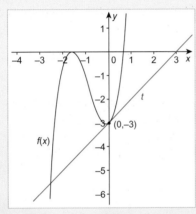

   (i) Write down $f'(x)$, the derivative of $f(x)$.

   (ii) Hence, find the slope of the tangent to $f(x)$ at $(0,-3)$.

   (iii) Find the equation of the tangent to the curve at $(0,-3)$.

Solution

   (i) $f(x) = 2x^3 + 5x^2 + x - 3$

      $\Rightarrow f'(x) = 6x^2 + 10x + 1$

   (ii) To find the slope of the tangent at a particular point, substitute the x co-ordinate of the point into the derivative.

      $\therefore f'(0) = 6(0)^2 + 10(0) + 1$

      $\Rightarrow f'(0) = 1$

      Therefore, the slope of the tangent to the curve at $x = 0$ is 1.

   (iii) $y - y_1 = m(x - x_1)$ Point $(0,-3)$ $m = 1$

      $\therefore y + 3 = 1(x - 0)$

      $y + 3 = x$

      $\therefore y = x - 3$

 ## Worked Example 12.6

Find a point on the curve $y = x^2 - 8x + 21$ where the tangent to the curve has a slope of 4.

Solution

$y = x^2 - 8x + 21$

$\Rightarrow \dfrac{dy}{dx} = 2x - 8$ (slope of all tangents to the curve)

The slope of the required tangent to the curve is 4.

$\therefore 2x - 8 = 4$

$\quad\quad 2x = 12$

$\therefore x = 6$

We must now find the y co-ordinate when $x = 6$.

$y = x^2 - 8x + 21$

$\therefore y = (6)^2 - 8(6) + 21$ at $x = 6$

$\Rightarrow y = 9$

Therefore, the required point is $(6,9)$.

Exercise 12.3

1. The diagram shows a tangent to the curve $f(x) = x^2$ at the point (1,1).

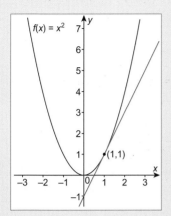

(i) Write down $f'(x)$, the derivative of $f(x)$. $f'(x) = 2x$

(ii) Hence, find the slope of the tangent to $f(x)$ at (1,1). $f'(1) = 2(1)$

$f(x) = 2$

(iii) Find the equation of the tangent to the curve at the point (1,1).

2. The diagram shows a tangent to the curve $f(x) = x^2 + 2x + 1$ at the point (0,1).

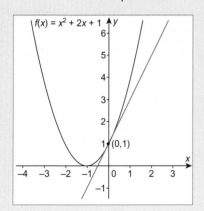

(i) Write down $f'(x)$, the derivative of $f(x)$.

(ii) Hence, find the slope of the tangent to $f(x)$ at (0,1).

(iii) Find the equation of the tangent to the curve at (0,1).

3. Below is a diagram showing a tangent to the curve $f(x) = x^2 + 2x - 3$ at the point (−2,−3).

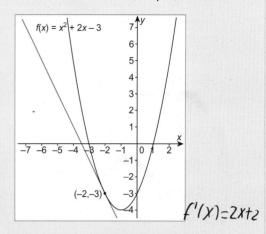

$f'(x) = 2x + 2$

(i) Write down $f'(x)$, the derivative of $f(x)$.

(ii) Hence, find the slope of the tangent to $f(x)$ at (−2,−3). $f'(-2) = 2(-2) + 2$

(iii) Find the equation of the tangent to $f(x)$ at (−2,−3). $= -2$

4. Below is a diagram showing a tangent to the curve $f(x) = 5 + 3x - x^2$ at the point (4,1).

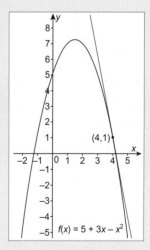

(i) Write down $f'(x)$, the derivative of $f(x)$.

(ii) Find the equation of the tangent to $f(x)$ at (4,1).

5. The function $f(x) = 5 + 2x - 2x^2$ is shown together with the tangent to $f(x)$ at the point (2,1).

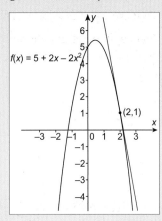

(i) Write down $f'(x)$, the derivative of $f(x)$.

(ii) Hence, find the slope of the tangent to $f(x)$ at (2,1).

(iii) Find the equation of the tangent to the curve at (2,1).

(iv) Find the co-ordinates of the point where the tangent intersects the y-axis.

6. A graph of the cubic function $f(x) = x^3 + 5x^2 + 5x + 1$ is shown. The tangent to $f(x)$ at the point (0,1) is also shown on the diagram.

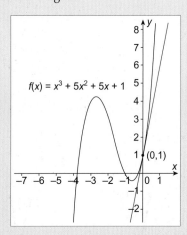

(i) Write down $f'(x)$, the derivative of $f(x)$.

(ii) Hence, find the slope of the tangent to $f(x)$ at (0,1).

(iii) Find the equation of the tangent to the curve at (0,1).

(iv) Find the co-ordinates of the points where the tangent intersects the x-axis and the y-axis.

(v) Hence, calculate the area enclosed between the tangent, the x-axis and the y-axis.

7. A graph of the cubic function $f(x) = 1 + 2x + 3x^2 - x^3$ is shown. The tangent to $f(x)$ at the point (0,1) is also shown on the diagram.

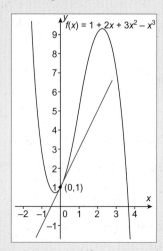

(i) Write down $f'(x)$, the derivative of $f(x)$.

(ii) Hence, find the slope of the tangent to $f(x)$ at (0,1).

(iii) Find the equation of the tangent to the curve at (0,1).

(iv) Find the co-ordinates of the points where the tangent intersects the x-axis and the y-axis.

(v) Hence, calculate the area enclosed between the tangent, the x-axis and the y-axis.

(vi) Show that the tangent intersects the curve at the point (3,7).

8. Show that the tangent to the curve $y = x^2 - 2x + 5$ at the point (1,4) has a slope of zero.

9. Find the point on the curve $f(x) = x^2 - 6x + 11$ where the tangent is parallel to the x-axis.

10. Find the point on the curve $y = x^2 - 2x + 11$ where the slope is equal to 6.

11. The function $f(x) = x^2 - 2x + 9$ is defined for all real values of x.

(i) Find the value of x for which $f'(x) = 8$.

(ii) Hence, find the equation of the tangent to the curve of $f(x)$ that has a slope of 8.

12. The function $f(x) = x^2 - 4x + 12$ is defined for all $x \in R$.

   (i) Find the value of x for which $f'(x) = 2$.

   (ii) Hence, find the equation of the tangent to the curve of $f(x)$ that has a slope of 2.

13. The function $f(x) = 3 + 4x - x^2$ is defined for all real values of x.

   (i) Find the value of x for which $f'(x) = 6$.

   (ii) Hence, find the equation of the tangent to the curve of $f(x)$ that has a slope of 6.

12.5 INCREASING AND DECREASING FUNCTIONS

Consider the curve $f(x) = x^2$, $x \in R$.

- For $x < 0$, as x increases, y decreases. We say $f(x)$ decreases for $x < 0$. Tangents drawn to a decreasing function will have a negative slope; i.e. $\dfrac{dy}{dx} < 0$ if a function is decreasing on an interval.

- For $x > 0$, as x increases, y increases. We say $f(x)$ increases for $x > 0$. Tangents drawn to an increasing function will have a positive slope; i.e. $\dfrac{dy}{dx} > 0$ if a function is increasing on an interval.

- For $x = 0$, y is neither increasing nor decreasing. The slope of the tangent at $x = 0$ is zero.

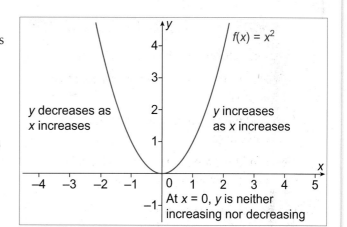

y decreases as x increases

$f(x) = x^2$

y increases as x increases

At $x = 0$, y is neither increasing nor decreasing

Worked Example 12.7

Let $f(x) = x^3 - 3x^2 + 1$, $x \in R$.

   (i) Write down $f'(x)$, the derivative of $f(x)$.

   (ii) Hence, find the range of values of x for which $f(x)$ is increasing.

Solution

   (i) $f(x) = x^3 - 3x^2 + 1$

      $\Rightarrow f'(x) = 3x^2 - 6x$

   (ii) $f(x)$ increases when $f'(x) > 0$.

      A sketch of the graph of $f'(x)$ will show us the x-values for which $f'(x) > 0$.

      $f'(x) = 3x^2 - 6x$

            $= 3x(x - 2)$

      To find the x-intercepts:

      Let $f'(x) = 0$.

      $3x(x - 2) = 0$

      $x = 0$ **OR** $x = 2$

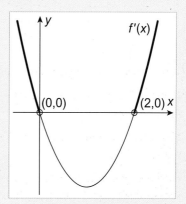

Reading from the graph, $f'(x) > 0$ when $x < 0$ or $x > 2$.

Therefore, $f(x)$ is increasing when $x < 0$ or $x > 2$.

Exercise 12.4

1. The diagrams below show the graphs of two cubic functions. For each function, write down the range of values of x for which the function is decreasing.

(i)

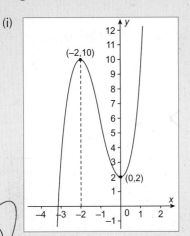

(ii)

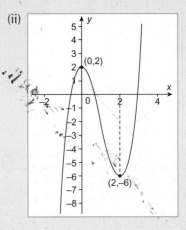

2. The diagrams below show the graphs of two cubic functions. For each function, write down the range of values of x for which the function is increasing.

(i)

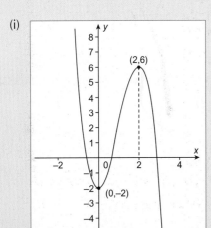

(ii)

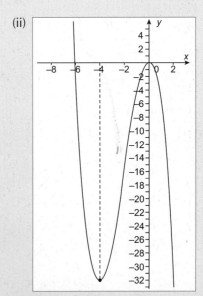

3. Find the range of values of x for which the following functions are increasing ($x \in R$):

   (i) $f(x) = x^2 - 2x - 8$

   (ii) $f(x) = 2 - 4x - x^2$

   (iii) $f(x) = 5x^2 - 2$

   (iv) $f(x) = x^2 + 3x - 5$

4. Find the range of values of x for which the following functions are decreasing ($x \in R$):

   (i) $f(x) = 2x^3 - 9x^2 + 12x - 5$

   (ii) $f(x) = x^3 - 48x$

   (iii) $f(x) = -27x + x^3$

   (iv) $f(x) = 2x^3 - 24x + 5$

5. Find the range of values of x for which the following functions are increasing ($x \in R$):

   (i) $f(x) = x^3 - x^2$

   (ii) $f(x) = 3x^3 - 9x + 2$

   (iii) $f(x) = x^3 - x$

   (iv) $f(x) = 18x - 15x^2 - 4x^3$

6. Show that for all values of $x, x \in R$, the function $f(x) = 2x^5 + x^3 + 7x$ is an increasing function.

7. Show that for all values of $x, x \in R$, the function $g(x) = -4x - 2x^3$ is a decreasing function.

12.6 SECOND DERIVATIVES

When a function $y = f(x)$ is differentiated with respect to x, the derivative is written as $\dfrac{dy}{dx}$ or $f'(x)$.

If the expression is differentiated again, the second derivative is obtained and is written as $\dfrac{d^2y}{dx^2}$ or $f''(x)$.

Second derivatives will be used later to help us locate the maximum and minimum points of various functions.

- $\dfrac{d^2y}{dx^2}$ is read as 'dee squared y dee x squared'.
- $f''(x)$ is read as 'f double prime of x'.

 ## Worked Example 12.8

For each of the following functions, find $\dfrac{d^2y}{dx^2}$.

   (i) $y = 5x^2 + 2x - 6$

   (ii) $y = 8x^3 + 10x$

Solution

   (i) $y = 5x^2 + 2x - 6$

       $\dfrac{dy}{dx} = 10x + 2$

       $\dfrac{d^2y}{dx^2} = 10$

   (ii) $y = 8x^3 + 10x$

       $\dfrac{dy}{dx} = 24x^2 + 10$

       $\dfrac{d^2y}{dx^2} = 48x$

 ## Worked Example 12.9

If $f(x) = 3x^3 - 5x^2 + 10x - 7$, find $f''(2)$.

Solution

  $f(x) = 3x^3 - 5x^2 + 10x - 7$

  $f'(x) = 9x^2 - 10x + 10$

  $f''(x) = 18x - 10$

Now substitute $x = 2$ into $f''(x)$.

  $\therefore f''(2) = 18(2) - 10$

          $= 36 - 10$

    $f''(2) = 26$

 ## Exercise 12.5

1. For each of the following functions, find $\dfrac{d^2y}{dx^2}$.

   (i) $y = 12x^2 - 2x - 6$

   (ii) $y = 8x^2 + 10x + 2$

   (iii) $y = 9x^2 + 9x + 12$

   (iv) $y = 23x^3 + 2x^2 - 3x - 9$

   (v) $y = 33x^2 + 4$

2. For each of the following functions, find $f''(x)$ at $x = -3$.

   (i) $f(x) = x^3 + x^2 + x$

   (ii) $f(x) = x^2 - x$

   (iii) $f(x) = x^3 + x$

   (iv) $f(x) = 10x^3 + 11x^2$

   (v) $f(x) = 9x^2 - 8x^3$

3. For each of the following, find $\dfrac{d^2s}{dt^2}$:

   (i) $s = 4.9t^2$

   (ii) $s = 5t - 4.9t^2$

   (iii) $s = t^3 + t^2 - 5t$

   (iv) $s = t^4 - t^2$

4. Find the second derivative of each of the following functions:

  (i) $f(x) = x^3$

  (ii) $f(x) = x^3 - 3x^2$

  (iii) $g(t) = -4t^2$

  (iv) $A(r) = \pi r^2$

5. For each of the following functions find $\dfrac{d^2s}{dt^2}$:

  (i) $s = (t^2 - 3)(t + 5)$

  (ii) $s = (t - 2)(t^2 - 3t - 8)$

  (iii) $s = (t^3 - t^2 - 3t)(t + 1)$

  (iv) $s = (t - 3)(t + 3)$

6. The function $f(x) = 3x^3 - 9x + 2$ is defined for all real values of x.

  (i) Find $f''(x)$, the second derivative of $f(x)$.

  (ii) Hence, find $f''(2)$.

7. The function $f(x) = x^3 + 3x + 2$ is defined for all real values of x.

  (i) Find $f''(x)$, the second derivative of $f(x)$.

  (ii) Hence, find the value of x for which $f''(x) = f'(x)$.

12.7 STATIONARY POINTS

At a stationary point on a curve, the gradient is zero. For our course, we will look at two types of stationary points called **local maximum** and **local minimum** points. These are also called **turning points** because the graph turns at these points.

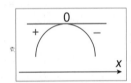

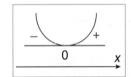

Maximum points – 'humps'

As x increases, the gradient goes positive → 0 → negative.

Minimum points – 'troughs'

As x increases, the gradient goes negative → 0 → positive.

At a stationary point on a curve, the gradient is zero,

i.e. $\dfrac{dy}{dx} = 0$.

ACTIVITY 12.2

$\dfrac{dy}{dx} = 0$ and $\dfrac{d^2y}{dx^2} < 0 \Rightarrow$ local maximum point

$\dfrac{dy}{dx} = 0$ and $\dfrac{d^2y}{dx^2} > 0 \Rightarrow$ local minimum point

Let $f(x) = 2 - 9x + 6x^2 - x^3$ for $x \in R$.

(i) Find $f'(x)$, the derivative of $f(x)$.

(ii) Find the co-ordinates of the stationary points of $f(x)$.

(iii) Use the second derivative test to determine the nature of the stationary points.

(iv) Hence, sketch a graph of $f(x)$ in the domain $-1 \leqslant x \leqslant 5$, $x \in R$.

Solution

(i) $f(x) = 2 - 9x + 6x^2 - x^3$

$\Rightarrow f'(x) = -9 + 12x - 3x^2$

(ii) $f'(x) = 0$ for a stationary point

$-9 + 12x - 3x^2 = 0$

$x^2 - 4x + 3 = 0$

$(x - 3)(x - 1) = 0$

$x = 3$ **OR** $x = 1$

We need to find the corresponding y-values.

$x = 1 \Rightarrow y = 2 - 9(1) + 6(1)^2 - (1)^3$

$\therefore y = -2$

$x = 3 \Rightarrow y = 2 - 9(3) + 6(3)^2 - (3)^3$

$\therefore y = 2$

Therefore, the stationary points are $(1, -2)$ and $(3, 2)$.

(iii) $f''(x) = 12 - 6x$

$f''(1) = 6 > 0$. Therefore, at $x = 1$ there is a local minimum.

$f''(3) = -6 < 0$. Therefore, at $x = 3$ there is a local maximum.

The co-ordinates of the local minimum are $(1, -2)$, and the co-ordinates of the local maximum are $(3, 2)$.

(iv) $f(x) = 2 - 9x + 6x^2 - x^3$

We are required to sketch a graph for $-1 \leqslant x \leqslant 5$.

Therefore, we should find $f(-1)$ and $f(5)$.

$f(-1) = 2 - 9(-1) + 6(-1)^2 - (-1)^3$

$= 2 + 9 + 6 + 1$

$\Rightarrow f(-1) = 18$

$f(5) = 2 - 9(5) + 6(5)^2 - (5)^3$

$= 2 - 45 + 150 - 125$

$\Rightarrow f(5) = -18$

Also, $f(0) = 2$.

Using these points and the stationary points, we sketch the curve.

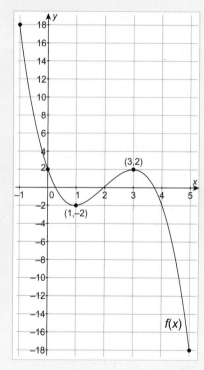

CALCULUS

The graph of a cubic function *f* is shown.

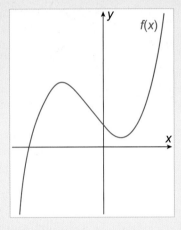

One of the four diagrams A, B, C and D below shows the graph of the derivative of *f*. State which one it is and justify your answer.

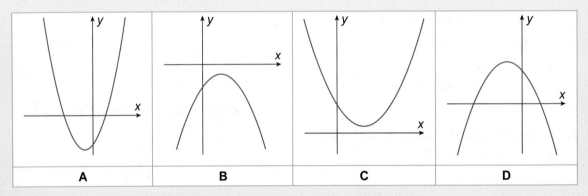

| A | B | C | D |

Solution

Graphs B and C can be eliminated for the following reasons:

- Graph B lies entirely below the *x*-axis, which implies that the derivative is negative for all values of *x*. If the derivative is always negative, then the function is a decreasing function. *f* is not a decreasing function.

- Graph C lies entirely above the *x*-axis, which implies that the derivative is positive for all values of *x*. If the derivative is always positive, then the function is an increasing function. *f* is not an increasing function.

Graph D can also be eliminated for the following reason:

- Graph D begins below the *x*-axis, i.e. the function is decreasing initially. However, the function *f* shown is increasing initially.

Graph A is the correct solution.

- The graph begins above the *x*-axis. Therefore, the function is increasing initially. The graph of the derivative then crosses the *x*-axis. The *x*-value of this intercept corresponds to the value of *x* for which *f* has a local maximum point. The derivative then becomes negative, showing that *f* is decreasing here. The graph then cuts the *x*-axis once more; this corresponds to the *x*-value of *f* for which the function has a local minimum. The derivative becomes positive once more, so *f* is increasing here.

1. The diagram shows the graph of the function
$f(x) = x^2 - 4x + 10, x \in R$.

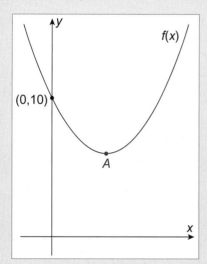

(i) Find a, the value of x for which $f'(x) = 0$.

(ii) Show that $f''(a) > 0$.

(iii) Hence, find the co-ordinates of the
point A, the minimum point on
the curve.

2. The diagram shows the graph of the function
$f(x) = x^2 - 6x + 17, x \in R$.

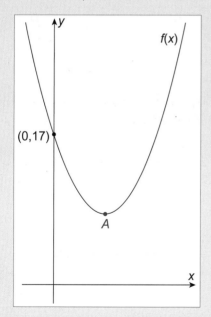

(i) Find a, the value of x for which $f'(x) = 0$.

(ii) Show that $f''(a) > 0$.

(iii) Hence, find the co-ordinates of the
point A, the minimum point on the curve.

3. The diagram shows the graph of the function
$f(x) = 1 + 8x - x^2, x \in R$.

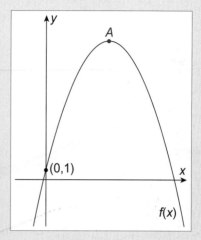

(i) Find a, the value of x for which $f'(x) = 0$.

(ii) Show that $f''(a) < 0$.

(iii) Hence, find the co-ordinates of the
point A, the maximum point on the
curve.

4. The diagram shows the graph of the function
$f(x) = 3 + 10x - x^2, x \in R$.

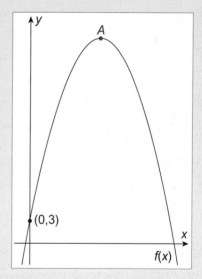

(i) Find a, the value of x for which $f'(x) = 0$.

(ii) Show that $f''(a) < 0$.

(iii) Hence, find the co-ordinates of the
point A, the maximum point on the
curve.

5. Let $f(x) = x^3 - 12x$, $x \in R$. The graph of $f(x)$ is shown. x_1 and x_2 are the x-values of the turning points of the curve of $f(x)$.

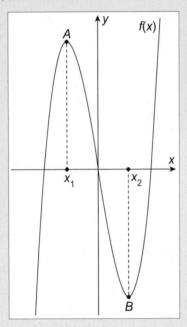

(i) Solve the quadratic equation $f'(x) = 0$.

(ii) Explain why the solutions to $f'(x) = 0$ are x_1 and x_2.

(iii) Find the co-ordinates of A and B.

(iv) Show that $f''(x_1) < 0$ and $f''(x_2) > 0$.

6. Let $f(x) = x^3 - 3x + 1$, $x \in R$. The graph of $f(x)$ is shown. x_1 and x_2 are the x-values of the turning points of the curve of $f(x)$.

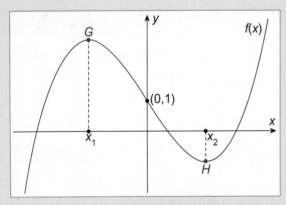

(i) Solve the quadratic equation $f'(x) = 0$.

(ii) Explain why the solutions to $f'(x) = 0$ are x_1 and x_2.

(iii) Find the co-ordinates of G and H.

(iv) Show that $f''(x_1) < 0$ and $f''(x_2) > 0$.

7. Find the co-ordinates of the local maximum point and the local minimum point on the curve $y = 2x^3 - 3x^2 - 36x + 10$.

8. Find the co-ordinates of the local maximum point and the local minimum point on the curve $y = 10 + 15x + 6x^2 - x^3$.

9. Let $f(x) = (x + 1)^2(2 - x)$, $x \in R$.

(i) Find the co-ordinates of the local maximum point and the local minimum point on the curve of $f(x)$.

(ii) Find the co-ordinates of the points where the curve intersects the x-axis and y-axis.

(iii) Draw a rough sketch of the curve.

(iv) Hence, write down the range of values of x for which $f(x)$ is increasing.

10. Let $f(x) = x^3 - 3x^2 - 24x$, $x \in R$.

(i) Find the co-ordinates of the local maximum point and the local minimum point on the curve of $f(x)$.

(ii) Show that the curve of $f(x)$ intersects the x-axis at $x = 0$.

(iii) Draw a rough sketch of the curve, given that its negative x-intercept lies between -4 and -3 and its positive x-intercept lies between 6 and 7.

11. Find the maximum and minimum values of the curve $y = x^3 - 3x + 5$ by:

(i) Examining the gradient on either side of the turning points

(ii) Determining the sign of the second derivative

12. The graph of a quadratic function h is shown.

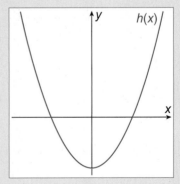

One of the two diagrams A and B below shows the graph of the derivative of *h*. State which one it is and justify your answer.

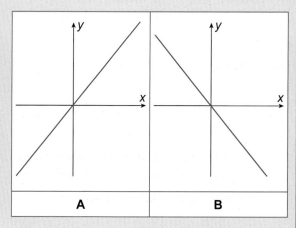

| A | B |

13. The graph of a quadratic function *g* is shown.

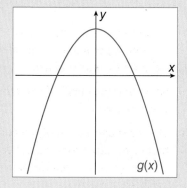

g(x)

One of the two diagrams A and B below shows the graph of the derivative of *g*. State which one it is and justify your answer.

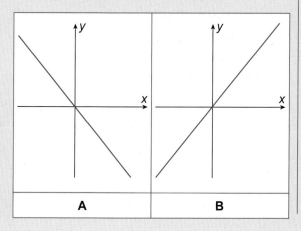

| A | B |

14. The graph of a cubic function *f* is shown.

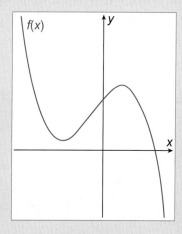

f(x)

One of the four diagrams A, B, C and D below shows the graph of the derivative of *f*. State which one it is and justify your answer.

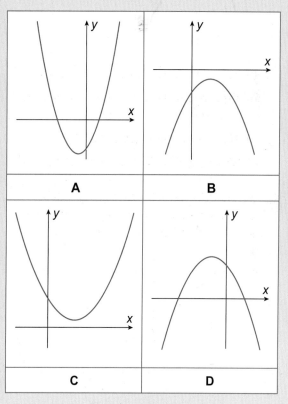

| A | B |
| C | D |

12.8 MAXIMUM AND MINIMUM PROBLEMS

Calculus is an important tool in solving maximum–minimum problems. We can use the analysis of stationary points to solve these real-life problems.

Worked Example 12.12

From a 30 cm × 30 cm sheet of cardboard, square corners are cut out so that the sides are folded up to make a box.

(i) What dimensions will yield a box of maximum volume?

(ii) What is the maximum volume of the box?

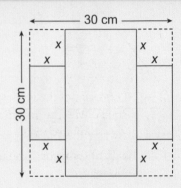

Solution

(i)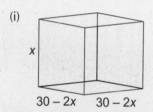

Side length in base = $30 - 2x$, height = x.

$\therefore$ Volume (V) = $(30 - 2x)(30 - 2x)(x)$

$= (900 - 120x + 4x^2)(x)$

$\therefore V = 900x - 120x^2 + 4x^3$

$\dfrac{dV}{dx} = 900 - 240x + 12x^2$

Let $\dfrac{dV}{dx} = 0$ and solve to find the stationary points:

$900 - 240x + 12x^2 = 0$

$4x^2 - 80x + 300 = 0$

$x^2 - 20x + 75 = 0$

$(x - 15)(x - 5) = 0$

$x = 15$ **OR** $x = 5$

$\dfrac{d^2V}{dx^2} = -240 + 24x$

At $x = 15$, $\dfrac{d^2V}{dx^2} = -240 + 24(15)$

$= -240 + 360$

$= 120 > 0$

Therefore, there is a local minimum at $x = 15$.

At $x = 5$, $\dfrac{d^2V}{dx^2} = -240 + 24(5)$

$= -240 + 120$

$= -120 < 0$

Therefore, there is a local maximum at $x = 5$.

Required dimensions for maximum volume (using $x = 5$):

Length = $30 - 2(5) = 20$ cm

Width = $30 - 2(5) = 20$ cm

Height = 5 cm

(ii) Maximum volume of box = $20 \times 20 \times 5$

$= 2{,}000$ cm^3

OR

Volume = $900x - 120x^2 + 4x^3$

So, maximum volume = $900(5) - 120(5)^2 + 4(5)^3$

$= 2{,}000$ cm^3

Exercise 12.7

1. A chicken coop is enclosed using 40 m of fencing. The enclosure is rectangular.

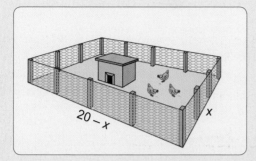

  (i) If one side of the enclosure is x metres long, explain why the adjacent side is $(20 - x)$ metres long.

  (ii) Find, in terms of x, the area of the enclosure.

  (iii) Find the value of x that maximises the area of the enclosure.

  (iv) What is the maximum area of the enclosure?

2. The speed v of a car (in metres/second) is related to time t (in seconds) by the equation $v = 3 + 12t - 3t^2$.

Determine the maximum speed of the car in kilometres/hour.

3. A farmer wishes to enclose a rectangular section of a field for grazing. She has purchased 200 m of electric fence to construct the enclosure. She designs the rectangular enclosure so that all 200 m of electric fence is just enough to enclose the grazing area.

  (i) If one side of the enclosure is x metres long, explain why the adjacent side is $(100 - x)$ metres long.

  (ii) Find, in terms of x, the area of the enclosure.

  (iii) Find the value of x that maximises the area of the enclosure.

  (iv) If the farmer decides to use a circular enclosure, find the radius length of such an enclosure. Assume all 200 m of fencing is needed to form this enclosure. Answer correct to two places of decimals.

  (v) Find the area of the circular enclosure, correct to the nearest square metre.

  (vi) If the farmer wants to have a maximum grazing area, which design should she use – rectangular or circular?

4. A wealthy businessman has a property on the shores of a quiet inlet. He wishes to enclose a rectangular swimming area in the inlet. He has purchased 300 m of pontoon with which to construct the swimming area.

  (i) If one side of the enclosure is x metres long, explain why the adjacent side is $(150 - x)$ metres long.

  (ii) Find, in terms of x, the area of the enclosure.

  (iii) Find the value of x that maximises the area of the enclosure.

  (iv) What is the maximum area of the enclosure?

5. A lifeguard needs to rope off a rectangular swimming area in front of a beach, using 200 m of rope and floats. The beach will form one side of the swimming area.

  (i) The left- and right-hand sides of the swimming area are each x metres long. Find the length of the adjacent side in terms of x.

  (ii) Find, in terms of x, the area of the enclosure.

ACTIVE MATHS   **315**

(iii) Find the value of x that maximises the area of the enclosure.

(iv) What is the maximum area of the enclosure?

6. A farmer wants to enclose two rectangular paddocks, which are equal in area. A river runs along the side of both paddocks. The farmer has 300 m of fencing.

(i) If x represents the length (from the river bank) of each paddock and y represents the width, show that $y = 150 - \frac{3}{2}x$.

(ii) Find, in terms of x, the area of one of the paddocks.

(iii) Find the value of x that maximises the area of each paddock.

(iv) What is the maximum area of the enclosure?

7. A Norman window is shaped like a rectangle with a semicircle on top. Suppose that the perimeter of a Norman window is to be 8 m.

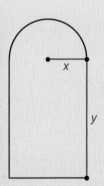

(i) Assume that $2x$ represents the base length of the rectangular part of the window and that y represents the height of the rectangular part. Taking $\pi = 3.14$, show that $y = 4 - 2.57x$.

(ii) Find, in terms of x, the area of the window.

(iii) What dimensions should the window have to allow the maximum amount of light to enter through the window?

8. Of all the numbers whose sum is 80, find the two that have the maximum product; that is, maximise $P = xy$, where $x + y = 80$.

9. Of all the numbers whose sum is 100, find the two that have the maximum product; that is, maximise $P = xy$, where $x + y = 100$.

10. A sports area is to be designed in the form of a rectangular field with a semicircular area at each end. The perimeter of the sports area is to be 1,400 m.

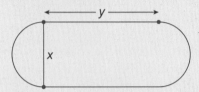

(i) Write the perimeter in terms of x and y.

(ii) Express y in terms of x.

(iii) What should the dimensions of the sports area be if the rectangular field is to have as large an area as possible? Give your answers in metres correct to one decimal place.

11. From a 50 cm × 50 cm sheet of aluminium, square corners are cut out so that the sides are folded up to make a box.

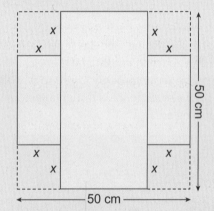

(i) What dimensions will yield a box of maximum volume?

(ii) What is the maximum volume?

12. From a 20 cm × 20 cm sheet of cardboard, square corners are cut out so that the sides are folded up to make a box.

(i) What dimensions will yield a box of maximum volume?

(ii) What is the maximum volume?

13. Liffey Appliances is marketing a new washing machine. It determines that in order to sell x machines, the price per machine (in euros) must be $440 - 0.3x$.

    It also determines that the cost of producing x washing machines is given by $C(x) = 6{,}000 + 0.5x^2$.

    (i) If x machines are sold, find $R(x)$, the total revenue received. Your answer will be a quadratic expression in x.

    (ii) Find $P(x)$, the profit function, if x machines are sold. [$P(x) = R(x) - C(x)$]

    (iii) How many machines must be produced to maximise profit?

    (iv) What is the maximum profit?

14. The output for a firm over time is given by the function:

    $$Q = \frac{t^3}{30} - \frac{t^2}{5} + \frac{3t}{10} + 120$$

    Determine the years (t) in which output is at a maximum and a minimum.

12.9 RATES OF CHANGE

ACTIVITY 12.3

Suppose that y is a function of x, i.e. $y = f(x)$.
Now suppose that x is a function of t. It follows that y is also a function of t.

The Chain Rule, which was explained in Activity 12.3, gives the formula:

Thus, the rate of change of y is related to the rate of change of x. We will use this idea to solve some real-life problems.

FORMULA
$$\frac{dy}{dt} = \frac{dy}{dx} \cdot \frac{dx}{dt}$$

Worked Example 12.13

The cost of extracting T tonnes of ore from a copper mine is $C = f(T)$ euros, i.e. the cost of extraction is a function of the amount of ore mined.

   (i) Explain the meaning of $f'(T)$, the derivative of $f(T)$.

   (ii) What are the units of measurement for $f'(T)$?

Solution

   (i) $f'(T)$ is the rate of change of C (cost) with respect to the amount of ore mined. For example, if $f'(3{,}000) = 500$, this means that when 3,000 tonnes has been mined, the cost of mining the next tonne of ore will be €500.

   (ii) Euros per tonne

Worked Example 12.14

Differentiate $y = (3x + 1)^3$ using the Chain Rule.

Solution

Let $u = 3x + 1$

$\frac{du}{dx} = 3$

$y = u^3$

$\therefore \frac{dy}{du} = 3u^2$

$\frac{dy}{dx} = \frac{dy}{du} \cdot \frac{du}{dx}$

$\frac{dy}{dx} = (3u^2)(3)$

$\quad = 9u^2$

$\therefore \frac{dy}{dx} = 9(3x + 1)^2$

Worked Example 12.15

The area of a healing wound is given by $A = \pi r^2$, where r is the radius length of the wound.

If the radius length is decreasing at a rate of 0.5 mm per day, how fast is the area decreasing at the instant when the radius length is 10 mm?

Solution

$A = \pi r^2$

$\therefore \dfrac{dA}{dr} = 2\pi r$ (The rate at which the area of the wound is changing with respect to its radius length)

$\dfrac{dr}{dt} = 0.5$ mm/day

We require $\dfrac{dA}{dt}$, the rate of decrease of the area.

$\dfrac{dA}{dt} = \dfrac{dA}{dr} \cdot \dfrac{dr}{dt}$ (Chain Rule)

$= (2\pi r)(0.5)$

$= \pi r$

When $r = 10$, $\dfrac{dA}{dt} = 10\pi$ mm^2/day.

 ## Worked Example 12.16

A stone is dropped from the top of a building of height 250 m. The distance (x) fallen in a time t seconds is given by $x = \frac{1}{2}gt^2$, where $g = 9.8$ m s^{-2} (air resistance ignored).

(i) Determine the velocity of the stone after 3 seconds.

(ii) Find the acceleration of the stone.

(iii) Show that the stone reaches the ground in $7\frac{1}{7}$ seconds.

Solution

(i) Velocity (or speed) is the rate of change of distance with respect to time,

i.e. velocity $= \dfrac{dx}{dt}$.

$x = \frac{1}{2}gt^2 \Rightarrow \dfrac{dx}{dt} = gt$

At $t = 3$,

$\dfrac{dx}{dt} = 3g$

$= 3(9.8)$

Velocity $= 29.4$ m s^{-1} after 3 seconds

(ii) Acceleration is the rate of change of velocity with respect to time.

$v = gt = 9.8t$ [from part (i)]

$\therefore \dfrac{dv}{dt} = 9.8$

Acceleration $= 9.8$ m s^{-2}

(iii) Find t, when $x = 250$.

$\frac{1}{2}gt^2 = 250$

$t^2 = \dfrac{500}{g}$

$t^2 = \dfrac{500}{9.8}$

$t = \sqrt{\dfrac{500}{9.8}}$

$t = \sqrt{\dfrac{5{,}000}{98}}$

$t = \sqrt{\dfrac{2{,}500}{49}}$

$t = \dfrac{50}{7}$

$\therefore t = 7\frac{1}{7}$ seconds

 ## Exercise 12.8

1. The length l (in metres) of a certain metal rod at temperature $\theta°C$ is given by:

$l = 1 + 0.00005\theta + 0.0000004\theta^2$

Determine the rate of change of length (in millimetres/°C), when the temperature is:

(i) 150°C (ii) 500°C

2. The luminous intensity I (in candelas) of a lamp is given by $I = 6 \times 10^{-4}V^2$, where V is the voltage.

(i) Find the rate of change of luminous intensity when $V = 200$ volts.

(ii) Find the voltage at which the light is increasing at a rate of 0.3 candelas per volt.

ACTIVE MATHS

3. Supplies are dropped from a helicopter and the distance fallen in a time t seconds is given by $x = \frac{1}{2}gt^2$, where $g = 9.8$ m/s^2.

   Determine the velocity and acceleration of the supplies after they have fallen for 2 seconds.

   > Velocity $= \dfrac{ds}{dt}$; acceleration $= \dfrac{dv}{dt}$
   >
   > where s = displacement
   > v = velocity
   > t = time

4. The average weight W (in kilograms) of an ash tree is given by the function $W = f(x)$, where x is the height of the tree in metres.

   (i) Explain the meaning of $f'(x)$, the derivative of $f(x)$.

   (ii) Will $f'(x)$ be positive or negative? Explain.

   (iii) What are the units of measurement for $f'(x)$?

5. A rock is dropped from the top of the Spire on Dublin's O'Connell Street. After it falls x metres, its speed V is $V = h(x)$; that is, V is a function of x. What is the meaning of:

   (i) $h(5)$ (ii) $h'(5)$?

6. A loaf of bread has just been taken out of the oven and is cooling off before being eaten. The temperature T of the bread (measured in degrees Celsius) is a function of t (measured in minutes), the length of time the bread has been out of the oven. Therefore, we have $T = f(t)$.

   (i) What is the meaning of $f(5)$?

   (ii) Is $f'(t)$ positive or negative? Explain.

   (iii) What are the units for $f'(t)$?

7. The weight W of an infant in kilograms is a function of its age, m (measured in months), so $W = f(m)$.

   (i) Would you expect $f'(m)$ to be positive or negative? Explain.

   (ii) What does $f(7) = 7.65$ tell you?

   (iii) What are the units of $f'(m)$?

8. A car accelerates in a straight line so that its distance s (in metres) from its starting point p after t seconds is given by the function $s(t) = t^2$. Find:

   (i) The distance of the car from p after 4 seconds

   (ii) The distance of the car from p after 5 seconds

   (iii) The speed of the car in terms of t

   (iv) The speed of the car after 4 seconds

9. A ball is thrown straight up into the air. The height h (measured in metres) of the ball after t seconds is given by the function $h(t) = 40t - 5t^2$.

   (i) Find the height of the ball after 1 second.

   (ii) Explain why $h'(t)$ represents the speed of the ball after t seconds.

   (iii) Find the speed of the ball after t seconds.

   (iv) What is the speed of the ball when it reaches its maximum height?

   (v) Find the time at which the ball reaches its maximum height.

   (vi) Find the maximum height reached.

10. The temperature T of a patient during an illness is given by $T(t) = -0.6t^2 + 0.67t + 37$, where T is the temperature (in degrees Celsius) at time t (in days).

    (Time is measured from the onset of the illness.)

    (i) Find $T'(t)$, the rate at which the temperature is changing with respect to time.

    (ii) Find the rate at which the temperature is changing at $t = 3$ days.

    (iii) When will the patient's temperature begin to fall? Answer correct to the nearest hour.

11. As soon as it touches down, an aeroplane applies its brakes. The distance s which the plane has travelled along the runway at any subsequent time t is given by the function $s(t) = 200t - 4t^2$, where s is measured in metres and t in seconds.

Find:

(i) The distance travelled after 10 seconds .

(ii) The plane's speed at any time t

(iii) The speed of the plane at $t = 10$

(iv) The plane's speed as it touches down

(v) The time at which the plane comes to rest

(vi) The distance that the plane has travelled along the runway when it stops

12. Differentiate the following using the Chain Rule:

(i) $y = (3x + 1)^3$

(ii) $y = (x^2 + 7)^3$

(iii) $y = (x^3 - 3x^2 + 2)^2$

(iv) $y = (8x + 3)^3$

(v) $y = (x^3 - 25)^2$

13. A square is constructed using CAD software. The square is slowly enlarged by increasing the lengths of the sides at a constant rate of 0.01 cm/s.

(i) Explain why the rate at which the area of the square increases is not constant.

(ii) Find the rate at which the area of the square is increasing when the side length of the square is 2 cm.

14. The length of the edge of a cube is decreasing at a rate of 4 cm per minute.

(i) What is the value of n if V, the volume of the cube, is given by $V(x) = x^n$, where x is the length of an edge of the cube?

(ii) What is the value of m and n if S, the surface area of the cube, is given by $S(x) = mx^n$, where x is the length of an edge of the cube?

(iii) Explain why $x'(t)$ or $\dfrac{dx}{dt}$ is negative.

(iv) Find the rate at which the volume of the cube is decreasing when $x = 10$ cm.

(v) Find the rate at which the surface area of the cube is decreasing when $x = 10$ cm.

15. The length of the radius of a spherical balloon is increasing at a rate of 1 cm per second.

(i) Write down an expression for V, the volume of the balloon, in terms of r, the radius of the balloon.

(ii) Write down an expression for S, the surface area of the balloon, in terms of r, the radius of the balloon.

(iii) Explain why $r'(t)$ or $\dfrac{dr}{dt}$ is positive.

(iv) Find the rate at which the volume of the balloon is increasing when $r = 12$ cm.

(v) Find the rate at which the surface area of the balloon is increasing when $r = 12$ cm.

Revision Exercises

1. Differentiate the following with respect to x:

(i) $y = 2x^2 + 12x + 16$

(ii) $y = 15x^2 + 10x - 12$

(iii) $y = x^3 - 19x + 120$

(iv) $y = 3x^3 - 12x^2 - 4x + 12$

(v) $y = 4x^3 + 4$

2. Differentiate the following functions with respect to the letter in brackets:

(i) $f(t) = (t^2 - 1)(t + 2)$ [t]

(ii) $A(y) = (y + 2)(y^2 - y + 3)$ [y]

(iii) $g(x) = (x - 4)(x + 4)$ [x]

(iv) $h(t) = \frac{1}{2}(10t - 9.8t^2)$ [t]

3. A graph of the cubic function $f(x) = x^3 - 3x + 2$ is shown. The tangent to $f(x)$ at the point $(1.5, 0.875)$ is also shown on the diagram.

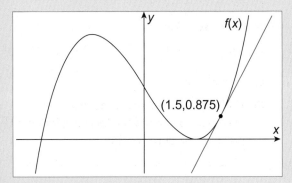

(i) Write down $f'(x)$, the derivative of $f(x)$.

(ii) Hence, find the slope of the tangent to $f(x)$ at $(1.5, 0.875)$.

(iii) Find the equation of the tangent to the curve at this point.

(iv) Find the co-ordinates of the points where the tangent intersects the x-axis and the y-axis.

(v) Hence, calculate the area enclosed between the tangent, the x-axis and the y-axis.

4. A graph of the cubic function $f(x) = x^3 - 3x^2 - 10x + 24$ is shown. The tangent to $f(x)$ at the point $(3.5, -4.875)$ is also shown on the diagram.

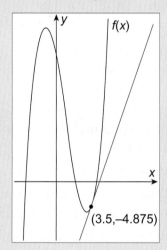

(i) Write down $f'(x)$, the derivative of $f(x)$.

(ii) Hence, find the slope of the tangent to $f(x)$ at $x = 3.5$.

(iii) Find the equation of the tangent to the curve at this point.

5. For each of the following functions, find $f''(x)$ and, hence, $f''(-3)$:

(i) $f(x) = 3x^3 + 2x^2 + x$

(ii) $f(x) = 5x^3 - 12x$

(iii) $f(x) = -3x^3 + 5x$

6. Let $f(x) = x^3 - 3x^2$, $x \in R$.

(i) Find the co-ordinates of the local maximum point and the local minimum point on the curve of $f(x)$.

(ii) Find the co-ordinates of the points where the curve intersects the x-axis and the y-axis.

(iii) Draw a rough sketch of the curve.

(iv) Hence, write down the range of values of x for which $f(x)$ is increasing.

7. The graph of a cubic function f is shown.

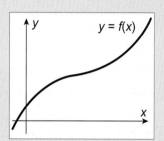

One of the four diagrams A, B, C and D below shows the graph of the derivative of f. State which one it is, and justify your answer.

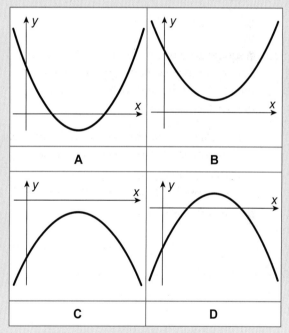

SEC Project Maths Sample Paper 1, Leaving Certificate Ordinary Level, 2012

8. The weight W (measured in kilograms) of a young calf is a function of its age, m (measured in months), so $W = f(m)$.

(i) What are the units of $f'(m)$?

(ii) Interpret the meaning of $f'(3) = 4$.

9. A pebble is dropped into still water, and circular ripples spread out from the point of entry. The radius of the circles increases at a rate of 10 cm/s.

(i) If r is the radius of one of the circles, then write down the area of the circle.

(ii) What is $\dfrac{dA}{dr}$ in terms of r?

(iii) Write down $\dfrac{dr}{dt}$.

(iv) Explain why $\dfrac{dA}{dt} = \dfrac{dA}{dr} \cdot \dfrac{dr}{dt}$.

(v) Find the rate at which the area of the circles is increasing when the radius length is 25 cm.

10. The function $f(x) = 2x^3 + 4x + 2$ is defined for all values of x.

(i) Find the values of x for which $f'(x) = 10$.

(ii) Find $f''(8)$.

11. A particle moves in a straight line so that its distance s from a fixed point o at any subsequent time t is given by $s(t) = t^3 - 2t^2 + t$, where s is measured in metres and t is measured in seconds.

Find:

(i) The distance of the particle from o after 2 seconds

(ii) The particle's speed after 2 seconds

(iii) The times at which the particle is at rest

12. The force of attraction F (measured in Newtons) between two bodies is a function of the distance r between the two bodies (measured in metres), i.e. $F = f(r)$.

For two given bodies, A and B:

$$f(r) = \frac{1{,}000}{r^2} \quad \text{and} \quad f'(r) = -\frac{2{,}000}{r^3}$$

(i) What are the units of $f'(r)$?

(ii) Find the force of attraction F between the two bodies when $r = 10$ m.

(iii) Find the rate of change of F with respect to r when $r = 10$ m.

13. Find x and y, if $x + y = 50$ and xy is to be a maximum.

Answers

Chapter 1

Exercise 1.1

1. (i) 2   (ii) -6 (iii) -6 (iv) 17   (v) 1   (vi) 4   (vii) 27   (viii) -3 (ix) -3 (x) 9   (xi) -27 (xii) -27 **2.** (i) -2 (ii) -10 (iii) 20   (iv) 0   (v) 228   (vi) 6   (vii) -1 (viii) 10   (ix) 2   (x) 10
3. (i) -48 (ii) 14   (iii) 30   (iv) -44 (v) -20 (vi) -248 (vii) 3,952   (viii) 4,000   (ix) 2,304   (x) 1,048,540   **4.** (i) 2   (ii) 32   (iii) -5 (iv) 110   (v) $\frac{2}{17}$ (vi) $\frac{-47}{10}$ (vii) 6   (viii) 1   (ix) 1   (x) 100
5. (i) $261\frac{2}{3}$ cm³   (ii) 83.73 m³   (iii) 70,650 mm³   (iv) $3,901\frac{1}{3}$ cm³   (v) $657,066\frac{2}{3}$ mm³   **6.** (i) 32 m²   (ii) 363 cm²   (iii) 14.04 m²   (iv) 388 cm²   (v) 552 m²   **7.** (ii) 45 metres   (iii) 3 seconds   (iv) 4 seconds

Exercise 1.2

1. (i) $3a$ (ii) 116   (iii) 0   (iv) d (v) $-4a$ **2.** (i) $-2b$ (ii) $-3c$ (iii) $-6d$ (iv) $-7p + 3$ (v) $-10x - 6$ **3.** (i) $e - 5f$ (ii) $5g + 4h - 7$ (iii) $17j - 2k$ (iv) $8m - 7n$ (v) $-p - 2q$ **4.** (i) $10x - 2y$ (ii) $4x + 5y - 14z$ (iii) $7a + 3b - 3c$ (iv) $9l - 8m$ (v) $-3p - q - 4r + 2$ **5.** (i) $4ab$ (ii) $-5ab$ (iii) $4xy$ (iv) 0   (v) $3pq$ **6.** (i) $-11pq$ (ii) $-mn$ (iii) $3pq - 3qr$ (iv) $2xy + 4x + 6y$ (v) $-3ab + 2cd + c$ **7.** (i) $2a^2$ (ii) $2a^3$ (iii) $10ab^2 + b^2$ (iv) $2b^3$ (v) $2xy^2 - 2x^2y$ **8.** (i) $2p^2 + p^3$ (ii) $5p^4$ (iii) $7x^2 + x$ (iv) $a^2x - ax^2$ (v) $x^3y^2 - 2x^3y - 2x^3$ **9.** (i) $16p^2 + 5q^2$ (ii) $6x^3 - 5y^2$ (iii) $7m^2 - 11n^2$ (iv) $-2mn^2 + 3m^2n$ (v) $3yz^2 - 3y^2z$ **10.** (i) $4x^3y - 2xy^3$ (ii) $2pr^2 + 3p^2r$ (iii) $2ab^2$ (iv) $-2x^2y - 7xy^2$ (v) $2x^2y^2 - 3xy^2 + 2xy$

Exercise 1.3

1. (i) $10a^2$ (ii) $12b$ (iii) $8c^2$ (iv) $-d^2$ (v) $10e^2$ **2.** (i) $3ab$ (ii) $-2bc$ (iii) $4cd$ (iv) $2ed^2$ (v) e^2f **3.** (i) x^4 (ii) x^3y^2 (iii) $6x^7$ (iv) $-2y^5$ (v) $20y^5$ **4.** (i) x^8 (ii) $6a^{10}$ (iii) $-10y^5$ (iv) $4b^{15}$ (v) $10x^6$ **5.** (i) a^2b (ii) a^2b^2 (iii) $6cd^2$ (iv) a^3b (v) $4x^2y^3$ **6.** (i) $-6x^6y^5$ (ii) a^3 (iii) $-2x^3$ (iv) $-3y^5$ (v) $10y^2$ **7.** (i) $-8x^2y$ (ii) $-9x^2y^3$ (iii) $50m^2n^2$ (iv) $-24a^8$ (v) $12a^2b$ **8.** (i) $8x^3y^3$ (ii) $2x^3y^2$ (iii) $10p^4q^4$ (iv) $-8p^8q^3$ (v) $10t^7p^4$ **9.** (i) b^2 (ii) $4b^2$ (iii) $9b^2$ (iv) $-27b^3$ (v) $64a^3b^3$ **10.** (i) $4a^2b^2$ (ii) $16x^4y^2$ (iii) $-8x^6y^3$ (iv) x^4y^8 (v) $64x^9y^6$

Exercise 1.4

1. (i) $3a + 9$ (ii) $2a + 4$ (iii) $5b + 10$ (iv) $3b - 9$ (v) $-4c + 16$ (vi) $4x + 2y - 6$ (vii) $5x - 15y - 5$ (viii) $-4x + 4y - 4$ (ix) $-2x + y + 1$ (x) $4x + 20y - 28$ **2.** (i) $7x + 10$ (ii) $7x + 18$ (iii) $6y - 16$ (iv) $-y + 28$ (v) $-3a - 3$ **3.** (i) $8a + 4$ (ii) $2b + 11$ (iii) $9b + 6$ (iv) $-6x - 14$ (v) -2 **4.** (i) $15y + 11$ (ii) $9y - 14$ (iii) $4a^2 + 8a + 10$ (iv) $-16a^2 - 2a + 8$ (v) $7b^2 - 6b - 3$ **5.** (i) $x^2 + 3x$ (ii) $2x^2 + 8x$ (iii) $5y^2 - 10y$ (iv) $y^2 - 6y$ (v) $2a^2 - a$ **6.** (i) $4a^2 + 2a$ (ii) $8b^2 - 8b$ (iii) $-4b^2 + 3b$ (iv) $x^3 + x^2$ (v) $2x^3 - 2x$ **7.** (i) $3y^3 + 9y^2 - 6y$ (ii) $2a^3 - 3a^2 + a$ (iii) $10a^3 - 8a^2 - 8a$ (iv) $-4b^3 - 4b^2 + 18b$ (v) $b + 3b^2 + b^3$ **8.** (i) $2a^2 + 2a$ (ii) $8a^2 + 9a$ (iii) $3b^2 - b$ (iv) $-3b^2 - 9b$ (v) $4x^2 - 4x$ **9.** (i) $9a^2 - 10a$

(ii) $-7a^2 + 15a$ (iii) $18b^2 - 61b$ (iv) $13b^2 + 14b$ (v) $-10q^2 - 14q$ **10.** (i) $6q - 9q^2$ (ii) $8x^2 + 6x + 3$ (iii) $4y^2 - 15y$ (iv) $-2a^3 + 3a^2 - 3a$ (v) $6x^3 + 6x^2 + 4x$

Exercise 1.5

1. $\frac{7x}{10}$ **2.** $\frac{3y}{8}$ **3.** $-\frac{2a}{15}$ **4.** $\frac{3b - 20}{10}$ **5.** $\frac{5c}{4}$ **6.** $\frac{26x}{21}$ **7.** $\frac{7x + 12}{4}$ **8.** $\frac{31x}{10}$
9. $\frac{18y}{7}$ **10.** $\frac{56x - 15}{18}$ **11.** $\frac{10a + 23}{12}$ **12.** $\frac{27a - 2}{15}$ **13.** $\frac{5x - 8}{8}$
14. $\frac{2x - 3}{9}$ **15.** $\frac{3}{2}$ **16.** $\frac{-23y + 37}{24}$ **17.** $\frac{20x + 79}{18}$ **18.** $\frac{1}{5}$ **19.** $\frac{7x - 18}{24}$
20. $\frac{12}{5}$ **21.** $\frac{9a - 26}{12}$ **22.** $\frac{-x + 11}{15}$ **23.** $\frac{-8x - 3}{5}$ **24.** $\frac{x + 1}{3}$
25. $\frac{-7x - 16}{15}$ **26.** $\frac{7x - 19}{12}$ **27.** $\frac{2}{9}$ **28.** $\frac{-15x + 20}{3}$ **29.** $\frac{26a + 39}{12}$
30. $\frac{5x + 5}{3}$

Exercise 1.6

1. (i) $x^2 + 5x + 6$ (ii) $x^2 + 5x + 4$ (iii) $x^2 + 9x + 14$ (iv) $x^2 - 4x - 21$ (v) $x^2 + 4x - 5$ **2.** (i) $y^2 - 12y + 32$ (ii) $y^2 - 49$ (iii) $y^2 - 6y + 8$ (iv) $y^2 - 9$ (v) $y^2 - 17y + 60$ **3.** (i) $a^2 - 11a + 18$ (ii) $a^2 - 8a - 33$ (iii) $a^2 + 7x - 98$ (iv) $a^2 - 2a + 1$ (v) $25 - a^2$ **4.** (i) $3x^2 + 8x + 4$ (ii) $8x^2 + 6x + 1$ (iii) $4x^2 - 5x - 6$ (iv) $15x^2 - 21x + 6$ (v) $6x^2 - 42x + 72$ **5.** (i) $6y^2 - 10y - 4$ (ii) $12y^2 - 30y + 12$ (iii) $21y^2 - 38y + 5$ (iv) $3y^2 - 26y + 16$ (v) $-6y^2 + 5y - 1$ **6.** (i) $5b^2 - 9b + 4$ (ii) $24b^2 - 58b - 5$ (iii) $8b^2 - 22b + 12$ (iv) $-45b^2 + 73b - 14$ (v) $-4b^2 + 6b - 2$ **7.** (i) $x^3 + 2x^2 + 2x + 1$ (ii) $2x^3 - 5x^2 - 4x + 3$ (iii) $16x^3 - 4x^2 - 14x - 3$ (iv) $3x^3 - 11x^2 + 4x + 6$ (v) $-7x^3 + 11x^2 - 3x - 1$ **8.** (i) $x^2 + 2x + 1$ (ii) $x^2 + 6x + 9$ (iii) $x^2 - 4x + 4$ (iv) $x^2 - 10x + 25$ (v) $4y^2 + 4y + 1$ **9.** (i) $9y^2 - 12y + 4$ (ii) $y^3 - 6y^2 + 12y - 8$ (iii) $8y^2 - 32y + 32$ (iv) $2y^2 + 9y - 5$ (v) -2

Exercise 1.7

1. $(x + 3)^2$ **2.** $(x + 7)(x + 1)$ **3.** $(x + 9)(x + 4)$ **4.** $(x + 2)(x + 6)$ **5.** $x(x + 5)$ **6.** $x(x - 7)$ **7.** $(x + 4)(x + 10)$ **8.** $(x - 4)(x + 4)$ **9.** $(x + 8)(x + 3)$ **10.** $(x - 3)(x - 9)$ **11.** $(x + 2)^2$ **12.** $(x + 7)(x - 2)$ **13.** $x(x - 9)$ **14.** $(x - 3)(x + 3)$ **15.** $(x - 8)^2$ **16.** $(x - 7)(x + 2)$ **17.** $(x - 6)(x + 3)$ **18.** $(x + 3)(x + 6)$ **19.** $(x - 9)(x + 3)$ **20.** $(x + 8)(x - 2)$ **21.** $(x - 3)(x - 7)$ **22.** $(x + 9)^2$ **23.** $x(x - 2)$ **24.** $(x - 10)(x + 10)$ **25.** $(x - 4)(x - 8)$ **26.** $(x - 4)(x + 1)$ **27.** $(x - 2)(x + 2)$ **28.** $(x - 5)(x + 3)$ **29.** $(x - 9)(x - 1)$ **30.** $(x + 8)(x - 6)$ **31.** $(x - 4)(x - 6)$ **32.** $(b - 5)(b + 5)$ **33.** $x(x + 12)$ **34.** $(x + 9)(x - 8)$ **35.** $(y - 13)(y + 13)$ **36.** $(x + 7)(x + 8)$ **37.** $(x - 15)(x + 15)$ **38.** $(x - 9)(x + 7)$ **39.** $x(x - 15)$ **40.** $(x + 9)(x - 2)$ **41.** $(x + 9)(x - 4)$ **42.** $x(x - 14)$ **43.** $(x - 3)(x - 1)$ **44.** $(x - 6)(x + 4)$ **45.** $(y - 11)(y + 11)$ **46.** $(x - 10)(x + 9)$ **47.** $(x + 9)(x - 7)$ **48.** $(x - 7)(x - 8)$ **49.** $(x + 7)(x - 6)$ **50.** $(x + 10)(x - 7)$ **51.** $(x - 13)(x + 3)$ **52.** $(3 - x)(3 + x)$ **53.** $(x - 6)(x - 5)$ **54.** $(x + 9)(x - 5)$ **55.** $(x - 15)(x + 5)$ **56.** $(x - 3)(x - 2)$

Exercise 1.8

1. $2x(x + 3)$ **2.** $3x(x + 7)$ **3.** $(7x - 5)(x + 1)$ **4.** $(2x + 3)(x + 1)$
5. $(7x + 1)(x + 2)$ **6.** $(8x - 7)(8x + 7)$ **7.** $(x + 1)(5x + 1)$
8. $4(x - 2)(x + 2)$ **9.** $3(x + 1)^2$ **10.** $(7x + 2)(x + 1)$ **11.** $2(x - 1)^2$
12. $5x(x - 5)$ **13.** $(3x - 5)(x - 1)$ **14.** $(5x + 3)(x + 2)$ **15.** $b(2b + 3)$
16. $25(x - 2)(x + 2)$ **17.** $(3x + 2)(x + 5)$ **18.** $(2x - 5)(x + 2)$
19. $7(x + 3)(x - 1)$ **20.** $(5x - 7)(x + 3)$ **21.** $(11x - 5)(11x + 5)$
22. $2(x - 4)(x + 3)$ **23.** $3(x - 6)(x - 2)$ **24.** $y(5y - 7)$
25. $(2x - 3)(x - 6)$ **26.** $(5x - 3)(x + 4)$ **27.** $4(15x - 7)(15x + 7)$
28. $(4x - 1)(x - 3)$ **29.** $(9y - 14)(9y + 14)$ **30.** $x(5x + 2)$
31. $(7x - 8)(x + 1)$ **32.** $(3x + 4)(x + 1)$ **33.** $4x(x - 4)$
34. $(3x + 2)(x + 2)$ **35.** $(3x - 7)(x + 1)$ **36.** $(2x + 5)(x - 3)$
37. $(5x - 7)(x + 7)$ **38.** $(2x - 3)(x - 5)$ **39.** $(8x + 1)(x + 2)$
40. $(5x + 2)(x + 2)$ **41.** $3(x - 4)(x - 2)$ **42.** $2(x + 2)(x + 3)$
43. $2(x - 3)(x + 2)$ **44.** $(5x - 3)(x - 3)$ **45.** $3(2x - 1)(x + 1)$
46. $2(x - 5)(x - 2)$ **47.** $(4x - 5)(x + 1)$ **48.** $2(3x - 1)(x + 1)$
49. $(10x + 3)(x + 3)$ **50.** $2(3x + 2)(x + 1)$ **51.** $(4x - 7)(x + 3)$

Exercise 1.9

1. a^4 **2.** a^3 **3.** a^6 **4.** a^9 **5.** $7a^2$ **6.** 3 **7.** $5a^5$ **8.** $8a$ **9.** $3a$
10. $2a^5$ **11.** $3a^4$ **12.** $5a^2b$ **13.** $5a^5b$ **14.** $3ab$ **15.** $7b$ **16.** $9b$
17. $-3x^4$ **18.** -3 **19.** $3x^2$ **20.** $-2x$ **21.** $3x$ **22.** $2xy^2$ **23.** $2xy$
24. $7x^4y^2$ **25.** $9x^2y$ **26.** $8xy^3z^2$ **27.** x **28.** $x + 8$ **29.** $x + 5$
30. $x + 2$ **31.** $x - 6$ **32.** $x + 3$ **33.** $\frac{5x - 3}{x + 4}$ **34.** $\frac{3x + 4}{x + 2}$ **35.** $\frac{3x - 2}{x + 2}$
36. $2x + 3$ **37.** $3x + 1$ **38.** $x - 2$ **39.** $2x - 3$ **40.** $2x - 5$
41. $12x - 5$ **42.** $5x + 13$ **43.** $-2x + 1$ **44.** $-5x - 13$

Exercise 1.10

1. $\frac{14}{3x}$ **2.** $\frac{9}{4x}$ **3.** $\frac{5x + 3}{x(2x - 1)}$ **4.** $\frac{2x + 2}{x(x + 2)}$ **5.** $\frac{3x - 4}{x(x - 2)}$ **6.** $\frac{6x - 8}{(x - 3)(x + 2)}$
7. $\frac{32 - x}{(x - 8)(x + 4)}$ **8.** $\frac{17 - x}{(2x + 1)(x + 4)}$ **9.** $\frac{1 - 10x}{(3x - 1)(2x - 3)}$ **10.** $\frac{8x + 10}{(2x - 1)(1 + 2x)}$
11. $\frac{19 - 2x}{3(2x + 5)}$ **12.** $\frac{1}{4x - 3}$ **13.** $\frac{-8x - 9}{(4x + 1)(2x - 3)}$ **14.** $\frac{6}{3x - 2}$

Revision Exercises

1. (a) (i) 1   (ii) -5 (iii) 5   (iv) -6 (v) 6   (vi) 0   (b) (i) -3 (ii) -7
(iii) 12   (iv) 0   (v) 1   (vi) 12   (c) (i) 4   (ii) -6 (iii) $\frac{5}{4}$ (iv) 2   (v) $\frac{3}{4}$
2. (a) (i) $12a - 2b$ (ii) $7x + 12xy$ (iii) $11a^2 + 3a$ (iv) $12x^2 + 11x$
(v) $12y + 6$ (vi) $10x - 20$ (b) (i) $15ab + 4$ (ii) $12x^2 + 11xy + 2$
(iii) $11x^2 + 3x - 13$ (iv) $2x^2 + 21x - 16$ (v) $2x^2 + 7x - 2$
(vi) $-2x^2 + 2y^2 + 6xy$ (c) (i) $9xy - y$ (ii) $2x^2$ (iii) $10y^2 + 2xy$
(iv) $2x^3 + 5x^2$ (v) $a^2 + 3a$ (vi) $3a^3 + 11a^2 + 12a + 5$ **3.** (a) (i) $14a^3$
(ii) $32b^{11}$ (iii) $30c^3$ (iv) $60d^3$ (v) $44e^3$ (b) (i) $20a^3b^2$ (ii) $12a^5b^{11}$
(iii) $15a^6c^3$ (iv) $12x^2y^3$ (v) $8p^2q^4$ (c) (i) $2a^2$ (ii) $2b^{11}$ (iii) c^4
(iv) $-36d^3$ (v) $-6e^3$ **4.** (a) (i) $121a^2$ (ii) $8b^3$ (iii) $125c^3$ (iv) $1000d^3$
(v) $27e^3$ (b) (i) $16a^4$ (ii) $-8b^3$ (iii) $64c^3$ (iv) $10,000d^4$ (v) $81e^4$
(c) (i) $-32a^5$ (ii) $-64b^3$ (iii) $256x^3y^2$ (iv) $27m^6$ (v) $4k^4$
5. (a) (i) $6a + 8b$ (ii) $12a + 30b$ (iii) $6x + 12y + 18z$ (iv) $-4x - 10y$
(v) $-30x + 6y$ (vi) $15a^2 - 6ab$ (b) (i) $8x + 9y$ (ii) $13m + 25n$
(iii) $11x^2 - 10x - 15$ (iv) $x + 26y - 4$ (v) $5x^2 - 13x + 11$
(vi) $3x^2 - 23x$ (c) (i) $a + 5b$ (ii) $-5a - 9b$ (iii) $5a - 22$ (iv) 11
(v) $-ab$ (vi) $x^3 + x^2 + 5x$ **6.** (i) $\frac{8x + 65}{15}$ (ii) $\frac{8x + 5}{5}$ (iii) $\frac{9x + 3}{7}$
(iv) $\frac{13x - 1}{6}$ (v) $\frac{8x + 15}{10}$ (vi) $\frac{19x - 14}{8}$ **7.** (i) $\frac{5x + 17}{(x + 1)(x + 7)}$
(ii) $\frac{3x + 16}{(x + 5)(x + 6)}$ (iii) $\frac{9x - 39}{(x + 1)(x - 7)}$ (iv) $\frac{3x - 22}{(x + 10)(6x + 8)}$
(v) $\frac{4x - 5}{(2x + 1)(5x - 1)}$ (vi) $\frac{-87}{(4x + 1)(x - 7)}$ (vii) $\frac{-2x - 7}{(2x + 1)(2x - 1)}$ (viii) $\frac{16}{(x - 9)(x + 7)}$
8. (a) (i) $x^2 + 6x + 5$ (ii) $x^2 + 6x + 8$ (iii) $y^2 + 9y + 14$
(iv) $a^2 + 4a + 4$ (v) $a^2 - 3a - 40$ (vi) $k^2 - 6k - 7$
(b) (i) $x^2 - 5x + 6$ (ii) $x^2 - 11x + 18$ (iii) $6x^2 + 13x + 5$

(iv) $4a^2 + 16a + 16$ (v) $9y^2 + 12y + 4$ (vi) $16y^2 - 8y + 1$
(c) (i) $x^3 + 5x^2 + 6x$ (ii) $2x^3 + 12x^2 + 10x$ (iii) $x^3 + 2x^2 - x - 2$
(iv) $x^3 - 8$ (v) $8x^3 + 27$ (vi) $8x^3 - 36x^2 + 54x - 27$
9. (a) (i) $(x - 5)(x + 4)$ (ii) $(y - 6)(y + 6)$ (iii) $x(x - 50)$
(iv) $(x - 9)(x + 9)$ (v) $(x - 4)(x - 3)$ (vi) $(x + 5)(x - 2)$
(vii) $(x + 6)(x - 2)$ (viii) $(x - 1)(x - 5)$ (ix) $(x - 2)(x - 3)$
(x) $(x - 25)(x + 4)$ (b) (i) $(2x - 1)(x - 1)$ (ii) $(5x - 2)(x + 3)$
(iii) $16(2y - 1)(2y + 1)$ (iv) $3x(4x + 5)$ (v) $x(8x - 11)$ (vi) $(2x + 1)^2$
(vii) $(3x + 1)(2x - 1)$ (viii) $(7x - 2)(2x + 1)$ (ix) $(5x + 1)(3x + 2)$
(x) $(6x - 1)(3x - 1)$ (c) (i) $(2x - 5)(x - 4)$ (ii) $2(x - 9)(x - 6)$
(iii) $(5x - 1)(x + 7)$ (iv) $(2x - 7)(x - 1)$ (v) $2(2x - 1)(x + 1)$
(vi) $(4x - 13)(x - 1)$ (vii) $(7x + 4)(x + 3)$ (viii) $2(x - 3)(x - 7)$
(ix) $(4x - 5)(x - 4)$ (x) $2(3x - 1)(x - 4)$ **10.** (a) (i) $12y^2$ (ii) $6x^2$
(iii) $6x^2y$ (iv) $6p^7q^2$ (b) (i) $x + 3$ (ii) $x + 7$ (iii) $3x + 7$ (iv) $2x + 5$
(c) (i) $2x + 9$ (ii) $x + 5$ (iii) $\frac{x + 3}{x - 1}$ (iv) $\frac{x}{x + 2}$ (v) $\frac{x + 4}{x + 5}$ (vi) $\frac{x + 3}{x + 5}$
(d) (i) $x + 5$ (ii) $2x - 1$ (iii) $3x - 4$ (iv) $2x - 9$ (v) $10x - 9$ (vi) $-5x - 8$
11. (a) 1: 4 m²; 2: 20.25 cm²; 3: 520 mm²; 4: 1.125 m²; 5: 700 cm²
(b) (i) 1: 2.47 seconds   2: 24.73 seconds   3: 28.56 seconds
4: 14.28 seconds   5: 12.37 seconds   (ii) 1.98 seconds   (iii) $h \approx 19$ m

Chapter 2

Exercise 2.1

2. (i) {1, 2, 4, 5, 8, 10, 20, 40}   (ii) {1, 2, 4, 8, 16, 32, 64}
(iii) {1, 2, 4, 7, 14, 28}   (iv) {1, 5, 7, 35}   (v) {1, 2, 3, 4, 6, 8, 12,
16, 24, 32, 48, 96}   (vi) {1, 2, 3, 4, 6, 8, 12, 16, 24, 48}
3. (i) {4, 8, 12, 16, 20, 24}   (ii) {6, 12, 18, 24, 30, 36}
(iii) {8, 16, 24, 32, 40, 48}   (iv) {9, 18, 27, 36, 45, 54}
(v) {12, 24, 36, 48, 60, 72}   (vi) {14, 28, 42, 56, 70, 84}
5. (i) HCF = 2   (ii) HCF = 5   (iii) HCF = 6   (iv) HCF = 1
(v) HCF = 12   (vi) HCF = 15   (vii) HCF = 3   (viii) HCF = 5
(ix) HCF = 4   (x) HCF = 3   **6.** (i) LCM = 12   (ii) LCM = 24
(iii) LCM = 60   (iv) LCM = 45   (v) LCM = 90   (vi) LCM = 80
(vii) LCM = 12   (viii) LCM = 20   (ix) LCM = 40   (x) LCM = 90
7. (i) $64 = 2^6$ (ii) $184 = 2^3 \times 23$ (iii) $2310 = 2 \times 3 \times 5 \times 7 \times 11$
(iv) $1870 = 2 \times 5 \times 11 \times 17$ (v) $102 = 2 \times 3 \times 17$ (vi) $368 = 2^4 \times 23$
(vii) $5250 = 2 \times 3 \times 5^3 \times 7$ (viii) $374 = 2 \times 11 \times 17$
(ix) $273 = 3 \times 7 \times 13$ (x) $170 = 2 \times 5 \times 17$ **8.** (i) (a) $136 = 2^3 \times 17$;
$102 = 2 \times 3 \times 17$ (b) HCF = 34; LCM = 408   (ii)(a) $117 = 3^2 \times 13$;
$130 = 2 \times 5 \times 13$ (b) HCF = 13; LCM = 1170   (iii)(a) $368 = 2^4 \times 23$;
$621 = 3^3 \times 23$ (b) HCF = 23; LCM = 9936   (iv) (a) $58 = 2 \times 29$;
$174 = 2 \times 3 \times 29$ (b) HCF = 58; LCM = 174   (v)(a) $60 = 2^2 \times 3 \times 5$;
$765 = 3^2 \times 5 \times 17$ (b) HCF = 15; LCM = 3,060   (vi) (a) $123 = 3 \times 41$;
$615 = 3 \times 5 \times 41$ (b) HCF = 123; LCM = 615   (vii) $69 = 3 \times 23$;
$123 = 3 \times 41$ (b) HCF = 3; LCM = 2,829   (viii)(a) $102 = 2 \times 3 \times 17$;
$170 = 2 \times 5 \times 17$ (b) HCF = 34; LCM = 510   **9.** (i) 56 (or 55 or 57)
(ii) 17   (iii) 13   (iv) 21 or 28   (v) 2   (vi) 12   (vii) 2,310   **10.** 42
11. 20th step   **12.** 60 sec   **13.** (i) 28 m   (ii) 42   (iii) 784 m²   **14.** 72
15. (i) 220   (ii) 660

Exercise 2.2

1. (i) 3   (ii) 5   (iii) -4 (iv) -5 (v) -11 (vi) -15 **2.** (i) -12 (ii) 7
(iii) -10 (iv) -15 (v) -60 (vi) -3 **3.** (i) 2   (ii) -7 (iii) 0   (iv) 2
(v) -18 (vi) 2   **4.** (i) 6   (ii) 0   (iii) -14 (iv) -2 (v) 0   (vi) -5
5. €1,000   **6.** Alice = 14; Bob = 35; Kylie = 25   **7.** (i) 20   (ii) -20
(iii) -20 (iv) 20   **8.** (i) 40   (ii) -32 (iii) -56 (iv) 90   (v) 90
(vi) -150 **9.** (i) 5   (ii) -4 (iii) 3   (iv) -3 (v) 4   (vi) -12
10. (i) 3   (ii) -6 (iii) -12 (iv) 2   (v) -11 (vi) -8 **12.** (i) 4
(ii) 9   (iii) 16   (iv) -1 (v) 1   **13.** (i) 8   (ii) -27 (iii) 25   (iv) 36
(v) 64   (vi) $-1,000$

Exercise 2.3

1. (i) $1\frac{1}{12}$ (ii) $\frac{5}{8}$ (iii) $\frac{1}{2}$ (iv) $\frac{29}{36}$ (v) $\frac{1}{4}$ (vi) $5\frac{3}{4}$ (vii) $2\frac{5}{8}$ (viii) $11\frac{13}{24}$
(ix) $6\frac{7}{24}$ (x) $1\frac{3}{4}$. **2.** (i) $\frac{2}{15}$ (ii) $\frac{1}{6}$ (iii) $\frac{5}{24}$ (iv) $\frac{16}{45}$ (v) $\frac{9}{20}$ (vi) $\frac{17}{15}$ (vii) 7
(viii) $\frac{15}{2}$ (ix) $\frac{231}{8}$ (x) $\frac{49}{16}$ **3.** (i) $\frac{1}{4}$ (ii) 1 (iii) $\frac{3}{8}$ (iv) $\frac{4}{3}$ (v) $\frac{12}{5}$ (vi) 4
(vii) $\frac{4}{15}$ (viii) 12 (ix) $\frac{7}{6}$ (x) $\frac{21}{5}$ **4.** $15\frac{11}{40}$ km **5.** 28 **6.** (i) $78\frac{17}{28}$ kg
(ii) $5\frac{1}{2}$ weeks **7.** (i) 24 (ii) 48 (iii) 36 **8.** (i) 3.12 (ii) 3.22 Option;
as it gives more pocket money in year 1 **9.** 21 bars **10.** €35
11. 64 km each day **12.** 200 cm

Exercise 2.4

1. (i) 8.4 (ii) 8.43 (iii) 8.426 (iv) 6.2 (v) 6.16 (vi) 6.164
(vii) 7.5 (viii) 7.55 (ix) 7.550 **2.** (i) $40 = 2^3 \times 5$; $2 = 2$; $5 = 5$;
$400 = 2^4 \times 5^2$ (ii) All terminating **3.** (i) 2.2361 (ii) 2.8284
(iii) 4.1231 (iv) 4.3589 **4.** (i) 2 (ii) 11 (iii) 3 (iv) 15 (v) 5 (vi) 13
5. (i) 4.414 (ii) 2.7639 (iii) 5.2915 (iv) 2.8038 **6.** (i) 50 (ii) 8
(iii) 20,000 (iv) 7,000 (v) 6,000 (vi) 10,000 **7.** (i) 0.0089 (ii) 0.022
(iii) 0.0023 (iv) 0.00000085 (v) 2.0 (vi) 0.000048 (vii) 960,000
(viii) 0.24 (ix) 0.00091 (x) 0.000000080 **8.** (i) 5 (ii) 6 (iii) 10 (iv) 3
(v) 2.8699 **9.** (i) ≈ 9 (ii) ≈ 20 (iii) 1 **10.** (i) 9.9954 (ii) 16.7358
(iii) 1.0581 **11.** (i) Est. = 4; Calc. = 3.7218 (ii) Est. = 3;
Calc. = 3.1652 (iii) Est. $\approx$ 2.5; Calc. = 2.0293 (iv) Est. = 4;
Calc. = 3.0691 (v) Est. = 5; Calc. = 4.9067 **12.** (i) 18.5856 m²
(ii) 17.6 m (iii) 20 m² (area); 18 m (perimeter)
(iv) 1.4144 m²; 0.4 m **13.** (i) $\approx$ 13,892 m (ii) 42 km²

Exercise 2.5

1. (i) 3.8×10^3 (ii) 7.5×10^4 (iii) 2.4×10^2 (iv) 8.48×10^5
(v) 5.376×10^6 (vi) 1×10^{-2} (vii) 1×10^{-3} (viii) 1×10^{-4}
(ix) 1.2×10^{-3} (x) 3×10^{-5} **2.** (i) 5,000 (ii) 800 (iii) 2,400
(iv) 62,000,000 (v) 840 (vi) 0.0019 (vii) 0.000364 (viii) 0.026
(ix) 0.26 (x) 0.00000506 **3.** (i) 3.4×10^7 (ii) 2.5×10^{-1}
(iii) 4.57×10^3 (iv) 1.258×10^{-4} (v) 7.206×10^3 (vi) 3.2×10^{-5}
(vii) 5×10^6 (viii) 6.464×10^{-1} (ix) 5.326×10^5 (x) 5×10^3
4. (i) 265 (ii) 0.00453 (iii) 7,200,000 (iv) 0.000017 (v) 300
(vi) 0.04 (vii) 26,400,000 (viii) 7,612 (ix) 276,000,000
(x) 0.00000000302 **5.** (i) 2,000,000 (ii) 16,900 (iii) 2,480
(iv) 647,000 (v) 61.2 (vi) 79,300 **6.** (i) 3.6×10^{-5} (ii) 5.613×10^{-4}
(iii) 3.45×10^{-2} (iv) 6.3×10^{-4} (v) 7.8×10^{-3} **7.** (i) 6.8×10^{-4}
(ii) 3.28×10^{-5} (iii) 6.57×10^{-2} (iv) 9.7×10^{-9} (v) 5.6×10^{-7}
8. (i) 0.0015 (ii) 0.000254 (iii) 0.000035 (iv) 0.00000667
(v) 0.0815 **9.** (i) 4 (ii) 5 (iii) 5 (iv) 4 (v) 2 **10.** 7
11. 5×10^2 sec **12.** 4.26 light years **13.** 1.53×10^{11} bits/sec
14. 5,706.8 kg m⁻³ **15.** 10^{13}

Exercise 2.6

1. (i) 10 (ii) 0 (iii) 25 (iv) 1 (v) 125 **2.** (i) 313 (ii) 1,897
(iii) 365 (iv) 2 **4.** (i) $\frac{2}{9}$ (ii) $8\frac{125}{252}$ (iii) 139 (iv) $14\frac{8}{27}$ **5.** (i) 2
(ii) 15 (iii) 66 (iv) 64 **6.** (i) $-\frac{1069}{1323}$ (ii) $42\frac{3}{32}$ (iii) 1,169 (iv) 0
7. (i) $\frac{11}{30}$ (ii) 4 (iii) $16\frac{2}{3}$ (iv) $7\frac{3}{5}$ **8.** (i) 48.88 (ii) ≈ 37.81
9. (i) ≈ 209.52 (ii) 521.25 (iii) $\approx 19,975.26$

Revision Exercises

1. (a) (i) 5, 10, 15, 20, 25, 30 (ii) 2, 4, 6, 8, 10, 12 (iii) 10, 20, 30, 40, 50, 60 (iv) 12, 24, 36, 48, 60, 72 (v) 13, 26, 39, 52, 65, 78 (vi) 25, 50, 75, 100, 125, 150 (b) (i) {1, 2, 5, 7, 10, 14, 35, 70}
(ii) {1, 2, 4, 5, 8, 10, 16, 20, 40, 80} (iii) {1, 2, 4, 7, 8, 14, 28, 56}
(iv) {1, 2, 4, 8, 16, 32, 64, 128} (v) {1, 2, 4, 8, 16, 32, 64, 128, 256}
(vi) 1, 2, 4, 5, 10, 20, 25, 50, 100 (c) (i) 2^7 (ii) $2^2 \times 3 \times 17$ (iii) $2 \times 5 \times 17$
(iv) $2^2 \times 11 \times 17$ (v) $2^2 \times 3 \times 5 \times 31$ (vi) $2^2 \times 3 \times 13 \times 17$ **2.** (i) LCM = 204;
HCF = 34 (ii) LCM = 2,829; HCF = 3 (iii) LCM = 2,808; HCF = 13
(iv) LCM = 615; HCF = 41 **3.** (i) Est. = 1; Calc. = 0.9710
(ii) Est. = 1; Calc. = 1.0473 (iii) Est. = 20.25; Calc. = 22.2501
(iv) Est. = 1; Calc. = 0.9361 **4.** (i) 850,000 (ii) 0.13 (iii) 2.0
(iv) 0.000054 (v) 650,000 (vi) 0.00081 **5.** (a) ≈ 0.068
(b) HCF = 26 (c) (i) 58,344 (ii) $\frac{1043}{6250}$ **6.** (a) (i) $p = 2$; $q = 17$
(ii) $m = 7$; $n = 19$ (iii) HCF = 8; LCM = 705,432 (b) 4×10^{-4}
7. (a) $2^2 \times 11 \times 53$ (i) $2^3 \times 7 \times 11^2$ (ii) HCF = 44; LCM = 359,128
(b) (i) €135 (ii) €3,500 **8.** (a) Any four fractions strictly between
0.4 and 0.6 (b) 2 is chosen integer. (i) ½ (ii) –1 (iii) 2 (iv) 2
9. (a) 1×10^{-4} m (b) 280 **10.** (i) 83,138
(ii) Any decimal strictly between 0.6 and 0.625 (iii) 6×10^{16}
11. (a) $\frac{1}{12}$ (b) (i) 3 children (ii) 17, 19, 23 **12.** (a) 0.227
(b) 24 mins **13.** (i) 0.0025 (ii) €99 (iii) 14.2 **14.** (i) 7 + 47;
11 + 43; 13 + 41; 17 + 37; 23 + 31 (ii) 3.61 (iii) 2, 3, 5, 6, 7
(iv) $n = 4$ (v) $\frac{6}{25}$

Chapter 3

Exercise 3.1

1. (i) 25 (ii) 8 (iii) 25 (iv) –216 (v) 16 (vi) –3 (vii) 16 (viii) 1
2. (i) -3^3 (ii) 2^{20} (iii) -5^{19} (iv) 3^3 (v) 4^{12} (vi) -1^{100} (vii) -6^3 (viii) 6^3
5. (a) $x = 2$, $y = 1$ **or** $x = 4$, $y = 2$ **or** $x = 6$, $y = 3$, etc. (b) $x = 1$,
$y = 2$ **or** $x = 2$, $y = 4$ **or** $x = 3$, $y = 6$, etc. **6.** (i) $b = 729$ (ii) $n = 6$
(iii) $a = 10$ **7.** (i) 5^5 (ii) 8^{10} (iii) 6^3 (iv) 4^8 (v) 2^{21} (vi) $\left(\frac{1}{2}\right)^{12}$
(vii) $\left(\frac{1}{4}\right)^{11}$ (viii) $\left(\frac{2}{7}\right)^8$ (ix) $(0.2)^5$ (x) $(2.4)^{13}$ **8.** (i) 5^{10} (ii) -2^9 (iii) -3^7
(iv) -5^5 (v) 7^8 (vi) $-\left(\frac{1}{6}\right)^5$ (vii) $\left(\frac{3}{8}\right)^8$ (viii) $\left(\frac{2}{3}\right)^{18}$ (ix) $-\left(\frac{3}{5}\right)^7$ (x) -2.7^7
9. (i) 3 (ii) 2^6 (iii) 10^3 (iv) 7^7 (v) 10^{-6} (vi) 4^{-5} (vii) 4^0 (viii) 8^{-6}
(ix) 5^0 (x) 7^{-2} **10.** (i) 8^4 (ii) -6^3 (iii) 4^4 (iv) 2^4 (v) -10^5 (vi) -12^5
(vii) -2^3 (viii) $\left(\frac{1}{2}\right)^4$ (ix) $-\left(\frac{3}{4}\right)^{-7}$ (x) $-\left(\frac{3}{4}\right)^0$ **11.** (i) 3^{15} (ii) 6^{20} (iii) 10^{25}
(iv) 4^{30} (v) 7^{42} (vi) 8^{15} (vii) 16^6 (viii) 10^{36} (ix) 2^4 (x) 13^{27} **12.** (i) 8^{12}
(ii) -7^{45} (iii) -18^{13} (iv) 10^{20} (v) -12^{35} (vi) $-\left(\frac{3}{5}\right)^{25}$ (vii) $\left(\frac{3}{2}\right)^{36}$ (viii) $\left(\frac{3}{4}\right)^{42}$
(ix) 2.3^6 (x) $\left(\frac{3}{5}\right)^{18}$ **13.** (i) 5^5 (ii) 5^{11} (iii) 5^2 (iv) 5^{66} (v) 5^{26} (vi) 5^{15}

Exercise 3.2

1. (i) $\frac{1}{8}$ (ii) $\frac{1}{16}$ (iii) $\frac{1}{729}$ (iv) $\frac{1}{125}$ (v) $\frac{1}{36}$ (vi) $\frac{1}{49}$ (vii) $\frac{1}{81}$ (viii) $\frac{1}{64}$
(ix) $\frac{1}{64}$ (x) $\frac{1}{25}$ **2.** (i) $\frac{2}{125}$ (ii) $\frac{3}{64}$ (iii) $\frac{5}{16}$ (iv) $\frac{4}{81}$ (v) $\frac{1}{32}$ (vi) $\frac{3}{49}$
(vii) $\frac{1}{4}$ (viii) $\frac{1}{12}$ (ix) $\frac{1}{8}$ (x) $\frac{1}{200}$ **3.** (i) 5 (ii) 7 (iii) 3 (iv) 2 (v) 2
(vi) 1 (vii) 6 (viii) 3 (ix) 2 (x) 11 **6.** (i) 10 (ii) 8 (iii) 6 (iv) 8
(v) 4 (vi) 2 (vii) 3 (viii) 10 (ix) 4 (x) 6 **7.** (i) 2 (ii) 9 (iii) 16
(iv) 8 (v) 1,000 (vi) 25 (vii) 32 (viii) 27 (ix) 27 (x) 256
8. (i) $\frac{1}{10}$ (ii) $\frac{1}{6}$ (iii) $\frac{1}{2}$ (iv) $\frac{1}{27}$ (v) $\frac{1}{27}$ (vi) $\frac{1}{4}$ (vii) $\frac{1}{243}$ (viii) $\frac{1}{25}$
(ix) $\frac{1}{32}$ (x) $\frac{1}{100,000}$ **11.** (i) $\frac{1}{2}$ (ii) $\frac{1}{5}$ (iii) $\frac{2}{3}$ (iv) $\frac{9}{5}$ (v) $\frac{2}{3}$ (vi) $\frac{2}{5}$
(vii) $\frac{8}{27}$ (viii) $\frac{9}{16}$ **12.** (i) $\frac{5}{6}$ (ii) $\frac{11}{12}$ (iii) $\frac{5}{2}$ (iv) $\frac{100}{9}$ (v) $\frac{9}{25}$ (vi) $\frac{25}{4}$
(vii) $\frac{27}{8}$ (viii) $\frac{16}{9}$ **13.** (i) 3×5 (ii) $3^9 \times 5^9$. Prime factors are 3 and 5.
14. Prime factors are 2 and 3. **15.** Prime factors of $100^{1,601}$ are 2 and 5.
16. (i) 4.39 (ii) 57.19 (iii) 3.04 (iv) 1.90 (v) 15.61 (vi) 0.02
(vii) 11.5 (viii) 0.04 (ix) 2.02 (x) 2.15 **17.** (i) 2^2 (ii) 2^3 (iii) 2^4
(iv) 2^5 (v) 2^{-1} (vi) 2^{-2} (vii) $2^{1/2}$ (viii) $2^{1/3}$ (ix) $2^{-1/2}$ **18.** (i) 3^0 (ii) 3^2
(iii) 3^3 (iv) 3^4 (v) 3^{-1} (vi) 3^{-2} (vii) $3^{1/2}$ (viii) $3^{3/2}$ (ix) $3^{-1/2}$ **19.** (i) 5^2
(ii) 5^3 (iii) 5^{-1} (iv) 5^0 (v) 5^{-2} (vi) 5^{-3} (vii) $5^{1/2}$ (viii) $5^{1/5}$ (ix) $5^{-1/2}$
20. (i) 10^2 (ii) 10^3 (iii) 10^{-2} (iv) 10^4 (v) 10^{-1} (vi) 10^{-3} (vii) $10^{1/2}$
(viii) $10^{1/100}$ (ix) $10^{-1/2}$ (x) $10^{1/6}$ (xi) $10^{3/2}$ (xii) $10^{3/2}$

Exercise 3.3

1. (i) $x = 2$ (ii) $x = 3$ (iii) $x = 3$ (iv) $x = 3$ (v) $x = 3$ (vi) $x = 4$
(vii) $x = 4$ (viii) $x = 3$ (ix) $x = 2$ (x) $x = 6$ **2.** (i) $x = 2$ (ii) $x = 3$
(iii) $x = 4$ (iv) $x = 6$ (v) $x = 10$ (vi) $x = 20$ (vii) $x = \frac{9}{4}$ (viii) $x = 2$
(ix) $x = \frac{3}{2}$ (x) $x = 3$ **3.** (i) 2^4 (ii) 2^3 (iii) $2^{3/2}$ (iv) $2^{5/2}$; $x = \frac{17}{4}$ **4.** (i) 3^3 (ii) $3^{1/2}$;
$x = \frac{9}{2}$ **5.** (i) 5^2 (ii) $5^{3/2}$ (iii) $5^{1/3}$; $x = 7$ **6.** (i) 7^2 (ii) $7^{1/3}$ (iii) $x = -24$
7. (i) 2 (ii) $2^{1/2}$ (iii) $x = \frac{7}{2}$ **8.** $x = 4$ **9.** (i) $x = 7^{1/2}$ (ii) $x = 5$
(iii) $x = 2^{1/2}$ (iv) $x = \frac{1}{2}$ (v) $x = 1^{1/2}$ (vi) $x = 1^{2/3}$ (vii) $x = \frac{3}{4}$
(viii) $x = \frac{9}{4}$ **10.** (i) $x = \frac{10}{3}$ (ii) $x = \frac{10}{3}$ **11.** 2^p **12.** $x = 8$
13. (i) $p = -\frac{1}{4}$ (ii) $p = 4$ **14.** $y = 14$

Exercise 3.4

1. (i) 3 (ii) 6 (iii) 17 (iv) 19 (v) 30 (vi) 28 (vii) 250 (viii) 20 (ix) 200
(x) 135   **2.** (i) False (ii) False (iii) True (iv) True   **3.** (i) 6 (ii) 10
(iii) 4 (iv) 8 (v) 10 (vi) 3 (vii) 5 (viii) 2 (ix) 3 (x) 5   **4.** (i) $2\sqrt{2}$
(ii) $3\sqrt{5}$ (iii) $10\sqrt{3}$ (iv) $2\sqrt{3}$ (v) $4\sqrt{2}$ (vi) $10\sqrt{5}$ (vii) $3\sqrt{3}$
(viii) $3\sqrt{6}$ (ix) $5\sqrt{3}$ (x) $7\sqrt{2}$ **5.** $7\sqrt{2}$ **6.** $5\sqrt{3}$ **7.** $7\sqrt{5}$ **8.** $5\sqrt{11}$

Revision Exercises

1. 5^{11} (ii) $8^0 = 1$ (iii) 3^6 (iv) 16^4 **2.** (i) 7^{-5} (ii) $15^{1/8}$ (iii) $17^{3/5}$ (iv) $5^{1/2}$
3. (i) 2^{16} (ii) 7^{22} (iii) 2^{24} (iv) 5^{35} **4.** (i) $5\sqrt{5}$ (ii) $7\sqrt{2}$ (iii) $8\sqrt{2}$
(iv) $3\sqrt{2}$ **5.** (i) a^{10} (ii) a^{24} (iii) $a^{3/2}$ (iv) a^2 **6.** (i) $17\sqrt{2}$ (ii) $20\sqrt{5}$
7. (i) 5 (ii) $x = \frac{3}{2}$ (iii) $n = 6$ **8.** (i) $\frac{1}{8}$ (ii) $x = \frac{11}{4}$ **9.** (i) $\frac{9}{2}$ (ii) $x = \frac{1}{4}$
10. (i) 2^6 (ii) $2^{9/4}$ (iii) 3^7 (iv) 3^{11}

Chapter 4

Exercise 4.1

1. (i) ◆ (ii) ÷ (iii) ∠ (iv) ≻ (v) ⊞   **2.** (i) Red, red, blue
(ii) blue, blue, red (iii) blue, red, green (iv) brown, blue, green
3. (a) (i) Red, blue, red (ii) Red, blue, red (iii) Red, red, red
(iv) Red, blue, blue (v) Red, yellow, red (b)(i) 50th: blue, 100th: blue,
150th: blue (ii) 50th: blue, 100th: blue, 150th: blue (iii) 50th: red,
100th: blue, 150th: red (iv) 50th: green, 100th: green, 150th: green
(v) 50th: yellow, 100th: green, 150th: brown   **4.** (i) Hexagon
(ii) Triangle (iii) Hexagon   **5.** (i) Triangle (ii) Square (iii) Square.
Reason: $3n \div 3$ has remainder 0.   **6.** (i) Triangle (ii) Hexagon
(iii) Yellow   **7.** (i) Red, red, red, red, red, blue, red, red, red
8. (i) 2, 3, 5, 7, 11, 13 (power of primes)... **or** 2, 3, 5, 7, 2, 3, 5, 7, 2, ...

Exercise 4.2

1. (iii) Arithmetic seq: 1st term 6, common diff. 3 (iv) 27 (v) $3n + 3$
2. (iii) Arithmetic seq: 1st term 4, common diff. 3 (iv) 28 (v) $3n + 1$
3. (iii) Arithmetic seq: 1st term 6, common diff. 2 (iv) 18 (v) $2n + 4$
(vi) $n - 1$ **4.** (iii) Arithmetic seq: 1st term 6, common diff. 3 (iv) 24
(v) $3n + 3$ **5.** (i) Yes; 1st term 3; common diff. 2 (ii) Yes; 1st term 2;
common diff. 2 (iii) No (no common diff.) (iv) No (no common diff.)
(v) Yes; 1st term 5; common diff. 5 (vi) Yes; 1st term 2; common diff. 0.5
(vii) Yes; 1st term 12; common diff. 3 (viii) No (no common diff.)
(ix) Yes; 1st term −5; common diff. 4 (x) Yes; 1st term 20;
common diff. 1   **6.** (i) (a) 2 (b) 4 (c) 14, 18, 22 (ii) (a) 5 (b) 2
(c) 13, 15, 17 (iii) (a) 19 (b) −3 (c) 10, 7, 4 (iv) (a) 100 (b) −10
(c) 70, 60, 50 (v) (a) 13 (b) 7 (c) 34, 41, 48 (vi) (a) −5 (b) 2
(c) 1, 3, 5 (vii) (a) 5.5 (b) 0.5 (c) 7, 7.5, 8 (viii) (a) 1 (b) $\frac{1}{4}$
(c) $1\frac{3}{4}$, 2, $2\frac{1}{4}$ (ix) (a) 72 (b) −11 (c) 39, 28, 17 (x) (a) $\frac{1}{6}$ (b) $\frac{1}{6}$
(c) $\frac{2}{3}, \frac{5}{6}, 1$ **7.** (i) (a) −3 (b) −12, −15, −18 (ii) (a) −10 (b) 80, 70, 60
(iii) (a) 1.6 (b) 9.2, 10.8, 12.4 (iv) (a) 4 (b) 4, 8, 12 (v) (a) $-2\frac{1}{2}$
(b) 5, $2\frac{1}{2}$, 0 (vi) (a) $-1\frac{1}{2}$ (b) $12\frac{1}{2}$, 11, $9\frac{1}{2}$ (vii) (a) $2\frac{3}{4}$ (b) $19\frac{1}{4}$, 22, $22\frac{3}{4}$

(viii) (a) 4.4 (b) 3.4, 7.8, 12.2 (ix) (a) $\frac{1}{10}$ (b) $\frac{3}{10}, \frac{2}{5}, \frac{1}{2}$ (x) (a) $-\frac{1}{8}$
(b) $\frac{5}{8}, \frac{1}{2}, \frac{3}{8}$ **8.** (i) (a) 1 (b) 5   (c) 16 (ii) (a) 3 (b) 4 (c) 15 (iii) (a) −5
(b) 4 (c) 7 (iv) (a) 40 (b) −5 (c) 25 (v) (a) −11 (b) 2 (c) −5
9. (a) (i) 3, 5, 7, 9 (ii) 2, 5, 8, 11 (iii) 4, 7, 12, 19 (iv) 10, 8, 6, 4
(v) 1, $\frac{1}{2}, \frac{1}{3}, \frac{1}{4}$ (b) (i), (ii) and (iv) are arithmetic.   **10.** (a) (i) 5, 9, 13, 17
(ii) 10, 7, 4, 1 (iii) 5, 11, 21, 35 (iv) 7, 4, 1, −2 (v) 4, 16, 64, 256
(b) (i), (ii) and (iv) are arithmetic.   **11.** (a) Sequence C (b) A: 2, 4, 8;
B: 1, 4, 9; C: 5, 9, 13 (c) 4   **12.** (a) C (b) A: 3, 9, 27; B: 2, 5, 10;
C: 3, 5, 7 (c) 2   **13.** (i) $d_A = 6, d_B = 2, d_C = 3$ (ii) $m_A = 6, m_B = 2$,
$m_C = 3$ (iii) Slope = common diff.   **14.** $x = 4$ **15.** $x = 3$
16. (i) 7 (ii) −3 (iii) 14   **17.** (i) 7 (ii) −4 (iii) $T_4 = 7$; $T_5 = 3$

Exercise 4.3

1. (i) (a) 5 (b) 2 (c) $2n + 3$ (ii) (a) 4 (b) 3 (c) $3n + 1$ (iii) (a) 1
(b) 4 (c) $4n - 3$ (iv) (a) 13 (b) 7 (c) $7n + 6$ (v) (a) 59 (b) −2
(c) $-2n + 61$ (vi) (a) −12 (b) 5 (c) $5n - 17$ (vii) (a) 43 (b) −3
(c) $-3n + 46$ (viii) (a) −16 (b) −4 (c) $-4n - 12$ (ix) (a) 75 (b) 9
(c) $9n + 66$ (x) (a) −20 (b) 3 (c) $3n - 23$ **2.** (i) $-4n - 7$ (ii) −227
3. (i) $12n - 2$ (ii) 766   **4.** (i) $7n - 7$ (ii) 588   **5.** (i) $6n + 1$ (ii) 197
6. (i) $8n - 5$ (ii) 763   **7.** (i) $-6n + 37$ (ii) −89   **8.** (i) $4n + 1$
(ii) 221   **9.** 35   **10.** 46   **11.** 21   **12.** 34   **13.** 8   **14.** −502
15. 285   **16.** (ii) 301 (iii) 298 (iv) Row 670 of Column A   **17.** (i) 95
(ii) 2020   **18.** (i) Day 3 = 2.5; Day 4 = 2.75; Day 5 = 3 (ii) Day 49
19. (i) Floor 6 = 540 rooms; Floor 7 = 630 rooms; Floor 8 = 720 rooms;
Floor 9 = 810 rooms; Floor 10 = 900 rooms (ii) 1,800 (iii) 101

Exercise 4.4

1. (i) 2,310 (ii) 480 (iii) 290 (iv) 780 (v) 1,590   **2.** (i) 1,425
(ii) 2,265 (iii) 2,895 (iv) 180 (v) 165   **3.** (i) 430 (ii) 190 (iii) −230
(iv) −170 (v) 50   **4.** 3,240   **5.** 900   **6.** 40 terms; $S_{40} = 1,640$
7. (i) 280 (ii) 1,160 (iii) 880   **8.** (i) 1,560 (ii) 6,320 (iii) 4,760
9. (i) 350 (ii) 1,500 (iii) 1,150   **10.** (i) 737 (ii) 4,785 (iii) 1,968
(iv) 396 (v) 1,683   **11.** (i) $4n - 1$ (ii) 221 (iii) 5,150   **12.** (i) €395
(ii) €14,850   **13.** (i) 9.25 km (ii) 33rd week (iii) 2,744 km
14. (i) 11 hours (ii) 110 cm   **15.** (i) 27 (ii) 50 (iii) 2,650

Exercise 4.5

1. (iii) Quadratic (iv) 28   **2.** (iii) Quadratic (iv) 64 (v) $L_n = n$
(vi) $H_n = n$ (vii) $T_n = n^2$ **3.** (iii) Quadratic (iv) 64 (v) $T_n = n^2$
4. (i) Quadratic (ii) Exponential (iii) Quadratic (iv) Quadratic
(v) Linear (vi) Exponential (vii) Quadratic (viii) Linear (ix) Exponential
(x) Exponential   **5.** (i) (a) 8 (b) 1st diff. = 6, 10, 14; 2nd diff. = 4;
(c) 56, 78, 104 (ii) (a) 1 (b) 1st diff. = 2, 3, 4; 2nd diff. = 1
(c) 15, 21, 28 (iii) (a) 7 (b) 1st diff. = 9, 15, 21; 2nd diff. = 6
(c) 79, 112, 151 (iv) (a) 3 (b) 1st diff. = 10, 14, 18; 2nd diff. = 4
(c) 67, 93, 123 (v) (a) 15 (b) 1st diff. = 8, 16, 24; 2nd diff. = 8
(c) 95, 135, 183 (vi) (a) 8 (b) 1st diff. = 4, 2, 0, −2; 2nd diff. = −2
(c) 8, 2, −6 (vii) (a) 5 (b) 1st diff. = 2, −2, −6, −10; 2nd diff. = −4
(c) −25, −43, −65 (viii) (a) 1 (b) 1st diff. = −3, 0, 13; 2nd diff. = 3
(c) 7, 16, 28 (ix) (a) 10 (b) 1st diff. = −6, −3, 0, 3; 2nd diff. = 3
(c) 10, 19, 31   **6.** (i) (a) Doubles (b) 256; 512; 1,024 (ii) (a) Triples
(b) 1,458; 4,374; 13,122 (iii) (a) Triples (b) 2,673; 8,019; 24,057
(iv) (a) Doubles (b) 416; 832; 1,664 (v) (a) Triples (b) −1,215;
−3,645; −10,935   **7.** (iii) No   **8.** (i) 125, 215, 343 (iii) The sequence
is cubic because the third difference is a constant.   **9.** (ii) The sequence
is cubic because the third difference is a constant. (iii) 207
10. (ii) $T_5 = 45$; $T_6 = 66$ (iv) Quadratic (second difference is constant)

Revision Exercises

1. (ii) $4n - 3$ (iii) 197 (iv) 60th term   **2.** (ii) $2n + 1$ (iii) 101 (iv) 99
3. (iii) Linear (first difference is constant) (iv) $4n + 1$ (v) 33   **4.** (i) 6
(ii) 5 (iii) 31 (iv) 402   **5.** (ii) Linear (iii) Quadratic   **6.** (i) 8 litres

(ii) 94 minutes **7.** (iii) Quadratic (iv) 35 **8.** (i) Quadratic (ii) $T_5 = 87$
9. (i) A: quadratic; B: linear (ii) A (Quadratic): 3, 9, 19, 33; B (Linear):
3, 5, 7, 9 (iii) 60 **10.** (i) 27 (ii) $\frac{1}{4}$ (iii) $\frac{37}{64}$ **11.** (a) Pattern 3: 45;
Pattern 4: 57; Pattern 5: 69 (b) $12n + 9$ (c) 129 (d) 32nd pattern
(e) $6n^2 + 15n$ (f) Seven patterns **12.** (b) Plant 1: $H = 4n + 12$;
Plant 2: $H = 3.5n + 20.5$ (n = no. of days) (d) (i) (17,80)
(ii) At day 17, both plants will be 80 cm tall. **13.** (a) 34, 30, 26
(b) T_{10} (c) $S_{15} = 90$; $n = 18$

Chapter 5

Exercise 5.1

1. €5,000 **2.** €7,750 **3.** €34,710 **4.** €34,700 **5.** (i) €30,100
(ii) €64,400 **6.** €30,530 **7.** 21% **8.** (i) €7,600 (ii) 20% **9.** 21%
10. €80,700 **11.** €10,460 **12.** €1,768.80 **13.** (i) €50.30
(ii) €148.85 (iii) €4,358.80 (iv) €880.23 **14.** (i) €41.07
(ii) €124.04 (iii) €3,518.80 (iv) €765.19 **15.** (i) €5,471.68
(ii) €79,801.32 **16.** €44,000 **17.** (i) €8,930 (ii) €56,829.27
(iii) Eoin: €3,296.85; Sorcha: €2,468.80

Exercise 5.2

1. (i) €2.70 (ii) €1.89 (iii) €2.16 (iv) €1.69 **2.** (i) €544.50
(ii) €229.90 (iii) €968 (iv) €1,087.79 **3.** €18.15 **4.** €363 **5.** €36
6. €250 **7.** €1,800 **8.** €171.99 **9.** (i) €3,375 (ii) €4,083.75
10. (i) €791 (ii) €87.50 (iii) €787.50 (iv) €819

Exercise 5.3

1. Cost price: (vii) €1.00 (viii) €2.10; Selling price: (iv) €28.00
(ix) €12.00 (x) €15.50; Profit: (ii) €5.00 (iii) €5.00 (vi) €0.90;
% Mark-up: (i) 20.00% (ii) 16.13% (iii) 33.33% (iv) 100.00%
(v) 50.00% (vi) 5.00% (vii) 300.00% (viii) 33.33% (ix) 20.00%
(x) 40.91%; % Margin: (i) 16.67% (ii) 13.89% (iii) 25.00%
(iv) 50.00% (v) 33.33% (vi) 4.76% (vii) 75.00% (viii) 25.00%
(ix) 16.67% (x) 29.03% **2.** (i) €157.50 (ii) €1,081.20 (iii) €2,520
(iv) €7,836.25 (v) €26,970 **3.** (i) €39.20 (ii) €80.75 (iii) €121.50
(iv) €99.50 (v) €1,518.05 **4.** (i) €47.50 (ii) €1,062.50 (iii) €25,500
(iv) €8,000 (v) €12,672 **5.** % Mark-up: 20%; % Margin; 16.67%
6. €11.25 **7.** (i) €138 (ii) 13% **8.** (a) (i) €60 (ii) €30 (iii) €240
(iv) €88 (v) €350 (vi) €180 (vii) €547.50 (viii) €3,408
(b) (i) €1,140 (ii) €170 (iii) €1,360 (iv) €4,312 (v) €1,050
(vi) €1,320 (vii) €912.50 (viii) €24,992 **9.** (i) 16.67% (ii) 8.33%
(iii) 11.11% (iv) 7.88% (v) 12.00% **10.** (i) €2.80 (ii) €67.20
11. (i) €79.86 (ii) €585.64 **12.** €212.50 **13.** €536.25 **14.** (i) €150
(ii) €31.25

Exercise 5.4

1. €26,046.56 **2.** €310.48 **3.** €13,959.40 **4.** €138,769.87
5. €35,513.69 **6.** €8,735.48 **7.** €7,555.67 **8.** €134,679.61
9. €1,418,299.58 **10.** €791.35 **11.** €1,958.82 **12.** €10,347.41
13. €1,400.27 **14.** €147,696 **15.** €16,177,050 **16.** €3,934.01
17. (i) €18,200 (ii) €231,065.97 (iii) €16,026.40 **18.** The first
option will cost less. **19.** €9,563.09 **20.** €6,333.85 **21.** 3.09%
22. 3.23% **23.** B (10-year bond) **24.** 3.58%

Exercise 5.5

1. (i) €180,000 (ii) €783,009.38 (iii) €47,494.85 (iv) €19,555.73
(v) €15,372.14 (vi) €14,173.48 (vii) €3,796.88 **2.** (i) €166,000
(ii) 15% (iii) €109,724.07 (iv) 3.5% (v) €15,372,139.84
(vi) €21,260.22 (vii) 25% **3.** €9,830.40 **4.** 150,859.81 m³
5. €60,000 **6.** ≈€979,100 **7.** ≈26% **8.** 20% **9.** ≈87.91% **10.** No

Revision Exercises

1. €15,060 **2.** €1,810.80 **3.** (i) €29.54 (ii) €93.03 (iii) €2,468.80
(iv) €612.99 **4.** €3,986.12 **5.** (i) €700 (ii) €700 (iii) 233.33%
(iv) 70% **6.** (i) €510.75 (ii) €60.75 (iii) €506.25 (iv) €517.50
7. €10,552.52 **8.** €187,103.54 **9.** (i) €13,250
(ii) €169,009.36 (iii) €11,037.25 **10.** Option 1: 1.41%; Option 2:
1.37%; Option 3: 1.74%; Option 4: 1.96% (ii) Option 2
11. €19,752.14 **12.** 2.80% **13.** (i) €4,081.49 (ii) 7.00%
(iii) The investments are identical in terms of AER. **14.** (i) €7,969.24
(ii) 2.31% **15.** (i) €14,762.25 (ii) €47,123.51 (iii) €1,361,220.84
(iv) €181,623.47 (v) €115,492.97 **16.** €177,006.66 **17.** 20%
18. No **19.** 45.07% **20.** (i) 37.00% (ii) Year 1: €148; Year 2: €93.24;
Year 3: €58.74

Chapter 6

Exercise 6.1

1. (i) 4 (ii) 7 (iii) –12 (iv) 5 (v) 3 (vi) –9 (vii) 9 (viii) 3
(ix) $\frac{1}{2}$ (x) 2 **2.** (i) (3, –3) is not a solution (ii) (1, 3) is a solution
(iii) (–4, 1) is not a solution (iv) (4, 2) is a solution
(v) (1, 5) is not a solution **3.** $x = 3$, $y = 2$

Exercise 6.2

1. $x = 3$ **2.** $y = 2$ **3.** $x = 4$ **4.** $a = 9$ **5.** $x = -1$ **6.** $x = -5$
7. $x = -3$ **8.** $y = 4$ **9.** $x = -6$ **10.** $x = 7$ **11.** $x = 4$
12. $t = 3$ **13.** $x = \frac{5}{6}$ **14.** $x = -2$ **15.** $x = -\frac{5}{2}$ **16.** $x = -1$
17. $x = -6$ **18.** $y = \frac{3}{8}$ **19.** $x = -2$ **20.** $x = 4$ **21.** $x = -\frac{1}{3}$
22. $x = 2.3$ **23.** $x = -3$ **24.** $x = -\frac{5}{9}$ **25.** $a = -3$ **26.** $x = -12$
27. $x = -7$ **28.** $x = -1$ **29.** $x = \frac{1}{2}$ **30.** $y = -4$ is a solution
31. $a = -1$ is a solution **32.** $b = -\frac{7}{3}$ is a solution

Exercise 6.3

1. $x = 2$ **2.** $x = 2$ **3.** $x = 12$ **4.** $a = -1$ **5.** $x = 2$ **6.** $x = \frac{4}{3}$
7. $x = -15$ **8.** $x = -\frac{1}{6}$ **9.** $x = 7$ **10.** $x = 11$ **11.** $x = 3$
12. $y = 5$ **13.** $x = 2$ **14.** $x = \frac{38}{11}$ **15.** $x = 10$ **16.** $t = \frac{15}{4}$
17. $x = -1$ **18.** $x = 5$ **19.** $x = 4$ **20.** $x = -1$ **21.** $x = 0$
22. $x = 9$ **23.** $x = 1$ **24.** $x = 6$ **25.** $x = 36$ **26.** $x = 9$

Exercise 6.4

1. $x = 4$, $y = 3$ **2.** $x = 8$, $y = 5$ **3.** $x = 7$, $y = -3$ **4.** $x = 1$, $y = 2$
5. $x = 3$, $y = 4$ **6.** $x = 2$, $y = 5$ **7.** $x = 7$, $y = 3$ **8.** $x = 5$, $y = 1$
9. $x = 2$, $y = 2$ **10.** $x = 0$, $y = -3$ **11.** $x = -1$, $y = 4$
12. $x = -4$, $y = 5$ **13.** $x = -3$, $y = -3$ **14.** $x = 5$, $y = 2$
15. $x = 7$, $y = 0$ **16.** $x = 4$, $y = -1$ **17.** $x = -4$, $y = 3$
18. $x = -2$, $y = -1$ **19.** $x = 11$, $y = 1$ **20.** $x = 2$, $y = 1$
21. $x = -5$, $y = -2$ **22.** $x = \frac{1}{2}$, $y = 3$ **23.** $x = 2$, $y = \frac{1}{3}$
24. $x = \frac{1}{4}$, $y = \frac{1}{5}$ **25.** $x = \frac{3}{10}$, $y = \frac{3}{5}$ **26.** $x = 1.5$, $y = 3.5$
27. $x = -1$, $y = 3$ **28.** $x = 3$, $y = 1$ **29.** $x = 14$, $y = 6$
30. $x = 2$, $y = 8$

Exercise 6.5

1. (i) $x = -\frac{2}{3}$ (ii) $x = 3$ (iii) $x = 2$ (iv) $x = -5$ (v) $x = 2$
(vi) $x = 4$ (vii) $x = -3$ (viii) $x = 8$ (ix) $x = -7$ (x) $x = -4$
2. (i) $x = 2\frac{6}{7}$, $y = 1\frac{5}{7}$ (ii) $x = 2$, $y = 2$ (iii) $x = -1$, $y = 3$
(iv) $x = 5\frac{1}{3}$, $y = 1\frac{2}{3}$ (v) $x = 3$, $y = -1$ (vi) $x = 1$, $y = -2$
3. (a) (i) $x = 2$, $y = 2$ (ii) $x = 1$, $y = \frac{1}{2}$ (b) (i) (2, 2) is a solution
(iii) (1, $\frac{1}{2}$) is a solution

Exercise 6.6

1. (i) 8, 9, 10   (ii) 6, 7, 8   (iii) −8, −7, −6   (iv) 1, 2, 3   (v) −4, −3, −2

Exercise 6.7

1. $x > 2$ **2.** $x \geqslant 3$ **3.** $x < 2$ **4.** $x \leqslant -1$ **5.** $x \leqslant -1$ **6.** $x > 4$
7. $x > -16$ **8.** $x \leqslant 2$ **9.** $x > -7$ **10.** $x \geqslant -1$ **11.** $x < 9$
12. $x \leqslant \frac{7}{2}$ **13.** $x > 7$ **14.** $x \geqslant 2$ **15.** $x > -4$ **16.** $x \geqslant \frac{1}{2}$
17. $x \geqslant 2$ **18.** $x \geqslant -\frac{1}{2}$ **20.** (i) $-4 < x < 6$ (ii) $3 \leqslant x < 9$
(iii) $-3 \leqslant x \leqslant 1$ (iv) $0 < x \leqslant 3$ (v) $-3 < x \leqslant 1$
21. $x \in \{1, 2, 3, 4, 5, 6\}$ **22.** (i) $x \leqslant 7, x \in Z$
(ii) $x \geqslant -1, x \in Z$ (iii) $E \cap F = \{-1, 0, 1, 2, 3, 4, 5, 6, 7\}$
23. $x < 3, x \in R$ **24.** $x > -7, x \in R$ **24.** (i) $x \geqslant 1, x \in R$
(ii) $x < 3, x \in R$ **25.** (i) $x > 5, x \in R$ (ii) $x \leqslant 7$ (iii) $M \cap N = \{ \}$
26. $x > 3$ (ii) $x < \frac{17}{4}$

Exercise 6.8

1. (i) $x = 3$ (ii) $y = 4$ (iii) $a = 1$ (iv) $b = 7$ (v) $r = -2$ (vi) $x = \frac{9-y}{3}$
(vii) $y = \frac{16-x}{4}$ (viii) $b = \frac{7-4a}{3}$ (ix) $\frac{2b-5}{3} = c$ (x) $r = -2t$ (xi) $x = \frac{9-y}{3y}$
(xii) $y = \frac{16-x}{4x}$ (xiii) $b = \frac{7-4a}{3b}$ (xiv) $\frac{2b-5}{3b} = c$ (xv) $r = -\frac{5t}{2}$
2. (i) $x = 20$ (ii) $y = 12$ (iii) $a = 12$ (iv) $b = \frac{35}{9}$ (v) $\frac{3}{2} = r$
(vi) $x = 20 - 4y$ (vii) $y = 12 - 6x$ (viii) $a - \frac{10}{4} = b$ (ix) $\frac{18b-10}{15} = c$
(x) $t = \frac{2r}{3}$ (xi) $\frac{4y}{5y-2} = x$ (xii) $\frac{2x}{2x-3} = y$ (xiii) $b = \frac{a}{2-5a}$
(xiv) $c = \frac{6b}{5-b}$ (xv) $r = \frac{2}{3p+t}$ **3.** $\frac{t-5}{4} = n$ **4.** $\frac{A}{l} = w$ **5.** $\frac{p}{m} = v$
6. $v - at = u$ **7.** $\frac{v-u}{t} = a$ **8.** $\frac{2K}{v^2} = m$ **9.** $\pm\sqrt{\frac{E}{m}} = c$ **10.** $\frac{Fr}{v^2} = m$
11. $r = \frac{mv^2}{F}$ **12.** $q = 2rs - p$ **13.** $\frac{b-a}{2} = c$ **14.** $3a - b = c$
15. $2s - a - c = b$ **16.** $b = \frac{c}{a+c}$ **17.** $\frac{s}{t} - \frac{1}{2}at = u$ **or** $u = \frac{2s-at^2}{2t}$
18. $\frac{2s}{t^2} - \frac{2u}{t} = a$ **or** $a = \frac{2s-ut}{t^2}$ **19.** $y = 6z - 3x$ **20.** $\frac{ac}{a-c} = b$
21. $\frac{2A}{x+y} = z$ **22.** $\frac{2A}{z} - y = x$ **23.** $x = \frac{c}{a-b}$ **24.** $q = \frac{c}{p-r}$
25. $b = \frac{x-a}{1-x}$ **26.** $a = \frac{2t}{2-c}$ **27.** $\frac{T^2g}{4x^2} = l$ **28.** $\frac{ac}{c-a} = b$
29. $\frac{v^2}{2h} = g$ **30.** (i) $V = \frac{M}{D}$ (ii) 63 cm^3 **31.** (i) $y = 3x - k(a + b)$
(ii) $x = \frac{k(a+b)+y}{3}$ **32.** (i) 1,570 cm^3 (ii) $h = 12$ cm
(iii) $r = 24.5$ cm   **33.** (i) 2.84 seconds   (ii) 2.24 m

Exercise 6.9

1. (i) 35   (ii) 49   (iii) $7n$ **2.** (i) 60   (ii) 240   (iii) $60t$ **3.** (i) 19
(ii) $3x + y$ **4.** (i) 26   (ii) $x + 4$ **5.** (i) 45 litres   (ii) $\frac{3}{4}$ m   **6.** $x + n$
7. (i) 5, 6, 7, 8, 9   (ii) $n + 1, n + 2, n + 3, n + 4, n + 5$
8. (i) 12, 14, 16, 18   (ii) $p + 2, p + 4, p + 6, p + 8$ **9.** (i) 37
(ii) $\frac{x}{2} - 3$ **10.** (i) €50   (ii) €30   (iii) €$(100 - x)$ **11.** (i) 12   (ii) $29 - x$
12. $(28x - 2)$ m   **13.** €x for eldest; €$\left(\frac{1,000-x}{3}\right)$ for 3 youngest
14. (i) xy (ii) $2(x + y)$ **15.** (i) 33, 35, 37   (ii) $q + 2, q + 4, q + 6$
16. (i) $xy - 16$ cm^2 (ii) $(x - 4)(y - 4)(2)$ cm^3

Exercise 6.10

1. $x = 9$ **2.** $x = 21$ **3.** $x = 11$ **4.** $x = 24$ **5.** $x = 7$ **6.** 41, 42
7. 6, 7   **8.** 9, 10, 11   **9.** 11 years old   **10.** 70 luxury seats
11. 10, 12   **12.** 11, 13   **13.** Emily: 14, Frances: 17, father: 62
14. 1st rectangle: 9, 4; 2nd rectangle: 6, 6   **15.** (a) 60°, 45°, 75°
(b) 65°, 30°, 85°   **16.** 12, 13, 14, 15
17. Small: 5 kg, Medium: 15 kg, Large: 20 kg
18. Yellow: 10, Blue: 15, Green: 7   **19.** 22
20. Amy: €100, Brendan: €300, Chloe: €150   **21.** €70

Exercise 6.11

1. $x = 10, y = 15$ **2.** $x = \frac{25}{2}, y = \frac{15}{2}$ **3.** $x = 28, y = 17$
4. Soft drinks: €2, Bar: €0.50   **5.** Pen: €0.70, Pencil: €0.30
6. Bar: €1.20, Drink: €0.70   **7.** $x = 5, y = 2$
8. Alan: 420 votes, Carol: 315 votes   **9.** Game: €33, CD: €6.60
10. 20 leather sofas, 30 fabric sofas   **11.** Coat: €60, Bag: €40
12. Toffee: €0.14, Ice-pop: €0.08   **13.** 1st section: 30 m;
2nd section: 120 m   **14.** $x = 45, y = 22$ **15.** Karl: 25, Eddie: 40

Revision Exercises

1. (a) (i) $x = 3$ (ii) $x = 6$ (iii) $x = 3$ (iv) $x = 8$ (v) $x = 8$
(b) (i) $x = 5$ (ii) $x = 9$ (iii) $x = 7$ (c) (i) $x = 1, y = 2$
(ii) $x = 5, y = 3$ (iii) $x = 2, y = 7$ (iv) $x = 7, y = 3$ **2.** (a) (i) $x = 4$
(ii) $x = 3$ (iii) $x = 9$ (iv) $x = 3$ (v) $x = -3$ (b) (i) $x \in \{1, 2, 3\}$
(ii) $x \in \{1, 2, 3, 4, 5\}$ (iii) $x \in \{1, 2, 3\}$ (c) (i) $44 - n$
(ii) 15 years old   **3.** (a) (i) $x = 1$ (ii) $x = 3$ (iii) $x = 2$ (iv) $x = 6$
(v) $x = -2$ (b) (i) $q = \frac{y+t}{p}$ (ii) $t = \frac{p}{v}$ (iii) $a = \frac{-by-c}{x}$ (iv) $x = \frac{z+\cdot 2y}{8}$
(v) $t - (n - 1)a = a$ (vi) $d = \frac{t-a}{n-1}$ (vii) $r = \frac{A}{2\pi h}$ (c) (i) $\frac{53-x}{2}$ (ii) $x = 11$
4. (a) (i) $x = -1$ (ii) $x = 2$ (iii) $x = \frac{5}{2}$ (iv) $x = \frac{9}{4}$ (v) $x = \frac{5}{2}$
(b) (i) $x = 5, y = -1$ (ii) $x = -2, y = 3$ (iii) $x = 1, y = -1$
(iv) $x = \frac{1}{2}, y = \frac{1}{2}$ (v) $x = 5, y = -2$ (c) (i) $\left(\frac{3n}{5} - 200\right)$ (ii) €1 : 2 coins;
50c : 18 coins   **5.** (a) (i) $x = 6$ (ii) $x = 13$ (iii) $x = 24$ (iv) $x = -1$
(c) (i) 18, 16   (ii) 3, 10   **6.** (b) (i) $t = \frac{2s-q}{6}$ (ii) $h = \frac{3v}{\pi r^2}$ (iii) $a = \frac{v^2-u^2}{2s}$
(iv) $u = \pm\sqrt{v^2 - 2as}$ (v) $s = \frac{v^2-u^2}{2a}$ (vi) $c = b - \frac{v(2-3a)}{u}$
(c) (i) Apple: 10c, Orange: 12c   (ii) 14, 15, 16   **7.** (a) (i) $x = 6$
(ii) $x = 3$ (iii) $x = 0$ (b) (i) $x = -2, y = -4$ (ii) $x = -4, y = 2$
8. (a) (i) (1) $x \leqslant \frac{7}{2}, x \in Z$ (2) $x \geqslant -2, x \in Z$
(3) $E \cap F = \{-2, -1, 0, 1, 2, 3\}$ (ii) (1) $x < 5, x \in R$
(2) $x \geqslant -4, x \in R$ (iii) (1) $x \leqslant 5, x \in N$ (2) $x \leqslant 2, x \in N$
(3) $E \setminus F = \{3, 4, 5\}$ (b) (i) $x = 10$ (ii) $x = 14$ (iii) $x = -1$
(iv) $x = 5$ (c) (i) 10c : 9 coins; 50c : 3 coins   (ii) Graham: 4, Hilda: 12
9. (a) (i) $x = 1, y = -2$ (ii) $x = 1, y = 0$ (iii) $x = 4, y = 1$ (iv) $x = 7$,
$y = \frac{3}{2}$ (v) $x = -3, y = 11$ (b) (i) $x = \frac{c}{a+k}$ (ii) $r = \frac{1+c}{1+s}$
(iii) $a = \frac{b}{1-k}$ (iv) $b = \frac{a-c}{c+1}$ (v) $c = \frac{a-d}{d+5}$ (c) (i) $x = 3, y = 7$
(ii) $x = 4$ **10.** (a) (i) (1) $x \geqslant 1$ (2) $x \leqslant 3$ (ii) (1) $x \leqslant 4$ (2) $x \leqslant \frac{19}{4}$
(b) (i) $a = \frac{3cx+b}{2}$ (ii) $a = 34$ (c) Stacey: 5 years old, Darren:
25 years old   **11.** (a) $x = 12, y = 5$ (b) (i) $r = \frac{s-a}{s}$ (ii) $r = \frac{3}{4}$ (c) 5, 7
12. (a) $x = 42$ (b) 7 two-person rooms, 3 three-person rooms   (c) 30, 7

Chapter 7

Exercise 7.1

1. $x = -3$ or -4 **2.** $x = -1$ or -9 **3.** $x = 5$ or -2 **4.** $x = -8$ or -9
5. $x = -5$ or 3 **6.** $x = 9$ or -8 **7.** $x = \frac{1}{2}$ or 2 **8.** $x = 0$ or $-\frac{3}{2}$
9. $x = \pm 9$ **10.** $x = -\frac{4}{5}$ or -3 **11.** $x = -\frac{3}{5}$ or -6 **12.** $x = \frac{3}{7}$ or 3
13. $x = 0$ or 3 **14.** $x = \pm 1$ **15.** $x = \frac{5}{2}$ or -9 **16.** $x = 5$ or -1
17. $x = -\frac{11}{5}$ or 3 **18.** $x = \frac{3}{4}$ or 3 **19.** $y = \pm\frac{15}{7}$ **20.** $x = -\frac{2}{7}$ or 6
21. $x = 0$ or 11 **22.** $x = -\frac{1}{9}$ or $\frac{1}{5}$ **23.** $x = \frac{1}{5}$ or -7 **24.** $x = 1$
25. $x = -\frac{2}{15}$ or $\frac{1}{10}$ **26.** $x = -\frac{6}{5}$ or 4 **27.** $x = -\frac{3}{2}$ or 4 **28.** $x = -\frac{8}{3}$ or 1
29. $\pm\frac{1}{3}$ **30.** $x = 8$ or -1 **31.** $x = -\frac{2}{7}$ or 6 **32.** $x = 3$ or 14
33. $x = -\frac{1}{6}$ or -2 **34.** $x = 0$ or $\frac{1}{3}$ **35.** $x = \pm\frac{1}{8}$ **36.** $x = \frac{1}{2}$ or -2
37. $x = -\frac{6}{7}$ or -5 **38.** $x = -\frac{5}{3}$ or $\frac{1}{2}$ **39.** $x = 0$ or $\frac{7}{10}$ **40.** $x = \pm 2$
41. $x = -\frac{4}{5}$ or -4 **42.** $x = -\frac{7}{3}$ or 1 **43.** $x = \frac{3}{7}$ or $-\frac{3}{2}$ **44.** $x = -\frac{2}{3}$ or -4
45. $x = \frac{1}{4}$ or $\frac{13}{2}$ **46.** $x = -\frac{1}{2}$ or 4 **47.** $x = -1$ or 7 **48.** $x = \pm 10$

49. $x = 7$ or -2 **50.** $x = -\frac{5}{3}$ or 6 **51.** $x = \frac{1}{5}$ or 6 **52.** $x = \frac{4}{5}$ or $-\frac{1}{2}$
53. $x = -\frac{7}{2}$ or 3 **54.** $x = -\frac{2}{5}$ or -1

Exercise 7.2

1. $x = -1$ or -5 **2.** $x = 2$ or -7 **3.** $x = 4$ or 3 **4.** $x = 3$ or -4
5. $x = 4$ or -9 **6.** $x = -4$ or $\frac{3}{2}$ **7.** $x = -2$ or $-\frac{7}{2}$ **8.** $x = 1$ or $-\frac{5}{3}$
9. $x = -\frac{7}{4}$ or 1 **10.** $x = 1$ or $-\frac{2}{7}$ **11.** $x = 9$ or $-\frac{1}{3}$ **12.** $x = \frac{3}{2}$ or -9
13. $x = 1$ or $-\frac{5}{13}$ **14.** $x = \frac{2}{5}$ or -6 **15.** $x = -\frac{1}{14}$ or $-\frac{1}{2}$ **16.** $x = 1$ or -2
17. $x = \frac{7}{2}$ or $\frac{1}{7}$ **18.** $y = 4$ or $\frac{7}{3}$ **19.** $x = \frac{5}{2}$ or -2 **20.** $x = 1$ or $\frac{4}{5}$
21. $x = \frac{1}{12}$ or $\frac{1}{2}$ **22.** $x = -2$ or -1 **23.** $x = -\frac{5}{6}$ or -2 **24.** $x = 11$ or -12
25. $x = 7$ or $\frac{1}{2}$ **26.** $x = -\frac{5}{2}$ or -17 **27.** $x = \frac{1}{12}$ or 0 **28.** $x = 4$ or $-\frac{3}{5}$
29. $x = \pm 8$ **30.** $x = \frac{5}{16}$ or $-\frac{1}{10}$ **31.** $x = \frac{5}{2}$ or 0 **32.** $x = 7$ or 0
33. $x = -3$ **34.** $x = -\frac{1}{2}$ or $\frac{2}{15}$

Exercise 7.3

1. $x = -0.6$ or -3.4 **2.** $x = -0.7$ or -8.3 **3.** $x = -0.11$ or -4.39
4. $x = 8.35$ or -3.35 **5.** $x = 1.21$ or -0.41 **6.** $x = -0.3$ or -1.2
7. $x = 4.22$ or -2.72 **8.** $x = -\frac{1}{3}$ or -0.333 **9.** $x = 1.4$ or -1.1
10. $x = 1.6$ or -0.7 **11.** $x = 1.55$ or -3.22 **12.** $x = 2.2$ or -1.0
13. $x = -3 \pm \sqrt{5}$ **14.** $x = 4 \pm \sqrt{7}$ **15.** $x = \frac{-1 \pm 3\sqrt{14}}{5}$
16. $x = 2.25$ or -1.92 **17.** $b = 0.9$ or -2.3 **18.** $x = \frac{5 \pm 2\sqrt{5}}{15}$
19. $x = \frac{-2 \pm \sqrt{10}}{4}$ **20.** $\frac{-2 \pm 4\sqrt{2}}{7}$ **21.** $x = 1.70$ or -1.30
22. $x = 2.1$ or -2.6 **23.** $x = 0.271$ or -0.396 **24.** $\frac{x = -2 \pm \sqrt{19}}{5}$
25. $x = \frac{-1 \pm \sqrt{141}}{5}$ **26.** $x = \frac{-2 \pm 3\sqrt{2}}{7}$ **27.** $x = 1.106$ or -1.356
28. $x = \pm 0.9428$ **29.** $x = \frac{-3 \pm \sqrt{39}}{3}$ **30.** $x = 1.15$ or 0.72

Exercise 7.4

1. $x = 1$ **2.** $x = 1$ **3.** $x = \frac{2}{3}$ or 1 **4.** $x = 4$ or -2 **5.** $x = -\frac{15}{7}$ or 2
6. $x = -3$ or 2 **7.** $x = -\frac{1}{2}$ or 2 **8.** $x = 1$ or $\frac{7}{3}$ **9.** $x = 0$ or $\frac{1}{2}$
10. $x = -\frac{21}{11}$ or 2 **11.** $x = \frac{26}{15}$ or $\frac{1}{2}$ **12.** $x = 1.62$ or 0.25
13. $x = -2.29$ or -3.71 **14.** $x = 6.70$ or 0.30 **15.** $x \approx 0.94$ or 0.26
16. $x = 16.08$ or -2.58

Exercise 7.5

1. $x^2 - 7x + 12 = 0$ **2.** $x^2 - 7x + 10 = 0$ **3.** $x^2 - x - 2 = 0$
4. $x^2 + 6x + 9 = 0$ **5.** $x^2 - 10x - 11 = 0$ **6.** $x^2 - 7x = 0$
7. $x^2 - 64 = 0$ **8.** $x^2 + 4x = 0$ **9.** $x^2 - 9 = 0$ **10.** $x^2 - 3px + 2p^2 = 0$
11. $x^2 - (p + q)x + pq = 0$ **12.** $x^2 - p^2 = 0$ **13.** $b = 18, c = 15$
14. $b = 6, c = 0$ **15.** $r = 16$ **16.** $c = 36$

Exercise 7.6

1. $(4,1)$ or $(1,4)$ **2.** $(-3,-4)$ or $(4,3)$ **3.** $(0,4)$ or $(4,0)$ **4.** $(5,-1)$ or $(1,-5)$
5. $(-16,14)$ **6.** $\left(-\frac{3}{5}, \frac{3}{5}\right)$ or $(-1,-1)$ **7.** $(1,1)$ or $(-1,-1)$ **8.** $(-2,3)$ or $(-3,-2)$
9. $(1,3)$ or $(-3,1)$ **10.** $(5,1)$ or $(1,3)$ **11.** $(7,6)$ or $(-9,-2)$ **12.** $(0,-4)$ or $(5,1)$
13. $(-7,-7)$ or $(5,5)$ **14.** $(2,-2)$ or $(-1,-5)$ **15.** $(-9,-5)$ or $(3,1)$
16. $(3,4)$ or $(4,3)$ **17.** $\left(4,\frac{7}{2}\right)$ or $(7,2)$ **18.** $\left(-4,-\frac{3}{2}\right)$ or $(5,3)$
19. $(2,-4)$ or $(-2,4)$ **20.** $(-9,-21)$ or $(6,9)$

Exercise 7.7

1. (i) $x = -1$ or -4 (ii) $x = 4$ or 8 (iii) $x = -3$ or 4 **2.** (i) $x = -1$
(ii) $x = -3$ (iii) $x = -3$ or -5 (iv) $x = -5$ **3.** 3.7

Exercise 7.8

1. (i) $x = -2$ or 3 (ii) $x = -2.7$ or -2 (iii) $x = -5$ or -1.5
(iv) $x = -0.5$ or 4.5 (v) $x = -3$ **2.** (i) $(-1,-2)$ and $(1,2)$
(ii) $(-1.5,-2.5)$ and $(2.5,1.5)$ (iii) $(-4,3)$ and $(4,-3)$
(iv) $(-1.2,0.3)$ and $(1.6,5.7)$ **3.** (i) Blue = C, Red = B, Green = A
(ii) $x = \pm 3$; $x = -3$ or 2; $x = -7$ or 3 **5.** $x = -1$ or 4 **6.** $x \approx 1.3$ or 4.7
7. $x = -2$ or 1.5 **8.** (i) The curve does not cut the x-axis.
(ii) The equation has no real roots.   **9.** (i) $x = -1$ or 4 (ii) $x = 2$

Exercise 7.9

1. $x = -6$ or 3 **2.** $x = -\frac{14}{5}$ or 2 **3.** $(7,4)$ and $(-4,-7)$ **4.** $7,8$
5. 13 m, 18 m   **6.** $x = 56$ **7.** $x = \frac{7}{2}$ or -1 **8.** 98 m, 34 m or 68 m, 49 m
9. 12   **10.** 21, 23   **11.** 1 m   **12.** $-1, 0, 1$ or $1, 2, 3$
13. Length: 13 m; breadth: 17 m   **14.** 3, 5, 7   **15.** 5 cm
16. Girl: 6, father: 36   **17.** Amy: 19, Bridget: 14, Caroline: 38
18. 5, 12, 13   **19.** 110 cm³   **20.** (i) Time A to B: $\frac{10}{x}$ hrs, B to C:
$\frac{12}{x-1}$ hrs   (ii) $x = 5$ **21.** (ii) 8   **22.** $x = 2$ **23.** $n = 10$ **24.** (i) 1st part:
4 km/hr; 2nd part: 6 km/hr   (ii) 2 hrs 30 mins   **25.** Mon: 8 km/hr,
Tue: 6 km/hr   **26.** Ann: 10 km/hr, Ben: 9 km/hr   **27.** $x = 2, y = 9$
28. Length: 0.7 m, width: 0.5 m   **29.** 4, 5   **30.** Length: 10 m,
width: 6 m   **31.** (i) 0%   (ii) $\approx$43% increase   **32.** (i) 130 km
(ii) 3 hours   **33.** (i) $(2,-5)$ or $(-5,2)$ (ii) 2 km east, 5 km west, 5 km
south, 2 km north   (iii) $\sqrt{29}$ km (each)

Revision Exercises

1. (a) (i) $x = -2$ or 4 (ii) $x = 2$ or 10 (iii) $x = -3$ or 2 (iv) $x = \pm 10$
(v) $x = -4$ or $\frac{3}{2}$ (vi) $x = \pm\frac{10}{7}$ (b) (i) -3 or -5 (ii) -2 or -5 (iii) -2
(c) (i) 5, 6   (ii) $x = -4$ or 7   (iii) $(7,4)$ or $(-4,-7)$ **2.** (a) (i) $x = -1$ or 6
(ii) $x = -\frac{5}{2}$ or $-\frac{4}{3}$ (iii) $x = -4$ or $\frac{1}{2}$ (iv) $x = -\frac{7}{5}$ or $\frac{3}{2}$ (b) (i) $x = \pm 2$
(ii) $x = -2$ or 4   (iii) $x = -2$ or ≈ 0.3 (c) (i) $(-2,-3)$ or $(2,3)$
(ii) $(-4,-2)$ or $(2,4)$ (iii) $(1,2)$ or $(2,1)$ (iv) $(2,-2)$ or $(-1,-5)$
3. (a) (i) $x = 1.45$ or -3.45 (ii) $x = 11.57$ or 0.43 (iii) $x = 2.70$ or -3.70
(iv) $x = 6.22$ or -3.22 (v) $x = 0.37$ or -1.37 (b) (i) $x = -1.3$ or 2.3
(ii) $x = -1.4$ or 0.7 (iii) $x = -1.2$ or 2.2 (c) (i) $x = -2$ or 7   (ii) $x = 2$ or 5
4. (a) (i) $x^2 - 8x + 12 = 0$ (ii) $x^2 - 6x + 5 = 0$ (iii) $x^2 - 9x - 22 = 0$
(iv) $x^2 + 6x - 40 = 0$ (v) $x^2 + 12x + 35 = 0$ (b) (i) $x \pm 5$ (ii) $x = 0$ or 2
(iii) $x = \frac{2}{3}$ or $-\frac{3}{4}$ (iv) $x = \frac{2}{3}$ (v) $x = 8$ or -2 (vi) $x = \frac{7}{5}$ or -6
(c) (i) $(-5,-8)$ or $(4,1)$ (ii) $(2,1)$ or $(-2,-1)$ (iii) $(1,0)$ or $(0,1)$
5. (a) (i) $x = \frac{3 \pm \sqrt{5}}{2}$ (ii) $x = \frac{6 \pm \sqrt{34}}{2}$ (iii) $x = \frac{6 \pm \sqrt{15}}{3}$ (iv) $\frac{7 \pm \sqrt{29}}{5}$
(v) $\frac{-2 \pm 3\sqrt{2}}{7}$ (b) (i) 7, 8   (ii) 6, 8   **6.** (a) (i) $x = 8$ or -7 (ii) $x = \frac{2}{5}$ or 1
(iii) $x = \frac{3}{2}$ or 5   (b) $x = -6$ or 3   (c) $x = \frac{1}{5}$ or 3   **7.** (a) (i) $x = 0.5$ or 3
(iii) $x = 0$ or 3.5 (b) (i) $p = 8$ or $q = 16$ (ii) $b = -20$ or $c = 100$
(iii) $k = 25$ (c) Length: 5 m, width: 6 m   **8.** (a) (i) $x = \pm 3$
(ii) $x = 0$ or 6   (iii) $x \approx -2.5$ or 4   (b) A → S, B → P,
C → R, D → Q   (c) (i) $\left(-\frac{3}{2},-10\right)$ or $(5,3)$ (ii) $\left(-4,-\frac{3}{2}\right)$ or $(5,3)$
(iii) $\left(\frac{1}{5},\frac{7}{5}\right)$ or $(1,1)$ **9.** (a) $x = \frac{2}{5}$ or $\frac{5}{2}$ (b) $x = 3$ (c) $x = 16$
10. (b) (i) $(-3,-4)$ and $(3,4)$ (ii) $(-5,-1)$ and $(5,1)$
(c) (iii) $x = -0.55$ or -5.45 **11.** (a) (i) $t = 4$ seconds   (b) $x = 13\frac{2}{3}$,
$y = 13\frac{1}{3}$ **12.** (c) $\approx$69.5 km   (d) After 26 seconds   (f) $t = 180$
(g) 1.1 km/s

Chapter 8

Exercise 8.1

1. (a) All except (c) represent functions.   **2.** (a), (b) and (d) are
functions.   **3.** (i) 10   (ii) 2   (iii) 6   (iv) 0   (v) 14   (vi) 13
4. (i) 1   (ii) 21   (iii) 1   (iv) 37   (v) 9   (vi) $-1\frac{1}{2}$ **5.** (i) 2   (ii) $\frac{1}{3}$
(iii) $-\frac{2}{3}$ (iv) 3   (v) $\frac{5}{6}$ (vi) $\frac{2}{3}$ **6.** (i) 3   (ii) 1   (iii) $\frac{5}{2}$ (iv) $\frac{1}{3}$

7. 8 **8.** 4 **9.** (i) $-\frac{1}{2}$ (ii) $-\frac{1}{2}$ (iii) $\frac{2}{11}$ (iv) $\frac{2x-1}{4x^2+2}$ (v) $\frac{x-x^2}{1+2x^2}$
(vi) $\frac{x+h-1}{x^2+2hx+h^2+2}$ **10.** B = {3, 7, 11, 15, 19, 23}
11. (i) Range = {1, 4, 9, 25, 36} (ii) Range: {4, 9, 25, 49, 121}
(iii) Range: {0, 1, 4, 9, 16} **12.** Domain: (i) {0, 1, 2, 3}
(ii) {2, 5, 7, 9} (iii) {−3, 3, 4} (iv) {1, 2, 4, 6}
Codomain: (i) {0, 3, 4, 6, 9} (ii) {4, 6, 7, 8, 11} (iii) {5, 8, 13, 20}
(iv) {5, 6, 7, 8, 11, 15, 19} Range: (i) {0, 3, 6, 9} (ii) {4, 7, 11}
(iii) {13, 20} (iv) {5, 6, 7, 8} **13.** (i) Yes; each input is mapped
to a unique output. (ii) Domain: {1, 2, 3, 4}
Range: {8, 9, 10, 11} (iii) $x \to x + 7$ (iv) 70
14. Range: {3, 4, 5, 6, 8} **15.** Possible domain: {snow, blackbird,
blood} **16.** (i) $f : x \to \frac{x}{2} + 3$ (ii) $f(4) = 5$; $f(18) = 12$; $f(-6) = 0$
(iii) $x = 12$ **18.** $f(4) = 19$ (ii) $g(4) = 12$ (iv) $k = 5$
19. $a = 3, b = 2$ **20.** $a = -\frac{5}{2}, b = \frac{17}{2}$ **21.** $a = 2, b = 3$
22. (i) $h(x) = 4x$ (iii) 80 (gold); 100 (total) **23.** (i) $y = f(x) = 200 - x^2$
(ii) $10\sqrt{2}$ minutes (iii) After 10 minutes

Exercise 8.2

1. (i) 0 (ii) 18 (iii) 32 (iv) 72 (v) 2 (vi) 8 (vii) 18 (viii) 72
2. (i) 6 (ii) 24 (iii) 38 (iv) 78 (v) 8 (vi) 14 (vii) 24 (viii) 78
3. (i) 5 (ii) 1 (iii) 37 (iv) 2 (v) 10 (vi) 17 (vii) $\frac{41}{16}$ (viii) $\frac{5}{4}$
4. (a) (i) $h = a \circ b$ where $b(x) = x^2$ and $a(x) = x + 1$ (ii) $f = a \circ b$
where $b(x) = x^2$ and $a(x) = 2x$ (b) (i) $g = a \circ b \circ c$ where $c(x) = x^2$,
$b(x) = 3x$ and $a(x) = x - 5$ (ii) $j = a \circ b \circ c$ where $c(x) = 4x$,
$b(x) = x - 3$ and $a(x) = x^2$ **5.** (i) (a) $f(x) = x^2 + 6$ (b) $f = a \circ b$ where
$b(x) = x^2$ and $a(x) = x + 6$ (ii) (a) $f(x) = 6(x - 2)^2$ (b) $f = a \circ b \circ c$
where $c(x) = x - 2$, $b(x) = x^2$ and $a(x) = 6x$ (iii) (a) $f(x) = (\sqrt{x} + 4)^3$
(b) $f = a \circ b \circ c$ where $c(x) = x^{\frac{1}{2}}$, $b(x) = x + 4$ and $a(x) = x^3$
(iv) (a) $f(x) = \frac{1}{4}(\sin^2(x))$ (b) $f = a \circ b \circ c$ where $c(x) = \sin x$, $b(x) = x^2$
and $a(x) = \frac{x}{4}$ **6.** (i) $h(x) = x + 3$ (ii) $h(x) = x - 6$ (iii) $h(x) = x^2$
(iv) $h(x) = x - 5$ **7.** (i) $3x^2 + 8$ (ii) $9x^2 + 12x + 6$ **8.** (i) 240 (ii) 38
9. (i) $16x + 15$ (ii) −17 **10.** (a) (i) 1 (ii) 4 (iii) 8 (iv) 1 (v) $\frac{4}{5}$
(b) (i) $\frac{4}{2^x}$ (ii) x (iii) $2^x + 1$ (iv) 2^{x+1} (c) $x = 3$ (d) $x = 3$

Revision Exercises

1. All except (c) and (e) are functions. **2.** (i) and (ii) are functions.
3. (i) Domain: {1, 2, 4, 8} (ii) Range: {2, 4, 8, 16} **4.** (i) $y = 5x$
(ii) Domain: {0, 1, 2, 3, ..., 14, 15} (iii) €65 **5.** (i) 2 (ii) 26
(iii) 6 (iv) 46 (v) 32 **6.** (i) 3 (ii) 0 (iii) $k \pm 2$ (iv) $p = 15$ **7.** 3
8. 3 **9.** (i) Range: {0, 3, 8, 24, 35} (ii) Range: {3, 8, 24, 48, 120}
(iii) Range: {−1, 0, 3, 8, 15} **10.** (i) 5 (ii) $x = 3$ or −2
11. (i) $y = \frac{x}{30} + 15$ (ii) 5 hours 15 minutes **12.** $a = -6, b = 11$
13. $a = 6, b = 8$ **14.** $a = -1, b = 8$ **15.** $a = 1, b = -10$
16. (i) 275 m (ii) 55 m/s (iii) 4 and 12 seconds **17.** (i) 4 (ii) 31
(iii) 52 (iv) 112 (v) 7 (vi) 16 (vii) 31 (viii) 112
18. $f(x) = x^3 + 15$; $f = h \circ g$ where $g(x) = x^3$ and $h(x) = x + 15$
19. $f(x) = \frac{(x-4)^2}{2}$; $f = h \circ g$ where $g(x) = x - 4$ and $h(x) = \frac{x^2}{2}$
20. $f(x) = (\sqrt{x} + 3)^3$; $f = j \circ h \circ g$ where $g(x) = \sqrt{x}$, $h(x) = x + 3$ and
$j(x) = x^3$ **21.** $f(x) = \frac{\sin^2(x)}{3}$; $f = j \circ h \circ g$ where $g(x) = \sin x$, $h(x) = x^2$
and $j(x) = \frac{x}{3}$ **22.** (i) $f(x) = x - 50$ (ii) $g(x) = 0.85x$

Chapter 9

Exercise 9.1

3. (i) 2.9 (ii) $-\frac{5}{3}$ **4.** (i) 7 (ii) $\frac{9}{4}$ (iii) −1 (iv) $x \geqslant 1$
5. Point of intersection: $\left(\frac{5}{3}, \frac{4}{3}\right)$ **6.** (i) 8.1 m/s (ii) $\frac{5}{3}$ seconds
(iii) 15 m/s (iv) 5 seconds **7.** (ii) 120 km (iii) $87\frac{1}{2}$ miles
(iv) [104 km, 120 km] **8.** (iii) Total costs = 5x + 45,000 (in euro)
(v) Sales revenue = 6x (in euro) (vii) 45,000 units

Exercise 9.2

3. (iii) 9 m (iv) 0.35 m or 5.65 m **4.** (i) −4.5 (ii) −1.45 or 3.45
(iii) $-1.45 \leqslant x \leqslant 3.45$ (iv) 6 **5.** (i) −9.75 (ii) −6.5 or 0.5
(iii) −6.75 or 0.75 (iv) −7.15 or 1.15 (v) −12 **6.** (ii) 0.25 seconds
or 4.15 seconds (iii) First ball: 31.25 m, second ball: 20 m
(iv) First ball: 2.5 seconds, second ball: 5 seconds (v) 3.9 seconds
7. (i) 6 (ii) $\frac{2}{3}$ (iii) 1 **8.** (i) 16 (ii) 0.6 or 6.9 (iii) $0.6 \leqslant x \leqslant 6.9$
(iv) $0 \leqslant x \leqslant 0.6$ or $6.9 \leqslant x \leqslant 8$ **9.** (i) −2 (ii) −1.3 or 2.8
(iii) −0.7 or 2.2 **10.** (iii) 16 m² **11.** (i) 5.75 (ii) −3 or 1 (iii) 6
(iv) $2 \leqslant k \leqslant 6$ **12.** (i) −2 or 1.5 (ii) −2.7 or 2.2 (iii) $-3 \leqslant x \leqslant -2$ or
$1.5 \leqslant x \leqslant 3$ **13.** (i) −2.6 or 0.6 (ii) $-3 \leqslant x \leqslant -2.6$ or
$0.6 \leqslant x \leqslant 2$ **14.** (ii) 2 seconds or 4 seconds (iv) 0.2 seconds
(v) 1.3 m **15.** (ii) 500 units (iii) €2,500 (iv) 400 units or 600 units
(v) It is more lucrative to produce 725 units; with 725 units, monthly
pay ≈ €2,000, whereas with 250 units, monthly pay ≈ €1,875.

Exercise 9.3

2. (i) −2, −0.5 or 2 (ii) −1.65, −1 or 2.15 **3.** (i) −1, 0 or 3 (ii) −1.5,
0.8 or 2.7 (iii) $-0.5 < x < 1.85$ **4.** (i) $\frac{2}{3}$ (ii) −2.8, −1.45 or 0.25
5. (i) −3, −1 or 1 (ii) $x < -3$ or $0.15 < x < 1$ (iii) 1.45 **6.** (i) 0 or $\frac{2}{3}$
(ii) −1 **7.** (i) 12,000 units (ii) 0.65 years (iii) 0 years and 2 years
(iv) 30,000 units **8.** $f(x) = g(x)$ at −1.4, −0.3 or 2.65 **9.** (i) 2
(ii) 2.2 **10.** (i) 4.9 (ii) −4.5 or 0.6 (iii) −0.4, 1.15 or 1.45
11. (i) 30°C (ii) 1 minute and 4 minutes (iii) [0.7 mins, 1.3 mins]
or [3.95 mins, 4 mins] (iv) 13°C **12.** (i) 1.85 years
(ii) 0.4 years or 3.8 years

Exercise 9.4

14. $a = 6, b = 2$ **15.** $a = 3, b = 2$ **16.** $a = 2.5, b = 2$
17. $a = 4, b = \frac{1}{2}$ **18.** $a = 2, b = \frac{1}{3}$ **19.** (i) 1 hour: 20 cm³;
2 hours: 40 cm³; 3 hours: 80 cm³; 4 hours: 160 cm³ (iii) 57 cm³
(iv) 3.3 hours **20.** (iii) $F = 60,000(0.8)^t$ **21.** (i) Base = (1 − i);
exponent = t (iv) €3,850 (v) €3,842.17

Exercise 9.6

8. (i) Shift four units to the left and three units downwards.
(ii) $(x + 4)^3 - 3$ **9.** x^3 **10.** $(x - 2)^3 - 6$

Exercise 9.7

6. (i) Shift two units to the left. (ii) 2^{x-2} **7.** 3^{x-3} **8.** $3(4^{x-3})$
9. $2^{x+2} + 3$

Revision Exercises

2. (i) 5.5 (ii) $\frac{8}{3}$ (iii) $-\frac{2}{3}$ (iv) $x \geqslant \frac{2}{3}$ **3.** Point of intersection: (3.2,1.6)
4. (ii) 12 (iii) €70 (iv) €35 or more **5.** (i) −5.75 (ii) −1.2
(iii) $-1 \leqslant x \leqslant 4$ (iv) −6.25 **6.** (i) 8.25 (ii) −4 or 1 (iii) 8.25
(iv) $-4 \leqslant k < 8.25$ **7.** (i) −1 or 1 (ii) $x \leqslant -1$ or $x \geqslant 1$
(iii) $-1 < x < 1$ **8.** $a = -1, b = -2, c = 4$ **10.** (i) $\frac{2}{3}$ (ii) −2, −1 or 0
(iii) One real root **11.** (i) 2.35 **12.** (i) −0.75 or 0.4 (ii) −0.5 or 0.8
14. $2(3^x)$ **15.** (i) 2.75 (ii) 3 (iii) −0.85, 1.3, 3.6 **17.** $a = 6$
18. $a = 2, b = -\frac{1}{4}$ **19.** (iii) Exponential (iv) Yes. It could have followed
a quadratic pattern. **21.** (i) Year 1: €448, Year 2: €501.76,
Year 3: €561.97, Year 4: €629.41, Year 5: €704.94 (iii) Base = (1 + i);
exponent = t (iv) €580 **22.** (i) €100,000 (iii) Roughly 0.5 years
(6 months) (iv) No **23.** (b) 0.25 or 2.15 (c) $g(k) = 2.25$

Chapter 10

Exercise 10.1

1. (i) 1:2 (ii) 4:3 (iii) 3:5 (iv) 1:2:3 (v) 3:7:12 (vi) 2:3 (vii) 1:3
(viii) 2:1:8 (ix) 4:6:3 (x) 1:1:1 **2.** (i) 350 g, 100 g (ii) €84, €48
(iii) 117 cm, 52 cm (iv) €1,800, €2,700 (v) 96 kg, 60 kg
(vi) 15 m, 30 m, 45 m (vii) 600 g, 120 g, 120 g (viii) €350, €400, €150
(ix) 136 g, 17 g, 68 g (x) 138 cm, 230 cm, 184 cm **3.** (i) 300 g, 150 g
(ii) €60, €90 (iii) 33 mm, 99 mm (iv) 800 g, 400 g, 3,200 g
(v) 48 kg, 72 kg, 36 kg (vi) 300 m, 300 m, 300 m
(vii) 111 g, 185 g, 148 g (viii) €600, €675, €150 (ix) 111 g, 74 g, 37 g
(x) 140 cm, 560 cm **4.** 50 ml **5.** Volleyball: €1,840, Soccer: €2,960
6. €9.40, €8.30, €6.30 **7.** (i) €1,200 (ii) 30 cm (iii) €765 (iv) 270 g
(v) 240 cm, 600 cm (vi) €150 (vii) B: 70 sweets, C: 50 sweets
8. $k = 5$ **9.** 256 pages **10.** The first option is better for Niamh.

Exercise 10.2

1. (i) Error: 1; Rel. error: $\frac{1}{150}$; % error: 0.67% (ii) Error: 0.9;
Rel. error: $\frac{1}{40}$; % error: 2.5% (iii) Error: 3; Rel. error: $\frac{1}{60}$;
% error: 1.67% (iv) Error: 0.2; Rel. error: $\frac{1}{24}$; % error: 4.17%
(v) Error: 0.3; Rel. error: $\frac{3}{67}$; % error: 4.48% (vi) Error: 0.85;
Rel. error: $\frac{17}{1,083}$; % error: 1.57% (vii) Error: 0.14; Rel. error: $\frac{7}{68}$;
% error: 10.29% (viii) Error: 2; Rel. error: $\frac{1}{251}$; % error: 0.40%
(iv) Error: 1; Rel. error: $\frac{1}{360}$; % error: 0.28% (x) Error: 1.4;
Rel. error: $\frac{7}{293}$; % error: 2.39% **2.** 1.08% **3.** 1.29% **4.** 1% **5.** 2.6%
6. (i) 0.0394 (ii) ≈ 0.8% **7.** (i) 0.05 (ii) ≈0.5% **8.** (i) €6,554
(ii) €6,555.60 (iii) €1.60 **9.** (i) 320 ± 2.5 g (ii) 640 ± 0.25 cm
(iii) 180 ± 0.05 cm (iv) 196 ± 0.25 cm (v) 3,400 ± 50 g
(vi) 5,300 ± 0.125 kg (vii) 14 cm ± 0.05 mm (viii) 25,000 ± 0.1 g
10. It will pass quality control. **11.** 2.2 ± 0.05 **12.** 54 ± 0.05 cm
13. (i) 450 ± 2.5 g (ii) Yes, since 453 g > 452.5 g, the upper limit.

Exercise 10.3

1. (i) $15\frac{3}{7}$ km/hr (ii) 100 km/hr (iii) 237.5 km (iv) 729 km
2. $6\frac{74}{75}$ miles per hour **3.** ≈ 28 km/hr **4.** (i) Arrival time: 14:55
(ii) Departure time: 09:30 (iii) Arrival time: 14.30
(iv) Arrival time: 09:08 **5.** (i) 68 km/hr (ii) ≈2 hrs 26 mins
(iii) 3 hrs 41 mins **6.** (i) ≈ 83 km/hr (ii) 80 litres (iii) €97.85
7. €2,000 **8.** €3 per month **9.** €241,200 **10.** (i) $59.50 (ii) No
11. John's story is more believable.

Exercise 10.4

1. (i) 160 km (ii) Between 10:00 and 10:30 (iii) 35.$\dot{5}$ km/hr
(iv) Between 12:00 and 12:30 (v) The final 40 km (highest average
speed recorded here) **2.** (i) Day 1 (ii) €4 (iii) Day 8 (iv) Days 3, 6, 9
(v) Not really (period of analysis too short) **4.** 1 → D, 2 → C, 3 → E,
4 → B, 5 → A **5.** (i) Day 8 (ii) Day 4 (iii) Day 6
(iv) No (productivity dropped by Day 9)

Exercise 10.5

1. A:1,508, B: 14.52, C: 212.63, D: 227.25, E: 30.68, F: 257.93
2. (i) Bill 1: €69, Bill 2: €1,451, Bill 3: €658, Bill 4: €633
(ii) Bill 1: €8.28, Bill 2: €174.12, Bill 3: €78.96, Bill 4: €75.96
(iii) Bill 1: €23.02, Bill 2: €211.25, Bill 3: €103.24, Bill 4: €99.83
3. Bill 1: €94.80, Bill 2: €107.64, Bill 3: €106.92, Bill 4: €118.20
4. (i) €9 (ii) €69 (iii) €83.49 **5.** (i) €283.12 (ii) €3.12 (iii) €26.88
(iv) €24.79 **6.** (i) €(25 + 7.5x) (iii) €70 (iv) €85 **7.** 181 minutes
8. (i) 250 messages (ii) 150 minutes (iii) Both networks cost the
same for this usage. **9.** (i) 1,162 units (ii) ≈ 12,765 kWh

(iii) €382.95 (iv) €434.65 **10.** (i) €3,313.80 (ii) €3,761.16
11. (i) 850 units (ii) €121.55 (iii) 13%

Exercise 10.6

2. (i) €67,500 (ii) €6.75 **3.** (i) 150 quiches (ii) €349 (iii) €2.60
(iv) €3.50 **4.** (i) 48,000 kg (ii) 45,000 kg (iii) €279,000
(iv) €305,000 **5.** (i) 40 m (ii) 120 m (iii) €1,540 (iv) €29.52
6. (i) 58,500 kg (ii) 55,500 kg (iii) 78,000 hours (iv) €858,000
(v) €1,778,000 (vi) €397,000 (vii) €179,500

Exercise 10.7

1. (i) $301.50 (ii) €234 **2.** (i) $356.44 (ii) €855.26
3. The Dublin O$_2$ tickets are more expensive. **4.** (i) $828.80
(ii) ¥99,314 (iii) £356 (iv) €574.48 (v) €71.96 (vi) Get ¥432,308
5. (a) (i) £738 (ii) €903.75 (iii) 0.41$\dot{6}$% (b) (i) €54 (ii) The bureau
de change is better for Alison. **6.** €240 **7.** It's cheaper in North
America. **8.** (i) €19.99 (ii) 2.5% **9.** €646.83

Exercise 10.8

1. 6 inches = 15.24 cm; 4.5 feet = 1.37 m; 5 miles = 8.05 km;
13 inches = 330.2 mm; 6 pints = 3.41 litres; 5 ounces = 141.75 g;
6 lbs = 2.72 kg; 3.5 tons = 3,048.15 kg; 22 yards = 20.12 m;
2.25 feet = 0.69 m **2.** 1,814.4 g **3.** (i) 22.05 km (ii) 13.70 miles
4. 10,200 kg of bricks is heavier. **5.** 7 m **6.** Store B is cheaper.

Revision Exercises

1. 9.6 cm **2.** 204 g, 102 g, 408 g; 14.39 ounces **3.** €975
4. 9 years old **5.** (i) 0.7666 (ii) 4.4% **6.** (i) €2,816 (ii) €2,816.06
(iii) €0.06 **7.** 26 ± 0.5 g **8.** (i) 477 ± 2.5 g (ii) Yes **9.** (i) €25 per year
(ii) €125 **10.** (i) 552 km/hr (ii) 285.84 miles **11.** (i) 306 units
(ii) ≈3,477 kWh (iii) €121.69 (iv) €138.12 **12.** 1,730 litres
13. (i) €769.50 (ii) €30.19 (iii) €179.07 (iv) €853.82
14. (i) 145,000 kg (ii) 95,000 kg (iii) 80,000 hours (iv) €600,000
(v) €1,449,000 (vi) €776,000 (vii) €553,500

Chapter 11

Exercise 11.1

1. (i) 10i (ii) 9i (iii) 5i (iv) 6i (v) 11i (vi) 7i (vii) 8i (viii) 13i
(ix) 12i (x) 4i **2.** $\sqrt{17}i$ (ii) $\sqrt{31}i$ (iii) $\sqrt{14}i$ (iv) $\sqrt{19}i$ (v) $\sqrt{21}i$
(vi) $\sqrt{23}i$ (vii) $\sqrt{29}i$ (viii) $\sqrt{43}i$ (ix) $\sqrt{5}i$ (x) $\sqrt{3}i$ **3.** (i) $2\sqrt{2}i$
(ii) $7\sqrt{2}i$ (iii) $3\sqrt{5}i$ (iv) $10\sqrt{3}i$ (v) $2\sqrt{3}i$ (vi) $4\sqrt{2}i$ (vii) $10\sqrt{5}i$
(viii) $3\sqrt{6}i$ (ix)$3\sqrt{3}i$ (x) $5\sqrt{5}i$ **4.** (i) $7\sqrt{2}i$ (ii) $\sqrt{3}i$ (iii) $7\sqrt{5}i$
(iv) $5\sqrt{11}i$ **5.** (i) ±3i (ii) ±2i (iii) ±5i (iv) ±6i (v) ±7i (vi) ±10i
6. (i) ±$\sqrt{7}i$ (ii) ±$\sqrt{11}i$ (iii) ±$\sqrt{15}i$ (iv) ±$\sqrt{17}i$ (v) ±$\sqrt{14}i$ (vi) ±$\sqrt{26}i$
7. (i) $-i$ (ii) -1 (iii) i (iv) 1 (v) i (vi) i **8.** (i) $-128i$ (ii) $-27i$
(iii) 625 (iv) 1,024i (v) 256 (vi) $-125i$ **10.** (i) $\frac{1}{8}$ (ii) $\frac{3}{8}$

Exercise 11.2

5. (i) Real (ii) Imaginary (iii) Imaginary (iv) Real (v) Imaginary
(vi) Real (vii) Real (as $i^2 = -i$) (viii) Imaginary (as $i^3 = -i$)
(ix) Real (as $i^4 = 1$) (x) Real (as $(2i)^4 = 16$) **6.** (i) 3 + 2i (ii) 5 + 7i
(iii) $-4 + 3i$ (iv) 8 − 5i (v) 10 − 6i (vi) $-2 + i$ **7.** (i) 1 − 12i
(ii) $-4 - i$ (iii) 7 − 9i (iv) $\frac{1}{2} + \frac{1}{4}i$ (v) $\frac{3}{2} + \frac{1}{5}i$ **8.** (i) $\frac{1}{2}, -\frac{3}{2}$
(ii) $\sqrt{2}, -3$ (iii) $\frac{22}{7}, -3.14$ (iv) 3, $-\frac{1}{\sqrt{3}}$ (v) $-\frac{5}{6}, 3$ (vi) 4, 0

Exercise 11.3

1. (i) $9 + 6i$ (ii) $5 + 4i$ (iii) $25 + 17i$ (iv) $8 + 7i$ **2.** (i) $5 + 2i$
(ii) $1 - 6i$ (iii) $9 + 10i$ (iv) $-4 - 24i$ **3.** $0 + 7i$ (ii) $-4 + i$
(iii) $7 + 10i$ (iv) $3 + i$ **4.** (i) $5 + i$ (ii) $2 + 4i$ (iii) $-4 - 2i$
(iv) $14 + 7i$ (v) $7 - i$ **5.** (i) $5 - 3i$ (ii) 4 (iii) $-1 + 3i$ (iv) $1 - i$
6. (a) (i) $1 + i$ (ii) $2 + 2i$ (iii) $3 + 3i$ (iv) $4 + 4i$ (v) $5 + 5i$
(b) (ii) Dilation of factor 2 (iii) Dilation of factor 3
(iii) Dilation of factor 4 (iv) Dilation of factor 5 **7.** (a) (i) $-1 + i$
(ii) $-2 + 2i$ (iii) $-3 + 3i$ (iv) $-4 + 4i$ (v) $-5 + 5i$ (b) (ii) Dilation
of factor 2 (iii) Dilation of factor 3 (iii) Dilation of factor 4
(iv) Dilation of factor 5 **8.** (a) (i) $-24 + 48i$ (ii) $-12 + 24i$
(iii) $-8 + 16i$ (iv) $-6 + 12i$ (v) $-4 + 8i$ (b) (i) Dilation of factor $\frac{1}{2}$
(ii) Dilation of factor $\frac{1}{3}$ (iii) Dilation of factor $\frac{1}{4}$ (iv) Dilation of factor $\frac{1}{6}$
9. (ii) $z_1 + \omega, z_2 + \omega, z_3 + \omega$ (iv) All numbers are translated a
distance of $\sqrt{2}$ units in the direction north-east. **10.** (ii) $z_1 + \omega$,
$z_2 + \omega, z_3 + \omega$ (iv) All numbers are translated a distance of $\sqrt{2}$ units
in the direction south-east.

Exercise 11.4

1. (i) 17 (ii) 41 (iii) 5 **2.** (i) 61 (ii) 5 (iii) 37 (iv) 85 (v) 65
(vi) 10 **3.** (i) $\sqrt{5}$ (ii) $\sqrt{8} = 2\sqrt{2}$ (iii) $\sqrt{10}$ (iv) $\sqrt{2}$ (v) $\sqrt{109}$
(vi) $\sqrt{58}$ **4.** (i) $\sqrt{11}$ (ii) 3 (iii) $\sqrt{43}$ (iv) 4 (v) 5 (vi) $\sqrt{69}$
5. ± 5 **6.** ± 6 **7.** ± 3 **8.** ± 5

Exercise 11.5

1. (i) $-35 + 21i$ (ii) $1 + 3i$ (iii) $14 + 2i$ (iv) $3 + 15i$ (v) $14 - 7i$
(vi) $-8 - 2i$ **2.** (i) $41 + 11i$ (ii) $-18 + 13i$ (iii) $-15 + 16i$ (iv) 13
(v) 25 (vi) $10 + 4i$ **3.** (i) $-12 + 6i$ (ii) 2 (iii) $30 - 5i$ (iv) 8
(v) $9 + 17i$ (vi) $14 + 21i$ **4.** (i) $\frac{5}{8} + \frac{5}{8}i$ (ii) $\frac{2}{5}$ (iii) $\frac{293}{1760} - \frac{23}{220}i$
(iv) $\frac{1}{2}$ (v) $\frac{43}{150} + \frac{73}{180}i$ (vi) $-\frac{11}{105} - \frac{47}{105}i$ **5.** (i) 7 (ii) 88 (iii) $7 + \sqrt{6}i$
(iv) $15 + 7\sqrt{3}i$ (v) 27 **6.** (i) $-1 + 3i$ (iii) 90° anti-clockwise rotation
about the origin **7.** $-2 - 3i$ (iii) 90° anti-clockwise rotation about
the origin **8.** (i) $4 + 3i$ (iii) 90° clockwise rotation about the origin
9. (i) $126 - 32i$ (ii) 130 **10.** (i) $-497 + 1275i$ **11.** (i) $-3 + 2i$
(iii) 90° clockwise rotation about the origin **12.** (i) $i, -1.5 + i$,
$-3 + i, -1.5 + 2i, -3 + 2.5i$ (iii) 90° anti-clockwise rotation about
the origin **13.** (i) $-i, 2 - i, 4 - i, -2i, 2 - 2i, 4 - 2i$
(iii) 90° clockwise rotation about the origin **14.** (i) $-4 + 2i, -3 + 4i$,
$-4 + 6i, -2 + 4i$ (iii) Rotation 90° anti-clockwise about origin with
a dilation factor 2

Exercise 11.6

1. (i) $-5 + 10i$ (ii) $\text{Arg}(z_1) = 63.43°$ $\text{Arg}(z_2) = 53.13°$ (iv) 116.56°
2. $-8 + i$ (ii) $\text{Arg}(z_1) = 26.57°$, $\text{Arg}(z_2) = 146.31°$ (iv) 172.87°
3. $|z_1| = 3.606$ $|z_2| = 5.385$ (ii) $16 - 11i$ (iii) 19.42 (iv) ≈ 19.42
4. (i) $|z_1| \approx 3.606$ $|z_2| \approx 4.472$ (ii) $-2 - 16i$ (iii) 16.1 (iv) ≈ 16.1

Exercise 11.7

1. (i) $7 - 5i$ (ii) $2 - i$ (iii) 14 (iv) 4 **2.** (i) $5 - 2i$ (ii) $3 + 4i$
(iii) $8 + 2i$ (iv) $8 - 2i$ (v) $8 + 2i$ **3.** (i) $-1 - 2i$ (ii) $2 - 3i$ (iii) $1 - 5i$
(iv) $1 + 5i$ (v) $1 - 5i$ **4.** (i) $a - bi$ (ii) $c + di$ (iii) $(a + c) + (d - b)i$
(iv) $(a + c) + (b - d)i$ (v) $(a + c) + (d - b)i$ **5.** (i) $5 - 6i$ (ii) $3 + i$
(iii) $21 + 13i$ (iv) $21 - 13i$ (v) $21 - 13i$

Exercise 11.8

1. (i) $3 + \frac{3}{2}i$ (ii) $3 - 4i$ (iii) $6 + 3i$ (iv) $2 - i$ (v) $\frac{5}{7} + \frac{12}{7}i$
2. (i) $3 - i$ (ii) $3 - 2i$ (iii) $1 + 3i$ (iv) $1 - 2i$ (v) $2 + i$
3. (i) $1 - 3i$ (ii) $3 + 3i$ (iii) $5 - i$ (iv) $4 - 3i$ (v) $3 + 4i$

4. (i) $\frac{1}{2} - \frac{1}{2}i$ (ii) $\frac{7}{10} - \frac{1}{10}i$ (iii) $-\frac{3}{5} + \frac{11}{5}i$ (iv) $2 - \frac{1}{2}i$ (v) $-\frac{9}{2} - \frac{1}{2}i$

5. (i) $1 - 2i$ (ii) $-2 - 4i$ (iii) $-6 - 9i$ (iv) $-12 - 4i$ (v) $\frac{1}{5} - \frac{1}{5}i$

6. (i) $0 - 16i$ (ii) $0 - 5i$ (iii) $0 - \frac{25}{3}i$ (iv) $-\frac{17}{5}i$ (v) $-\frac{11}{4}i$

7. (i) $-\frac{4}{5} + \frac{3}{5}i$ **10.** (i) $2 - 3i$ (ii) $\sqrt{17}$

Exercise 11.9

1. $-2 \pm 3i$ **2.** (i) $-3 - 4i$ (ii) $-2 + 4i$ **4.** $4 \pm i$ **6.** (i) $48 - 14i$
(ii) $-98 + 14i$ **7.** $6 \pm 2i$ **8.** $-5 \pm 3i$ **9.** (i) $2 \pm i$ (ii) $4 \pm 3i$
(iii) $-1 \pm 4i$ (iv) $-2 \pm 6i$ **10.** (i) $\pm 4i$ (ii) $\frac{3}{2} \pm 2i$ (iii) $\frac{1}{3} \pm \frac{2}{3}i$ (iv) $4 \pm 3i$

Revision Exercises

1. (i) $7 - i$ (ii) $-1 + 3i$ (iii) $14 - 2i$ (iv) $4 + 2i$ (v) $\frac{1}{2} + \frac{1}{2}i$ (vi) $2\sqrt{5}$
2. (i) $2 - 3i$ (ii) $12 + 5i$ (iii) $-31 - 33i$ (iv) $-5 + 4i$ (v) $\frac{-39}{41} + \frac{23}{41}i$
(vi) $5\sqrt{82}$ **3.** (i) $-9 - 8i$ (ii) $\frac{31}{202} + \frac{7}{202}i$ (iii) $\sqrt{5}$ (iv) $\sqrt{202}$
(v) $\sqrt{\frac{5}{202}}$ (vi) $13 - 29i$ **4.** (i) $1309 - 588i$ (ii) $1309 + 588i$
(iii) $21 - 28i$ (iv) $9 + 40i$ (v) $1309 + 588i$ (vi) $45 + 164i$
5. (i) $800 + 3150i$ (ii) 3250 (iii) 50 (iv) 65 (v) 3250 (vi) $3 + 140i$
6. (i) $-\frac{204}{325} + \frac{253}{325}i$ (ii) $-\frac{204}{325} + \frac{253}{325}i$ (iii) 65 (iv) 65 (v) $-7 - 178i$
(vi) $-46 - 230i$ **7.** (ii) $3 + 0i, 4 - 2i, -1 - 5i$ (iii) Each number is
moved a distance of $\sqrt{2}$ units in the direction south-east.
8. (i) $-10 - 2i$ (ii) $1 + i$ (iii) $-1 - 2i$ **9.** $2 \pm i$ **10.** (i) i (ii) -1
(iii) $-i$ **12.** $z = 37 + 0i$ **13.** $z = 33 + 7i$ **14.** (a) (i) $2i, -2 + 2i$
(iv) The points rotate in an anti-clockwise direction. (b) $z^8 = 16$,
$z^{12} = -64, z^{16} = 256$ (c) Positive (d) 2^{20}

Chapter 12

Exercise 12.1

1. (ii) 0 **2.** (ii) 46 **3.** (i) 6 (ii) 6 (iii) 2 (iv) 6 (v) 12 (vi) 6 **4.** (i) 7
(ii) -1 (iii) 4 (iv) 3 (v) 125 **5.** (i) 9 (ii) 5 (iii) 20 (iv) -2 (v) 26
6. (ii) 6 **7.** (ii) -8 **8.** (ii) 6

Exercise 12.2

1. $3x^2$ (ii) $6x$ (iii) $6x^2$ (iv) -8 (v) -16 (vi) x **2.** (i) 2 (ii) $6t$
(iii) $15t^2$ (iv) t^2 (v) t (vi) -15 **3.** (i) x (ii) t^2 (iii) $2\pi r$ (iv) πr (v) 2π
(vi) $3x^2$ **4.** (i) $8x + 2$ (ii) $6x + 10$ (iii) $2x + 9$ (iv) $9x^2 + 8x - 3$
(v) $6x$ **5.** (i) 3 (ii) -2 (iii) 17 (iv) -15 (v) -1 (vi) $2x - 3$ **6.** (i) 0
(ii) 0 (iii) 0 (iv) 0 (v) 0 (vi) 0 **7.** (i) $3x^2 + 2x + 1$ (ii) $3x^2 - 1$
(iii) $3x^2 + 1$ (iv) $30x^2 + 22x$ (v) $27x^2 - 16x$ (vi) $3x^2 + 12x - 3$
8. (i) $3x^2 + 2x - 1$ (ii) $9x^2 + 4x - 1$ **9.** (i) $2x - 2$ (ii) 198
10. (i) $3x^2 - 2x$ (ii) 85 **11.** (i) $3x^2 - 6x + 2$ (ii) 11
12. (i) $6x^2 + 6x - 2$ (ii) -2 **13.** (i) $15x^2 - 4x - 12$ (ii) -12
14. (i) $x^2 + x - 12$ (ii) $2x + 1$ **15.** (i) $2x^2 + x - 6$ (ii) $4x + 1$

Exercise 12.3

1. (i) $2x$ (ii) 2 (iii) $y = 2x - 1$ **2.** (i) $2x + 2$ (ii) 2 (iii) $y = 2x + 1$
3. (i) $2x + 2$ (ii) -2 (iii) $y = -2x - 7$ **4.** (i) $3 - 2x$ (ii) -5
(iii) $y = -5x + 21$ **5.** (i) $2 - 4x$ (ii) -6 (iii) $y = -6x + 13$ (iv) $(0,13)$
6. (i) $3x^2 + 10x + 5$ (ii) 5 (iii) $y = 5x + 1$ (iv) x-axis: $\left(-\frac{1}{5},0\right)$;
y-axis: $(0,1)$ (v) 0.1 units² **7.** (i) $2 + 6x - 3x^2$ (ii) 2 (iii) $y = 2x + 1$
(iv) x-axis: $\left(-\frac{1}{2},0\right)$; y-axis: $(0,1)$ (v) $\frac{1}{4}$ units² **9.** $(3,2)$ **10.** $(4,19)$
11. (i) 5 (ii) $y = 8x - 16$ **12.** (i) 3 (ii) $y = 2x + 3$ **13.** (i) -1
(ii) $y = 6x + 4$

Exercise 12.4

1. (i) $-2 < x < 0$ (ii) $0 < x < 2$ **2.** (i) $0 < x < 2$ (ii) $-4 < x < 0$
3. (i) $x > 1$ (ii) $x < -2$ (iii) $x > 0$ (iv) $x > -\frac{3}{2}$ **4.** (i) $1 < x < 2$
(ii) $-4 < x < 4$ (iii) $-3 < x < 3$ (iv) $-2 < x < 2$ **5.** (i) $x < 0$ or $x > \frac{2}{3}$
(ii) $x < -1$ or $x > 1$ (iii) $x < -\frac{1}{\sqrt{3}}$ or $x > \frac{1}{\sqrt{3}}$ (iv) $-3 < x < \frac{1}{2}$

Exercise 12.5

1. (i) 24   (ii) 16   (iii) 18   (iv) $138x + 4$ (v) 66   **2.** (i) -16 (ii) 2
(iii) -18 (iv) -158 (v) 162   **3.** (i) 9.8   (ii) -9.8 (iii) $6t + 2$
(iv) $12t^2 - 2$ **4.** (i) $6x$ (ii) $6x - 6$ (iii) -8 (iv) 2π **5.** (i) $6t + 10$
(ii) $6t - 10$ (iii) $12t^2 - 8$ **6.** (i) $18x$ (ii) 36   **7.** (i) $6x$ (ii) 1

Exercise 12.6

1. (i) 2   (iii) (2,6)   **2.** (i) 3   (iii) (3,8)   **3.** (i) 4   (iii) (4,17)   **4.** (i) 5
(iii) (5,28)   **5.** (i) $x = \pm 2$ (iii) $A(-2,16)$; $B(2,-16)$ **6.** (i) $x = \pm 1$
(iii) $G(-1,3)$; $H(1,-1)$ **7.** Local minimum: $(3,-71)$; local maximum:
$(-2,54)$ **8.** Local minimum: $(-1,2)$; local maximum: $(5,110)$
9. (i) Local minimum: $(-1,0)$; local maximum: $(1,4)$
(ii) x-axis: $(-1,0)$ and $(2,0)$; y-axis: $(0,2)$ (iv) $-1 < x < 1$
10. (i) Local minimum: $(4,-80)$; local maximum: $(-2,28)$
11. (i) & (ii) Local minimum: $(1,3)$; local maximum: $(-1,7)$
12. Graph A   **13.** Graph A   **14.** Graph D

Exercise 12.7

1. (ii) $20x - x^2$ m^2 (iii) $x = 10$ m   (iv) 100 m^2 **2.** 54 km/hr
3. (ii) $100x - x^2$ m^2 (iii) $x = 50$ m   (iv) $r \approx 31.83$ m   (v) 3,183 m^2
(vi) Circular   **4.** (ii) $150x - x^2$ m^2 (iii) $x = 75$ m   (iv) 5,625 m^2
5. (i) $200 - 2x$ m   (ii) $200x - 2x^2$ m^2 (iii) $x = 50$ m   (iv) 5,000 m^2
6. (ii) $150x - \frac{3}{2}x^2$ m^2 (iii) $x = 50$ m   (iv) 7,500 m^2 **7.** (ii) $8x - 3.57x^2$ m^2
(iii) $x = \frac{400}{357}$ m, $y = \frac{400}{357}$ m   **8.** (i) $x = y = 40$ **9.** $x = y = 50$
10. (i) Perimeter $= 2y + \pi x$ (ii) $y = 700 - \frac{\pi x}{2}$ (iii) Length: 350.0 m,
width: 222.8 m   **11.** (i) Side length (base): $33\frac{1}{3}$ cm; height: $8\frac{1}{3}$ cm
(ii) $9,259\frac{7}{27}$ cm^3 **12.** (i) Side length (base): $13\frac{1}{3}$ cm; height: $3\frac{1}{3}$ cm
(ii) $592\frac{16}{27}$ cm^3 **13.** (i) $R(x) = 440x - 0.3x^2$

(ii) $P(x) = -0.8x^2 + 440x - 6,000$ (iii) 275   (iv) €54,500
14. (i) Maximum: Year 1, Minimum: Year 3

Exercise 12.8

1. (i) 0.00017 m/°C   (ii) 0.00045 m/°C   **2.** (i) 2.4×10^{-1} candelas/
volt   (ii) 250 volts   **3.** Velocity: 19.6 m/s; acceleration: 9.8 m/s^2
4. (i) Rate of change in weight with respect to the height of the tree.
(ii) Positive, as taller trees weigh more, other things being equal.
(iii) kg/m   **5.** (i) Speed after falling 5 m   (ii) Acceleration after falling 5 m
6. (i) Temperature of the bread 5 minutes out of the oven
(ii) Negative, as the temperature drops with time.   (iii) °C/min
7. (i) Positive, since infants get heavier with time.   (ii) At seven
months, the infant's weight is 7.65 kg.   (iii) kg/month   **8.** (i) 16 m
(ii) 25 m   (iii) $2t$ m/s   (iv) 8 m/s   **9.** (i) 35 m   (ii) $h'(t) =$ rate of
change in displacement with respect to time; this is defined as the
speed.   (iii) $40 - 10t$ m/s   (iv) 0 m/s   (v) 4 seconds   (vi) 80 m
10. (i) $-1.2t + 0.67$ °C/day   (ii) -2.93 °C/day   (iii) $t \approx 13$ hours
11. (i) 1,600 m   (ii) $200 - 8t$ m/s   (iii) 120 m/s   (iv) 200 m/s
(v) 25 seconds   (vi) 2,500 m   **12.** (i) $9(3x + 1)^2$ (ii) $6x(x^2 + 7)^2$
(iii) $(6x^2 - 12x)(x^3 - 3x^2 + 2)$ (iv) $24(8x + 3)^2$ (v) $6x^2(x^3 - 25)$
13. (i) $\frac{dA}{dt}$ is not constant, as it depends on l.   (ii) 0.04 cm^2/s
14. (i) $n = 3$ (ii) $m = 6$, $n = 2$ (iii) The length x is decreasing with
respect to time.   (iv) 1,200 cm^3/min   (v) 480 cm^3/min
15. (i) $V = \frac{4}{3}\pi r^3$ (ii) $S = 4\pi r^2$ (iii) $r'(t)$ is positive, as the radius is
increasing with time.   (iv) 576π cm^3/s   (v) 96π cm^2/s

Revision Exercises

1. (i) $4x + 12$ (ii) $30x + 10$ (iii) $3x^2 - 19$ (iv) $9x^2 - 24x - 4$
(v) $12x^2$ **2.** (i) $3t^2 + 4t - 1$ (ii) $3y^2 + 2y + 1$ (iii) $2x$ (iv) $5 - 9.8t$
3. (i) $3x^2 - 3$ (ii) 3.75   (iii) $y = 3.75x - 4.75$ (iv) x-axis: $(1.2\dot{6},0)$,
y-axis: $(0,-4.75)$ (v) $3.008\dot{3}$ units^2 **4.** (i) $3x^2 - 6x - 10$ (ii) 5.75
(iii) $y = 5.75x - 25$ **5.** (i) $f''(x) = 18x + 4$, $f''(-3) = -50$ (ii) $f''(x) = 30x$,
$f''(-3) = -90$ (iii) $f''(x) = -18x$, $f''(-3) = 54$ **6.** (i) Local maximum:
$(0,0)$; local minimum: $(2,-4)$ (ii) x-axis: $(0,0)$ and $(3,0)$; y-axis: $(0,0)$
(iv) $x < 0$ or $x > 2$ **7.** Graph B   **8.** (i) kg/month   (ii) At 3 months,
the monthly growth rate is 4 kg/month.   **9.** (i) πr^2 (ii) $24\pi r$ (iii) 10
(iv) By the Chain Rule   (v) 500π cm^2/s   **10.** (i) $x = \pm 1$ (ii) 96
11. (i) 2 metres   (ii) 5 m/s   (iii) $\frac{1}{3}$ second or 1 second   **12.** (i) N/m
(ii) 10 N   (iii) $-\frac{2,000}{r^3}$ **13.** $x = 25$, $y = 25$

Notes